INNOVATIONS IN CLINICAL PRACTICE

Focus on Sexual Health

A Volume in the *Innovations in Clinical Practice* Series

Edited by
LEON VANDECREEK
FREDERICK L. PETERSON, JR.
JILL W. BLEY

PROFESSIONAL RESOURCE PRESS
P.O. Box 15560
Sarasota, FL 34277-1560

EARN HOME STUDY CONTINUING EDUCATION CREDITS*

Professional Resource Exchange, Inc. offers a home study continuing education program as a supplement to *Innovations in Clinical Practice: Focus on Sexual Health*. For further information, please call 1-800-443-3364, fax to 941-343-9201, write to the address below, or visit our website: http://www.prpress.com

*The Professional Resource Exchange, Inc. is approved by the American Psychological Association to sponsor continuing education for psychologists. The Professional Resource Exchange, Inc. maintains responsibility for this program and its content. We are also recognized by the National Board of Certified Counselors to offer continuing education for National Certified Counselors. We adhere to NBCC Continuing Education Guidelines (Provider #5474). Home study CE programs are accepted by most state licensing boards. Please consult your board if you have questions regarding that body's acceptance of structured home study programs offered by APA-approved sponsors. Our programs have also been specifically approved for MFCCs and LCSWs in California and MFTs, LCSWs, and MHCs in Florida.

Published by Professional Resource Press
(An imprint of Professional Resource Exchange, Inc.)
Post Office Box 15560
Sarasota, FL 34277-1560

Printed in the United States of America.

Library of Congress Cataloging-in-Publication Data

Focus on sexual health / edited by Leon VandeCreek, Frederick L. Peterson Jr., Jill W. Bley.
    p. ; cm. -- (Innovations in clinical practice)
    Includes bibliographical references and index.
    ISBN 13: 978-1-56887-106-6 (alk. paper)
    ISBN-10: 1-56887-106-6 (alk. paper)
    1. Sex therapy. 2. Sexual disorders--Treatment. 3. Psychosexual
disorders--Treatment. I. VandeCreek, Leon. II. Peterson, Frederick L., 1956- III. Bley,
Jill W., 1941- IV. Series: Innovations in clinical practice (Unnumbered)
    [DNLM: 1. Sexual Dysfunctions, Psychological--therapy. 2. Psychotherapy--methods.
3. Sexual Behavior--psychology. 4. Sexual Dysfunction, Physiological--psychology. 5.
Sexual Dysfunction, Physiological--therapy. WM 611 F652 2007]
    RC557.F63 2007
    616.85'8306--dc22
                                   2006051370

The copyeditor for this book was Patricia Rockwood, the managing editor was Debra Fink, the production coordinator was Laurie Girsch, and the typesetter was Richard Sullivan.

Preface

Volumes 1 through 20 in the *Innovations in Clinical Practice: A Source Book* series were not built around a particular theme. Instead, each of these volumes covered a wide range of topics of probable interest to clinicians. Our primary audience for these volumes was practicing mental health professionals. These practitioners consistently praised the timeliness of the topics that we covered, the highly applied focus and usefulness of the contributions, the expertise of contributors, and the quality of our editing.

Peter A. Keller was the senior editor of the series from its inception through Volume 10. Lawrence G. Ritt served as coeditor of the first five volumes and continues to consult about the development of subsequent volumes. Steven R. Heyman was coeditor of Volumes 6 to 10. Beginning with the 11th volume, Leon VandeCreek assumed the position of senior editor. Samuel Knapp served as associate editor for Volumes 11 through 16. Thomas L. Jackson has served as associate editor since Volume 11.

There are two other individuals who have made important contributions to the production of the original *Innovations* volumes. From the onset of this series, Debra Fink has supervised the final production of each volume and ensured careful attention to details that others might have missed. Laurie Girsch has ably assisted her since Volume 8. We appreciate their thoroughness and cooperative spirit. Each year they have become more important to the success of the series.

Other contributors to the preparation of these volumes include Patricia Rockwood and Jude Warinner, who have worked many hours copyediting and proofreading the manuscripts. Without their skilled assistance, this volume would not be a reality. We would also like to thank Richard Sullivan for his help in preparing the current volume for distribution.

CHANGES IN RECENT VOLUMES

Over the past several years, we began to notice a shift in interest (and sales) amongst our readers that appeared to correspond to changes that had occurred in their practices; namely, readers were reporting that their practices had become more "specialized" and they were now less interested in the broad range of topics that were included in each *Innovations* volume. They were also reporting lower incomes and a desire for less expensive books and other resources.

After reviewing responses to the survey questions in recent *Innovations* continuing education (CE) modules, reviewing the literature, and holding a series of focus groups and editorial conference calls, we decided to begin producing a series of somewhat smaller, less expensive, and more focused *Innovations* volumes to meet the current needs of the majority of our customers. The first five volumes are:

- *Innovations in Clinical Practice: Focus on Children and Adolescents*
- *Innovations in Clinical Practice: Focus on Violence Treatment and Prevention*
- *Innovations in Clinical Practice: Focus on Adults*
- *Innovations in Clinical Practice: Focus on Health and Wellness*
- *Innovations in Clinical Practice: Focus on Sexual Health*

The Senior Editor, Leon VandeCreek, along with coeditor, Jeffery B. Allen, have already begun work on the next *Innovations* volume; the tentative title is *Innovations in Clinical Practice: Focus on Group, Couples, and Family Therapy*.

All of these volumes follow the general format of prior *Innovations* volumes with timely, cutting-edge applied materials written with a "how to do it" emphasis, client handouts, forms, and informal instruments that clinicians can put to immediate use in their practices.

AN INVITATION TO SUBMIT A CONTRIBUTION

The editors are currently soliciting contributions for future volumes in the *Innovations* series. If you are doing something innovative in your work, please let us hear from you. Contact Dr. Jeffery B. Allen, Senior Editor, SOPP, Wright State University, 3640 Colonel Glenn Highway, Dayton, OH 45435-0001, if you would like more detailed information on becoming a contributor.

CONTINUING EDUCATION

The Professional Resource Exchange is approved as a continuing education (CE) sponsor by several national and state organizations including the American Psychological Association and the National Board for Certified Counselors. CE credits are available to readers who are required to participate in CE programs, as well as by those who simply wish to validate their learning. To learn how to obtain home study continuing education credits through the *Innovations in Clinical Practice* series, please visit our website (www.prpress.com) or call 800-443-3364. These programs provide an economical means of obtaining continuing education credits while acquiring relevant clinical knowledge. Readers have been consistently positive about the experience of obtaining CE credits through this series.

COPYRIGHT POLICIES

Most of the material in this volume may be duplicated. You may photocopy materials (such as office forms and instruments) or reproduce them for use in your practice or share contributions with your students in the classroom; however, no part of this publication may be stored in a retrieval system, scanned, recorded, posted on an Internet website, or transmitted by any other means or in any form. For materials on which the Professional Resource Exchange holds the copyright, no further permission is required for noncommercial, professional, or educational uses. However, unauthorized duplication or publication for resale or large-scale distribution of any material in this volume is expressly prohibited.

Any material that you duplicate from this volume (with the exceptions mentioned below) must be acknowledged as having been reprinted from this volume and must note that copyright is held by the Professional Resource Exchange, Inc. The format and exact wording required in the acknowledgment are shown on the copyright page of this volume. The only exception to this policy is that clinical and office forms (not instruments) for use with clients in your own office may be reprinted without the acknowledgment mentioned above.

There are exceptions to our liberal copyright policy. We do not hold copyright on some of the materials included in this volume and, therefore, cannot grant permission to freely duplicate those materials. When copyright is held by another publisher or author, such copyright is noted on the appropriate page of the contribution. Unless otherwise noted in the credit and copyright citation, any reproduction or duplication of these materials is strictly and expressly forbidden without the consent of the copyright holder.

Leon VandeCreek
Wright State University

Frederick L. Peterson, Jr.
Wright State University

Jill W. Bley
Private Practice

Biographies

Leon VandeCreek, PhD, Senior Editor, is a licensed psychologist who is the past dean and current professor in the School of Professional Psychology at Wright State University in Dayton, Ohio. He has been awarded a Diplomate in Clinical Psychology and is a Fellow of several divisions of the American Psychological Association. His interests include professional training and ethical/legal issues related to professional education and practice. Dr. VandeCreek has served as President of the Pennsylvania Psychological Association, Chair of the APA Insurance Trust, Chair of the Board of Educational Affairs of the APA, and Treasurer of the Ohio Psychological Association. In 2005 he served as President of the Division of Psychotherapy of the APA. He has authored and coauthored about 150 professional presentations and publications, including 15 books. Since 1992, he has served as Senior Editor of the *Innovations in Clinical Practice: A Source Book* series, published by Professional Resource Press. Dr. VandeCreek may be contacted at the Ellis Human Development Institute, 9 N. Edwin C. Moses Boulevard, Dayton, OH 45402. E-mail: leon.vandecreek@wright.edu

Frederick L. Peterson, Jr., PsyD, is an educator, clinical psychologist, and sexual health practitioner in Dayton, Ohio. He received his doctorate degree in psychology from the School of Professional Psychology (SOPP), Wright State University in 1984. He has academic appointments to the School of Professional Psychology, School of Medicine (Department of Psychiatry), and the College of Education and Human Services at Wright State University. Along with his academic teaching, he conducts the "Safe Schools Program" for Parents and Friends of Lesbians and Gays (PFLAG). Dr. Peterson completed two postdoctorate internships at the Supporting the Emotional Needs of the Gifted (SENG) Program at Wright State University (1984-1985) and a clinical fellowship at the Masters and Johnson Institute, St. Louis (1993-1994). He is affiliated with several professional organizations and has provided numerous presentations at national conferences in the fields of psychology, sexual health, education, and nursing. Dr. Peterson was Director of Medical Education (1987-1997) at the Dayton VA Medical Center before starting the Sexual Health Clinic, which offers treatment services, professional training, and research on sexuality and gender topics. He is currently the Director of the Sexual Health Clinic and Co-Director of the APA-Approved Psychology Internship Program. He also coordinates the Veteran's Writers Group, the Veteran's History Project, and the Smoking Cessation Program at the hospital. He conducts a private practice in sexual health and clinical psychology, including court evaluations involving sex offense cases, through The Flexman Clinic in Dayton, Ohio. His greatest interests are his family, especially his children Lex, Dane, Claudia, Mackenzie, and Joshua. He lives with his wife Christy and their two sons in Springfield, Ohio. Dr. Peterson can be reached at the Sexual Health Clinic, VA Medical Center, Dayton, OH 45428. E-mail: Docpete100@aol.com

Jill W. Bley, PhD, is a clinical psychologist. She received her PhD from the University of Cincinnati in 1980. She was affiliated with the University of Cincinnati as an adjunct associate professor of psychology from 1982 until 1994. During that time she taught sex therapy to graduate students in psychology. She was a founder of Women Helping Women/Rape Crisis Center in Cincinnati in 1972. Dr. Bley became certified as a sex therapist in 1982 and a sex therapy supervisor in 1988 by the American Association of Sexuality Educators, Counselors, and Therapists (ASSECT). She authored a column entitled "Speaking of Sex" which was published in the Cincinnati Downtowner newspaper from 1989 until 2002. Dr. Bley served for 2 years on the Board of the Cincinnati Academy of Professional Psychology. She has also been a member of the Board of Cincinnati Psychological Association. She has served as the Association's Secretary (1986-1987), Ethics Chair (1988-1989), Program Chair and President-Elect (1989-1990), and President (1991-1992). In 1995, she received the Distinguished Alumnae Award presented by the University of Cincinnati Alumni Association for Friends of Women's Studies. She is currently a Volunteer Associate Professor in the Department of Psychiatry, University of Cincinnati Medical Center. Dr. Bley may be contacted at 750 Red Bud Avenue, Cincinnati, OH 45229. E-mail: drjillbley@cinci.rr.com

Table of Contents

SECTION III: SEX THERAPY WITH SPECIAL POPULATIONS

SECTION IV: THERAPIST GUIDES AND PATIENT HANDOUTS

INNOVATIONS IN CLINICAL PRACTICE

Focus on Sexual Health

A Volume in the *Innovations in Clinical Practice* Series

Introduction
To the Volume

This volume of *Innovations in Clinical Practice* represents the fifth publication since we shifted from comprehensive books with about 35 contributions, to more focused volumes that provide more depth on specific topics. We hope the book brings the somewhat unfamiliar world of clinical sexology to mental health professionals, introduces them to new concepts, such as "sexual identity," and motivates them to promote sexual health through providing sex therapy services. As in prior volumes, contributions are grouped into sections with common themes.

The first section, INTRODUCTION TO THE SCIENCE AND ART OF SEX THERAPY, includes several contributions that provide a foundation for the practice of sex therapy. The topics include a rationale for making sexual health a part of one's practice, some pointers on how to do a sexual health assessment as a routine part of one's mental health practice, an overview of the effects of aging and of medications on sexual health, and a review of important ethical issues that may arise when working with clients on sexual health. We hope these contributions stimulate practitioners to consider expanding their services to this important area of clinical care.

The second section includes contributions on SEXUAL DYSFUNCTIONS AND DISORDERS. These contributions cover the most common forms of dysfunction and disorders. We focus on providing requisite clinical knowledge, informed by sexual science, that is necessary to expand practitioners' skills and practices. Our goal is to share practical information and solutions to the challenges people face with their sexuality.

The third section, SEX THERAPY WITH SPECIAL POPULATIONS, provides information on working with sexual minority and culturally diverse clients, people with chronic illness and disability, and with seniors. While members of these populations may experience any of the sexual dysfunctions and disorders discussed in the prior section, they may also bring sexual challenges unique to their group.

In the fourth section, THERAPIST GUIDES AND PATIENT HANDOUTS, we provide tools for practitioners to use to collect and organize information. The assessment tools are primarily informal and designed to assist clinicians in collecting information about their clients. Our goal is to publish screening instruments and forms that aid in the organization of data, rather than the making of formal inferences and diagnoses. The materials presented here should be useful to mental health professionals, with minimal potential for misuse. We assume that readers will be thoroughly familiar with any disorders or processes that they evaluate, and readers are advised to carefully review the introductory materials that accompany contributions to this section. We have included a copy of the Code of Ethics for sex therapists. This guide is a companion piece for the fifth contribution ("Ethics in Sex Therapy"). We have included two assessment instruments for sexual functioning, one each for male and female clients. We have also included a self-awareness exercise that assists clinicians and clients in considering their sexual identities. Finally, most approaches to sexual health include the client as an active participant in the assessment and treatment process. We have included two tools that facilitate client involvement: a copy of a treatment plan that is designed to be shared with the client, and a sex history questionnaire that the clinician can use to gather information with the client.

In this section, we have also included three handouts for use with clients. Two handouts provide exercises for clients that enhance sexual health and that can be used to help resolve sexual problems. The other handout identifies several common sexual myths that clients, and perhaps even clinicians, share.

Section I:
Introduction to the Science and
Art of Sex Therapy

The INTRODUCTION TO THE SCIENCE AND ART OF SEX THERAPY includes five contributions that provide foundational information for expanding one's practice into the areas of sexual health.

In the first contribution, Jill W. Bley and Frederick L. Peterson, Jr. make the case for considering sexual health within one's overall health and for expanding services for sexual health. Surgeon General Satcher made sexual health a national priority in 2001 when he issued a call to action. He encouraged health care professionals to develop programs that promote sexual awareness and prevention and treatment of sexual health problems. The authors describe several myths that plague both clients and clinicians. Accompanying this contribution is a handout entitled, "A Health Care Professional's Guide to Contemporary Sexual Myths" that is included in the THERAPIST GUIDES AND PATIENT HANDOUTS section of this volume. The authors also describe the origins of sex therapy and provide information about how and where to obtain training for sex therapy.

A key component to providing sexual health services is conducting a sexual health assessment. In the second contribution, Candace B. Risen describes the why, when, with whom, and how to incorporate a sexual health assessment into work with all clients. She makes the case that all clinicians should promote and advance sexual health, whether the client presents a sexual concern or not. She describes the process of conducting an assessment and the obstacles clinicians place in the way of engaging in that process. She also provides a conceptual framework for understanding what should be included in such an assessment. Readers may find the "Sex History Questionnaire" that is presented in the THERAPIST GUIDES AND PATIENT HANDOUTS section to be helpful as well in completing an assessment.

By the year 2030, nearly 20% of people in the United States will be 65 years of age or older and a similar trend is developing in many parts of the world. The maintenance of good health and general well-being in later life has implications for sexual relationships and behaviors. Sexuality in older adults is often misunderstood, misrepresented, or left invisible. In the next contribution, Andrea Bradford and Cindy M. Meston provide an overview of the influence of aging on the sexual lives of men and women.

Contemporary explanations for sexual concerns often focus on interpersonal anxiety, emotional turmoil, early life experiences, and relationship concerns. The impact of physiology and pharmacology also play a role in how we understand sexual health. Today, most sexual disorders are believed to be at least partially physical in nature, either as a direct result of medical conditions, or as a result of the medications used to treat these conditions. The contribution by William W. Finger reviews some of the hundreds of medications known to cause changes in sexual functioning. Advice on assessing potential sexual side effects of medications is included.

In the final contribution in the section, Catherine Dailey Ravella highlights some of the ethical issues that clinicians face when they work in the realm of sex therapy. She concludes that understanding and adhering to the code of ethics prescribed by our individual profession offers the soundest guide to ethical practice. In addition, she describes the Code of Ethics of the American Association of Sexuality Educators, Counselors, and Therapists (AASECT) and of the American Psychological Association. A copy of the AASECT Code of Ethics is included in this volume in the THERAPIST GUIDES AND PATIENT HANDOUTS section.

Making Sexual Health a Part Of Your Mental Health Practice

Jill W. Bley and Frederick L. Peterson, Jr.

"We as a nation must address the significant public health challenges regarding the sexual health of our citizens" (U.S. Surgeon General, 2001, p. i). In his call to action, Dr. Satcher was referring not only to the urgent need for health care professionals to respond to the AIDS epidemic and other sexually transmitted diseases, but also to the problems faced by teens as they attempt to cope with their sexuality, dissemination of accurate information about sexual health issues, intervention strategies, and a method of evaluating the effectiveness of those strategies. The report encouraged health care professionals to make programs available that promote awareness and prevention of sexual abuse and coercion. It also emphasized the fact that the health interests of adults and children can be hurt within relationships with sexual health problems. Therefore, when a mental health professional is entrusted with the task of helping couples and families, ignoring their sexual health may mean that those couples and families will not be able to achieve an optimal level of healthy functioning.

Recent studies show that there are an alarming number of people suffering from some type of sexual dysfunction. Bartlik and Goldberg (2000) found that "a significant proportion of women in all age groups are affected by female sexual arousal disorder" (p. 86). They estimated that one in five premenopausal women and two in five postmenopausal women suffer from this disorder. Women who come to therapy with this problem are usually baffled about what might be causing it. Similarly, therapists untrained in sex therapy are sometimes baffled, not only about what might be the cause of the problem but also what to do about it.

The National Health and Social Life Survey (a representative sample of men ages 18 to 59), which was conducted by Lauman et al. (1994), found that 10.4% of men reported being unable to achieve or maintain erection during the past year (complete erection dysfunction). Feldman et al. (1994) reported in The Massachusetts Male Aging Study (a community-based survey of men between the ages of 40 and 70 years) that 52% of respondents had some degree of erectile difficulty.

Mental health professionals are trained to treat both mental (psychological, emotional) and physical (somatic) manifestations of mental health issues. However, very few have been trained to assess, much less treat, the sexual problems that may affect their clients' minds and bodies. Mental health professionals who are not trained to deal with the sexual problems with which their clients may be struggling might, in some cases, be in danger of doing harm to them. Since there are so many sexual myths and misinformation in our culture, untrained mental health professionals often are prone to believing and endorsing those myths and misinformation, thereby passing them on to their clients.

AMERICA'S SEXUAL HERITAGE AND THE PROBLEM OF SEXUAL MYTHS

Sexual health is defined as the integration of the physical, emotional, intellectual, and social aspects of being sexual in ways that are positively enriching and enhance personality, communication, and love (World Health Organization [WHO], 2001). Hence, sexual misinformation and myths interfere with the intellectual understanding of sexuality, which in turn can affect perceptions of self and others (emotional and social aspects) as well as increase the risk for disease transmission and even sexual violence (physical aspects). Later conceptualizations of sexual health (developed by expert panels of the World Health Organization) offer more comprehensive and sophisticated definitions:

> Sexual health is a state of physical, emotional, mental and social well-being related to sexuality; it is not merely the absence of disease, dysfunction or infirmity. Sexual health requires a positive and respectful approach to sexuality and sexual relationships, as well as the possibility of having pleasurable and safe sexual experiences, free of coercion, discrimination and violence. (WHO, 2004, p. 3)

Sexual myths plague most of our sexual lives. The Kinsey Institute of Indiana University surveyed nearly 2,000 American adults to document how sexually illiterate we are as a nation. Of the 18 questions on basic sexual literacy, 55% of the sample failed to produce 10 correct answers (earning an "F") and another 27% supplied 10 to 11 correct answers, earning a "D" (Reinisch & Beasley, 1990). Less than one in five people sampled passed the sexual literacy test with a "C" or better. This study and others (Lewis & Bor, 1994; Muller & Lief, 1976) demonstrate the great prevalence of sexual misinformation in our culture and why the former Surgeon General felt compelled to implore health care professionals of all disciplines to aid Americans in achieving sexual health (U.S. Surgeon General, 2001).

It is easy to understand how sexual myths get perpetuated, as an estimated three of every five people in the Kinsey sample reported that they got their sexual information from either friends (42%) or a boy- or girlfriend (17%) (Reinisch & Beasley, 1990). Mental health professionals are not immune from sexual myths. Most of them grew up in homes where sex was a taboo topic, just like the vast majority of Americans. Therapists are encouraged to rid themselves of sexual myths and become more sexually literate in order to assist clients to correct sexual misinformation that may adversely affect their self-esteem and sexual relationships as well as complicate treatment.

Related to the problem of sexual myths, American culture has been described as sex-negative and sexophrenic (Peterson, 1999). "Sexophrenia" is an informal (nondiagnostic) term that describes a state of dissonance resulting from conflict between feeling pleasure from sexual activity and the negative messages learned about the same behavior. Sex-negative messages may be so potent within a person's thinking that they generate significant anxiety and guilt, which then either prevents the person from engaging in the activity or blocks enjoyment of the activity. Throughout American history, negative stereotypes about any sexual behavior other than heterosexual intercourse have been described as unnatural, sinful, selfish, immoral, unhealthy, or a sign of insanity and disease. In short, the perpetuation of sexual myths serves as an obstacle to an individual achieving sexual health.

A common sexual myth is that people have to be young and beautiful to be attractive to others and sexually happy. Many people reach a certain age and stop being sexually active, not because they do not have sexual feelings and thoughts but because they think they are not supposed to be sexual at their age. This particular sexual myth is derived from the primary directive of most world religions, to "go forth, be fruitful, and multiply." This clearly is a direct prescription for procreational sex. Over the millennia, most (far from all) societies have upheld the primary directive by creating traditions and incentives that support procreational sex while instituting significant social sanctions against all other forms of sexual expression. This historical process was accomplished in part by making all sexual variations (other than penile vaginal intercourse) either a crime or a medical condition, especially homosexuality, anal sex, and masturbation.

The sexual heritage of traditional American majority culture is based upon the Anglo-Puritan values of people who were so sex-negative they used to cover the legs of furniture with cloth skirts for propriety's sake. During the 18th and 19th centuries, a doctrine of health came to be accepted within the American scientific-medical community which perceived good health as the result of good food, good exercise, good rest (with plenty of fresh air), and good sex (the latter defined as sexual abstinence with occasional practice for procreation). Restraint even from marital procreational sex was advised as a caution to avoid excessive seminal loss and general overexcitement of the nervous system (Money, 1985).

Because every variety of nonprocreational sex was not socially sanctioned, each variety was considered deviant and quite literally believed to lead to disease and disability, including insanity and death. Perhaps the most fascinating example of the medicalization of sexuality in our American heritage is masturbation, also known at various times in this country as self-abuse, self-vice, self-pollution, and the disease of onanism (mistakenly referring to the Old Testament character Onan). During most of American history, masturbation was considered a disease requiring medical treatment. Medical experts of the time believed that masturbating would develop into a condition known as "sexual neuroanesthenia" and result in a host of dreaded symptoms ranging from acne and isolating oneself for long periods in the bathroom to general weakness, blindness, or insanity (Masters, Johnson, & Kolodny, 1995; Robinson, 1934). Countless youth were needlessly tormented by such antimasturbation home remedies as tying hands to the bedposts at bedtime and "medical treatments" such as circumcision (for both girls and boys) and castration. Masturbation and seminal loss were so vilified that even involuntary nocturnal ejaculations (wet dreams) were medicalized as the disease of spermatorhea (Robinson, 1934).

Did you know that graham crackers and cornflakes were invented as "antimasturbation foods" to prevent the ill effects of the disease of masturbation? Famous health advocates such as Rev. Sylvester Graham and Dr. John Harvey Kellogg popularized the 19th-century doctrine of good health (which excluded sex except for procreation). Rev. Graham was so closely associated with this doctrine of good health that some food products today still bear his name (graham flour and crackers). Dr. Kellogg and his wife Anna originally invented baked flakes of corn as an antimasturbation food and served it to the patients of the Battle Creek Sanitarium (Money, 1985). The story of Dr. Kellogg was popularized in the movie *The Road to Wellville* (Abraham, 1994).

Through the first half of the 20th century, masturbation was still referred to as "self-abuse" in medical dictionaries (Gould, 1949; Robinson, 1934). The sexual revolution of the 1960s helped to change the way we think about this activity. Masturbation is often referred to now as "self-pleasuring" and is considered a healthy part of sexual expression. Modern concerns about masturbation are usually centered around teaching children discretion about the "where and when" of masturbation, such as, "Yes, it is normal, son, but not at the dinner table." Parental overreaction and punitive responses are also a concern ("You will go to hell for that!"). However, even now guilt is a common problem ("This feels too good not to be bad"). Recently, mental health providers have become aware of and concerned about excessive, compulsive masturbation. Patients with this issue present with statements such as, "I can't seem to stop doing this even when I know it will cause trouble for me."

The sexual myth about masturbation has been addressed but is only one of a multitude of sexual myths that are far beyond the scope of this contribution. This myth was selected as an example of the devastating effects misinformation can have on the lives of everyday people. Sexual myths abound regarding children and adolescents, seniors, people living with disabilities, gays and lesbians, bisexual and transgendered individuals, and racial/ethnic groups, as well as pregnancy, contraception, abortion, and sexual performance (to name a few).

Sexual literacy is needed by mental health therapists to effectively respond to client needs for accurate sexual information. Therapists are referred to other sources for further reading (Peterson, 2000; Reinisch & Beasley, 1990). Alternatively, readers may reference the handout, "A Health Care Professional's Guide to Contemporary Sexual Myths" (by F. L. Peterson, Jr. & C. Peterson, on pp. 323-325). Health care professionals, especially mental health professionals, are encouraged to use this guide as a handout for the sexual health education of their clients.

THE ORIGINS OF SEX THERAPY

In the United States, the development of sex therapy over the last 40 years as an interdisciplinary profession has been built on a confluence of five significant historical influences: (a) the invention of the "talking cure" by Sigmund Freud and others, and the psychoanalytic movement within American psychiatry (Bankhart, 1996); (b) the reaction against psychoanalysis and the development of behaviorism within American psychology (O'Donohue & Kitchener 1999); (c) the application of empirical methods to the study of sexuality and the establishment of a sexual science in America, beginning with the pioneers Robert Dickinson (Hartman & Fithian, 1997), Alfred Kinsey (Kinsey, Pomeroy, & Martin, 1948; Kinsey et al., 1953), and William Masters and Virginia Johnson (1966). The empirical methods in sexology led, ultimately, to the advent of oral contraceptives and oral sexual stimulants; (d) the sexual revolution of the 1960s that began the relaxation of the social conventions of previous decades, the questioning of the sexual repression of American women, allowing access to sexual literacy, and creating a consumer demand for sexual health services; and (e) the social conservatism of American academia that prevented established professions, such as medicine or psychology, from overcoming the effects of the taboos surrounding the teaching of sexuality (other than the traditional teaching in medical schools related to making sure the "plumbing" works, fertility issues, and birthing).

There are likely to be nearly as many perspectives on the history of sex therapy as there are different sexological practitioners and researchers. We believe there are many ways to conceive and outline this history, depending on which set of lens you use to look back over the 20th century. To gain a perspective other than our own, we consulted Dennis Sugrue, a contributor to this volume and past president of the American Association of Sexuality Educators, Counselors, and Therapists (AASECT).

Confluent with the first three key historical influences the authors believe contributed to the advent of sex therapy as an interdisciplinary field, Dr. Sugrue summarizes the sex therapy field as developing over four distinct periods: orthodoxy predating sex therapy, the commercialization of sex therapy, the professionalization of sex therapy, and the postmodern period of sex therapy.

American psychiatry and the psychodynamic model were the gold standard of medical care in the first half of the century. All deviations from expectations of "normal sexuality" were viewed as pathology requiring psychoanalysis. Early behavioralists, such as Joseph Wolpe and Arnold Lazarus, countered this orthodoxy by quietly treating sexual dysfunctions and publishing results as a sort of "underground movement " toward sex therapy. The commercialization of sex therapy occurred with the enormous contributions of Masters and Johnson, who conducted pioneer sex research, applied their research results (as well as incorporating many of the behavioral strategies published by others), packaged it all into a "new sex therapy," and legitimized this treatment with the mantle of a medical context. This was the start of sex therapy proper.

The professionalization of sex therapy occurred over time with mental health professionals (see, e.g., Kaplan, 1974, 1995; Lief, 1977; LoPiccolo & Friedman, 1988) who, unable to replicate the results of Masters and Johnson, synthesized new approaches from their own research and clinical work to effectively resolve the sexual problems their patients presented. Related to the professionalization movement, new professional associations developed for the promotion of sexual literacy (SIECUS; Sexuality Information and Education Council of the United States), the continuation of sound sex research (SSSS; The Society for the Scientific Study of Sexuality), and the professional credentialing of sex therapy services (AASECT). The postmodern age of sex therapy, in which we are currently practicing, has brought many changes to the field, including, but not limited to, more sophisticated and integrative approaches to treatment (cognitive-behavioral, pharmacologic, systemic), the medicalization of sex therapy with the Viagra revolution, the reconceptualization and emphasis on female sexuality, and the broadening of sex therapy to be responsive to cultural and technological shifts such as compulsive sexual behaviors, the cybersex phemonenon, and transgenderism (Dennis Sugrue, personal communication, December, 2005).

We see the field of sex therapy as having evolved through four overlapping stages of development, or "generations." A brief review of the development of the field will show that the First Generation of sex therapists began with Masters and Johnson's initial launching from the sexual science base (1966) into the clinical application of their work (1974). The Second Generation sex therapists branched out from the medical model, took the basic behavioral exercises of Masters and Johnson, and added their own unique variations. Harold Lief and Helen Singer Kaplan were key sex researchers that contributed to the foundation for the work by Third Generation sex therapists. Therapists of this generation advocate a "systems" or "integrated" approach. The Fourth Generation of sex therapists must work within a post-Viagra context. Therefore, modern sex therapy reflects a dynamic tension between the medicalization of sexuality and the sexual health paradigm.

The First Generation

Dr. Alfred Kinsey's groundbreaking "Kinsey reports" (Kinsey et al., 1948, 1953) brought about numerous changes in how Americans perceive sex, including greater understanding of the incredible diversity in sexual behaviors, most of which are now considered within a typical "normal" range of sexual activity (e.g., masturbation and homosexuality). Many of the contributions Kinsey made to sexual science and his effect on shifting sexual norms are reflected in the Fox film release, *Kinsey* (Mutrux, 2004).

Although Alfred Kinsey opened the door to America's bedrooms, it was William Masters and Virginia Johnson who brought us to an understanding of what happens under the covers. Between 1954 and 1966 Masters and Johnson observed and measured over 10,000 orgasms under laboratory conditions (Masters et al., 1995). The publication of their 1966 volume marked the beginning of all contemporary sex therapy (Leiblum & Rosen, 2000). Their research led them to develop behavioral techniques that they labeled "Sensate Focus Exercises" (Masters & Johnson, 1974). Sensate focus exercises progress from nongenital pleasuring (Sensate Focus I) to intercourse pleasuring (Sensate Focus III) (see handout on pp. 317-319 for a description of these exercises). David Schnarch has called this linear, "stage," or "phase" theory and practice of sex therapy the "first generation" approach (1991).

The Second Generation

The basic sensate focus exercises provided the foundation for innovative techniques that were developed by a few sex therapists during the 1970s to help men and women who could not become aroused (lubrication in women and erection in men) and/or control their orgasm (inhibited or premature orgasm). Women and men learned to explore their bodies, relax, and overcome their fears, the anti-sex societal conditioning, and performance anxieties that inhibited their sexual response.

We see this as the second generation of sex therapists because these clinicians took the behavioral techniques of Masters and Johnson and added a cognitive therapy approach that allowed the therapist to explore the cognitions of the patients that may have contributed to the sexual problem. They recognized that sexual problems were not all related to performance anxiety that would easily respond to sensate focus exercises alone. They worked to help patients understand how their culture, lack of accurate information about sex, religion, and family attitudes, and values and morals impacted their sexual functioning. As mentioned previously, Sugrue refers to this development as the professionalization of sex therapy.

In 1976, Julia Heiman and Joseph LoPiccolo published their book *Becoming Orgasmic: A Sexual and Personal Growth Program for Women*. The focus was on helping individual women achieve orgasm by self-pleasuring as well as with a partner. The program provided information that increased their sexual pleasure by expanding sexual literacy and practicing specific exercises designed to help women gradually and systematically achieve orgasm with or without a partner.

In 1978, Bernie Zilbergeld's book *Male Sexuality* described the myths and misinformation that have contributed to the creation of many sexual problems for men. He also used the basic sensate focus techniques to describe exercises that men can do, individually, to help them learn to focus their attention on pleasure instead of performance. He guided men in learning how to achieve erections and to prolong the pleasures of arousal so that they could overcome the embarrassments created by premature ejaculation. He included advice on how to transfer these new experiences to a sexual encounter with a partner. In 1992 he published a revised edition, *The New Male Sexuality*, which included information about all of the newest techniques for enhancing male sexuality, such as the use of new medications that cause vasodilation and enhance erections.

In 1980, Lonnie Barbach published an important book (*Women Discover Orgasm: A Therapist's Guide to a New Treatment Approach*) that outlined her approach to helping women achieve orgasm using a group sex therapy modality. She designed a 10-week group therapy program with a step-by-step model for therapists to follow that incorporated individual therapy and group therapy techniques in a group therapy approach. During the first few weeks of the group, the therapist focuses on each woman's individual issues. The therapist uses this information to design a treatment plan for each woman in the group. As the group progresses and each woman begins to do her own individualized homeplays (exercises), the dynamics inherent in group therapy begin to enhance the therapeutic interventions made by the therapist.

The Third Generation

Masters and Johnson's conceptualization of the sexual response cycle was that sexual response progressed in phases that they called excitement, plateau, orgasm, and resolution. Helen Singer Kaplan's 1974 book pointed out that, although the plateau phase and the resolution phase may be useful to medical sexologists, they were of no practical use to sex therapists. The major thrust of her message was that sexual response is really "Tri-phasic" and that Masters and Johnson had failed to address the issue of sexual desire, probably because desire could not be measured in the laboratory. By highlighting the issue of desire phase disorders, Kaplan paved the way for the next generation of sex therapists. She forced them to recognize that sexual response in humans is much more than "stages" or "phases" of physical reactions to sexual stimuli. Understanding the many facets of sexual desire caused researchers, practitioners, and theorists to broaden their scope to take into consideration the context of the entire person, including the body, mind, spirit, and relationship.

Research on arousal disorders in males and females indicate that problems with lubrication in females and erection in males are widespread and cause much distress in those who experience these disorders. However, low sexual desire is the most common presenting complaint of clients seen in sex therapy clinics (Pridal & LoPiccolo, 2000) and probably in private sex therapy practices. Sexual desire disorders are also the most difficult to understand and treat.

Desire phase dysfunctions are resistant to the standard sensate focus exercises, because people who have no motivation to have sex have little to no motivation to do these exercises; the underlying causes of their avoidance of sex have not been explored. Therefore, the etiology is not understood and so cannot be treated. The treatment, according to Kaplan, must be a combination of psychodynamic, sexual, marital, and behavioral therapies.

Kaplan was perhaps the first, but not the only, clinician to recognize that the basic sensate focus exercises did not provide the therapist with enough tools to be as effective as possible. LoPiccolo and Friedman (1988) proposed a "broad-spectrum" treatment that would incorporate cognitive, behavioral, and systemic treatment approaches. Pridal and LoPiccolo (2000) maintain that "therapy with low desire clients can be quite successful if the treatment addresses cognitive, affective, behavioral, and systemic elements" (p. 57). Insight and understanding comprise part of their treatment as well.

In 1991, David Schnarch published *Constructing the Sexual Crucible: An Integration of Sexual and Marital Therapy*. His work represented a milestone contribution to the understanding and treatment of sexual problems. Schnarch demonstrated the need for clinicians to make a radical change in their treatment approach by shifting their emphases from sensate-based behavioral-only treatment, analyzing resistances, individual pathology, and/or relational dysfunctions to developing a nonpathological model that focuses on the natural unfolding of human differences. He stressed the need for the development of a multisystems approach to sexual therapy that allows for differentiation as it manifests in sex and intimacy in committed relationships (Schnarch, 1991). Gerald Weeks (a contributor to this volume) also espouses the use of an integrated model of marital and sex therapy (Weeks, 2005).

These important developments in the understanding of the treatment of sexual problems within the context of a committed relationship make it clear that practitioners must increase and expand their knowledge, training, and expertise if they hope to alleviate the distresses endured by couples who experience sexual/relationship issues. They need to become expert in the theory and practice of treating every aspect of sexuality including sexual addiction, sexual abuse, and intimacy disorders, because of the profound impact of these issues on the sexuality of the individual and the sexual relationship of a couple.

The Fourth Generation

Recently, there has been a focus on medicalizing sex therapy. The Fourth Generation of sex therapists are practicing in a post-Viagra world where they must inform themselves, as never before, about the pros and cons of the use of medications to resolve sexual problems. Pharmacological interventions for a patient's sexual concerns has a long history, going back to antiquity from the Ayurvedic medical texts in India (rock salt) and early philosophers in Greece (satyrion). In America, Robinson (1934) discussed using the bromides of strontium and sodium, small dosages of atropine, and "administrations of thyroid extract and adrenal substance" to treat the pseudodisease of masturbation (pp. 48-49). In the United States, as early as 1890, Robert Dickinson began to collect sex histories from his patients. He published extensively on the sexual problems of women (Hartman & Fithian, 1997).

William Masters, also a physician, along with Virginia Johnson, studied the anatomy and physiology of human sexual response and published those results in 1966. Masters and Johnson's research led them to the conclusion that many sexual dysfunctions were psychogenic and should be treated with behavioral-type therapy (1970), which took the emphasis of treatment away from the medical model for approximately 30 years.

In the 1980s a number of medical treatments became available for erection dysfunctions (ED). One, injections of vasodilators such as papaverine, was touted as a new "cure" for impotence, because it allowed full tumescence independent of sexual desire (Broderick, 1998; Montague, 1998). Americans had to wait until 1995, however, for the first prescription drug for impotence, prostaglandin E1, which was prescribed as the self-injected medication Caverject

(American Association of Clinical Endocrinologists [AACE], 1998). A year and many sore penises later, an intraurethral suppository form of alprostadil (another vasodilator) was approved and released under the commercial name of Muse (Process of Care Panel of the University of Medicine and Dentistry, New Jersey, 1998). The hormones testosterone and estrogen and yohimbine, which is a tree bark extract, have also been used as "sexual medicine." The surgical implantation of penile prostheses was also a fairly common medical answer to erectile dysfunctions. Those treatments, however, were isolated to the practice of urology.

When sildenafil citrate (Viagra) hit the market, medical practitioners were able to prescribe, for the first time in history, an oral medication that actually worked to "cure" many men with erectile dysfunction. The incredible impact of Viagra on American culture as a whole, and sex therapy specifically, is related to three key differences between Viagra and previous sexual medications. First, Viagra was an effective and easily taken oral medication perfect for a "take-a-pill-to-fix-it" American culture. Second, the release of Viagra was accompanied by an effective and unparalleled marketing campaign that recruited the likes of presidential candidates sharing their impotence with the world. Finally, and most importantly, there was a historical shift that occurred with consumers moving away from urology and psychiatry specialists and going to primary care, family medicine, and general internists, who are now the primary professionals prescribing Viagra (Peterson, 2000).

Sex therapists began to worry that there would be a "medicalization" of all erectile problems and possibly of all sexual problems, which would then cause most people with sexual issues to look for a pill that would fix them and would set the course for primary care physicians to be the only professionals involved in the evaluation and treatment of erection disorders. While recognizing that this has happened to some extent, it is important to acknowledge how beneficial these drugs have been to many men and to their relationships.

Since the advent of these drugs, drug companies have invested huge amounts of time and money in trying to develop medications that will cure/treat Female Sexual Dysfunction (FSD). Raymond Moynihan, a journalist, published an article in 2003 in which he reported on meetings between clinicians, researchers, and drug company representatives "to discuss the future direction of clinical trials" of medications intended to treat FSD. He stated that this was happening even though there is "widespread lack of agreement about the definition" of FSD. He wrote that Dr. Sandra Leiblum, Dr. John Bancroft, Dr. Leonore Tiefer, and Dr. Raymond Rosen, all leading sex therapists and researchers, have expressed concerns about the "medicalization" of sexuality. Dr. Tiefer was quoted as saying that pharmacological research may oversimplify sexual difficulties because it "promotes genital function as the centrepiece of sexuality and ignores everything else" (Moynihan, 2003, p. 46).

Some sex therapists have postulated that the major emphasis of the first-generation models of "phases" and "stages" has been too focused on what is known about male sexual response and often overlooked much evidence that suggested that female sexual response may be very different. Sally A. Kope has written an excellent contribution to this book titled "Female Sexual Arousal and Orgasm: Pleasures and Problems," in which she discusses the importance of alternative models that may help therapists better understand these differences (Stayton, Angelo, & Kaye, 2005; Whipple, 2002). Basson's (2003) Non-Linear Model postulates that responsive desire, which is the type of desire reported by most women, is probably more important than spontaneous desire, because intimacy is the important component of responsive desire. The new emphasis on a team approach (composed of sex therapist, medical doctor, and/or physical therapist) to the treatment of female genital pain disorders (as described in another contribution in this book; see pp. 107-117) is further evidence of the changes that are moving practitioners toward this Fourth Generation approach to sex therapy.

This historic shift necessitates that several demands be placed on modern mental health professionals as well as, and to a greater degree, sex therapists. First, mental health professionals need to be informed of product information related to the sexual psychopharmacology that is available to clients as well as the "clinical pathways" that have been developed to recommend sequential steps to assessment and treatment of some sexual concerns, such as erection dysfunction (Department of Veteran Affairs, 1999; Process of Care Panel of the University of Medicine and Dentistry, New Jersey, 1998).

Second, because of direct marketing (as opposed to traditional marketing only to providers) and the availability of information about sexual medicines over the Internet, mental health professionals and sex therapists find themselves working with consumers who are familiar with the product information of sexual medicines. These clients may be getting sexual medicine through medical providers or through the Internet, bypassing their primary care and specialty providers. Often, clients are presenting for therapy after, not before, trying one or more sexual medicines, such as oral medications or hormonal treatments.

Third, mental health and sex therapy practitioners have a greater need to work with colleagues with prescription privileges, which involves developing professional relations with physicians, physician assistants, or nurse practitioners. Gone are the days when mental health therapists could work "in a bubble" with little interaction with the client's medical care providers. The need for therapists to work collaboratively with medical care providers is not a one-way street, however. Mental health professionals who develop sex therapy competence will find that many medical care providers need them as well. They need someone to whom to refer patients who present with sexual concerns, which medical professionals often do not know how to treat effectively. Very few medical care providers have training in sexual health issues beyond the basics they learned in medical school and what they learn from drug company representatives. Therefore, most medical professionals are eager to provide a referral for their patients with sexual concerns to a competent mental health provider with expertise in this area.

It is imperative that Fourth Generation sex therapists make sure that they work together to provide men and women who come to them with sexual concerns with the best information about what is available to help them, whether it is sensate focus exercises, couples therapy, individual therapy, pharmacological therapy, understanding the cultural/historical/religious context of the problem, or some combination of these.

Raymond Rosen (2000) described a new process-of-care algorithm for the evaluation and treatment of ED, whereby psychological and sex therapy treatments are strongly emphasized either in conjunction with or as an alternative to medical therapies. This new process could be applied to the treatment of all sexual dysfunctions and usher in the Fourth Generation of sex therapists, who, by necessity, must be well educated, trained, and knowledgeable about all aspects of sexuality, including mind, body, spirit, culture, religion, relationship, and pharmacology.

HOW AND WHERE TO GET SEX THERAPIST/COUNSELOR TRAINING*

There are three paths to practicing as a sex therapist. First, get a graduate degree in human sexuality that has a clinical emphasis, for example, clinical sexology. Second, develop a specialty in a particular area of sex therapy, such as "sex addictions." Finally, work on certification through the American Association of Sexuality Educators, Counselors, and Therapists (AASECT).

With regard to the first option of getting an academic degree, the website for AASECT (www.aasect.org)** has a page titled, "How to Become a Sexuality Educator, Counselor

---

* Portions of this section were adapted from "The Development of a Sexual Health Component in Your Practice" by F. L. Peterson, Jr. and J. W. Bley. This article appeared in L. VandeCreek & J. B. Allen (Eds.), *Innovations in Clinical Practice: Focus on Health and Wellness* (pp. 159-168), 2005, Sarasota, FL: Professional Resource Press. Copyright © 2005 by Professional Resource Exchange, Inc. Adapted with permission.

** Although all websites cited in this contribution were correct at the time of publication, they are subject to change at any time.

or Therapist." Three programs are listed on this site that offer degrees in human sexuality. According to the website for The Society for the Scientific Study of Sexuality (SSSS) (www.sexscience.org), 44 universities offer sex therapy training in their graduate programs, but only the three programs mentioned above grant academic degrees in human sexuality.

Deciding to treat sexual problems only within special populations, such as men with erection dysfunction, is a second option. It is possible for a psychotherapist who has not been trained as a sex therapist to successfully treat some individuals who present with a particular sexual concern. However, as the foregoing information suggests, it is never advisable to try to treat any sexual problem with no training in the area whatsoever.

The third option, pursuing AASECT certification while continuing one's clinical practice, is recommended. Because this choice requires multiple steps, one should start by going to www.aasect.org/certification.asp. The requirements for certification as a sex counselor are less stringent than those required for certification as a sex therapist. Requirements for sex counselor and sex therapist certification are summarized here; details are listed on the AASECT website:

1. One must possess state certification or a license to practice in a related field, such as psychology, social work, medicine, and so on.
2. There is a requirement for sexuality education of 60 clock hours for a sex counselor and 90 clock hours for a sex therapist. One can also earn Continuing Education Units by reading books on the topic, such as this one.
3. At least 30 hours of clinical training in one's field must be in sex counseling. There are seven core areas of training listed for certification at the sex therapist level.
4. A minimum of 12 clock hours of Attitudes/Values Training are required.
5. A minimum of 100 hours of supervised sex counseling is required for sex counselor certification and 250 hours of supervised sex therapy for sex therapy certification.
6. Face-to-face supervision for a minimum of 30 hours for sex counselors and 50 hours for sex therapists is required.

Table 1 (p. 15) summarizes all of the information provided on the AASECT website for both sex therapists and sex counselors. For more complete information about both of these certifications, consult the website.

Although this third pathway for adding a sex therapy component to your practice is time-consuming, it is the best because you will be able to feel very confident that you are well trained and have had the opportunity to use the expertise of a supervisor who will have had many years of experience in the field.

CONCLUSION

Psychiatrists and psychologists are generally perceived today as having expertise in human behavior and behavior change through psychopharmacology and psychotherapy, respectively. However, neither professional organization has divisions or programs within their organizations designed to help its members overcome their own feelings of discomfort in dealing with client concerns about sexuality or developing clinical skills to resolve these concerns. The same can be said for the national associations for counselors and social workers. The challenge to all mental health disciplines is to expand efforts and resources devoted to promoting sexual health and developing skills in clinical sexology.

This volume, as well as other excellent references on sexual health (most notably, Leiblum & Rosen, 2000, and Levine, Risen, & Althof, 2003) is designed to assist mental health therapists of all disciplines to overcome obstacles, expand their knowledge base, increase their skills, and incorporate sexual health into their clinical practice.

TABLE 1: American Association of Sexuality Educators, Counselors, and Therapists Summary and Comparison of Certification Requirements

Requirement	Sex Counselor	Sex Therapist
Membership	Yes	Yes
Code of Ethics	Yes	Yes
Academic and Professional Experience	BA + 2 years (minimum)	MA + 2 years or Doc. + 1 year
General Eligibility	Clinical license not required	State license required
Human Sexuality Education	60 clock hours	90 clock hours
Sex Counseling or Sex Therapy Training	60 clock hours (30 general/30 sex)	60 clock hours (30 general/30 sex)
Sexual Attitudes and Values Training Experience	12 clock hours	12 clock hours
Clinical Training or Professional Experience	100 hours of supervised sex counseling	250 hours of supervised sex therapy
Supervision	30 hours (6 months minimum)	50 hours (50% group, 6 months >) (15 years experience = 25 hours)
Application Process	$250 and documentation	$250 and documentation

CONTRIBUTORS

Jill W. Bley, PhD, is a clinical psychologist. She is certified by the American Association of Sexuality Educators, Counselors, and Therapists as both a sex therapist and a supervisor. She taught sex therapy to graduate students in clinical psychology at the University of Cincinnati. During that time she trained and supervised many students. Dr. Bley wrote a syndicated column, "Speaking of Sex," which appeared in some downtown newspapers. Her columns addressed the diverse issues related to human sexuality. She is a founder of Women Helping Women/Rape Crisis Center and a Sex Therapy Clinic, both in Cincinnati. She has lectured extensively on topics of sexuality. Dr. Bley is a Volunteer Associate Professor in the Department of Psychiatry University of Cincinnati Medical Center. Dr. Bley may be contacted at 750 Red Bud Avenue, Cincinnati, OH 45229. E-mail: drjillbley@cinci.rr.com

Frederick L. Peterson, Jr., PsyD, is a health psychologist at the Veterans Healthcare System of Ohio, Dayton Campus, where he coordinates a Sexual Health Clinic and the Smoking Cessation Programs. Dr. Peterson is the Co-Director of the Psychology Internship Program. He completed postdoctorate training as a Clinical Fellow at the Masters and Johnson Institute. Research interests include sex therapy, tobacco use treatment, and the effects of masculinity-related personality factors on health. He holds three academic appointments at Wright State University, including the School of Medicine (Department of Psychiatry), the School of Professional Psychology, and the College of Education and Human Services. Dr. Peterson can be reached at the Sexual Health Clinic, VA Medical Center, Dayton, OH 45428. E-mail: Docpete100@aol.com

RESOURCES

Abraham, M. (Executive Producer), & Parker, A. (Director). (1994). *The Road to Wellville* [Film]. Culver City, CA: Columbia/Tristar Studios.

American Association of Clinical Endocrinologists (AACE). (1998). AACE Clinical Practice Guidelines for the Evaluation and Treatment of Male Sexualy Dysfunction. *Endocrine Practice, 4*(4), 220-235.

American Association of Sexuality Educators, Counselors, and Therapists. (2003). *Standards for Certification*. Retrieved June 30, 2004, from http://www.aasect.org

Bankhart, C. P. (1996). *Talking Cures: A History of Western and Eastern Psychotherapies*. Belmont, CA: Wadsworth.

Barbach, L. G. (1980). *Women Discover Orgasm: A Therapist's Guide to a New Treatment Approach*. New York: Free Press.

Bartlik, B., & Goldberg, J. (2000). Female sexual arousal disorder. In S. Leiblum & R. Rosen (Eds.), *Principles and Practices of Sex Therapy* (3rd ed., pp. 85-117). New York: Guilford.

Basson, R. (2003). Women's difficulties with low sexual desire and sexual avoidance. In S. B. Levine, C. B. Risen, & S. E. Althof (Eds.), *Handbook of Clinical Sexuality for Mental Health Professionals* (pp. 111-130). New York: Brunner-Routledge.

Broderick, G. (1998). Impotence and penile vascular testing: Who are these men and how do they evaluate the etiology and severity of their complaints? *Journal of Sex Education and Therapy, 23*(3), 197-206.

Department of Veteran Affairs. (1999). *The Primary Care Management of Erectile Dysfunction* (Published by the Pharmacy Benefits Management Strategic Health Care Group and the Medical Advisory Panel, Publication No. 99-0014). Washington, DC: U.S. Government Printing Office.

Feldman, H. E., Goldstein, I., Hatzichristov, D., Krane, R., & McKinlay, R. (1994). Impotence and its medical and psycho-social correlates: Results of the Massachusetts male aging study. *Journal of Urology, 151*, 54-61.

Gould, G. (1949). *Gould's Pocket Pronouncing Medical Dictionary of the Principal Words Used in Medicine and the Collateral Sciences* (11th ed.). Philadelphia: P. Blakiston's Son & Co.

Hartman W., & Fithian, M. (1997). Sexual dysfunctions, counseling, and therapies: A brief history of American sexual therapy. In R. T. Francoeur (Ed.), *The International Encyclopedia of Sexuality* (Vol. I-III). Retrieved October 28, 2005, from http://www2.rz.hu-berlin.de/sexology/GESUND/ARCHIV/IES/USA15.HTM

Heiman, J., & LoPiccolo, J. (1976). *Becoming Orgasmic: A Sexual and Personal Growth Program for Women*. New York: Prentice Hall.

Kaplan, H. S. (1974). *The New Sex Therapy*. New York: Brunner/Mazel.

Kaplan, H. S. (1995). *The Sexual Desire Disorders: Dysfunctional Regulations of Sexual Motivation*. Levittown, PA: Brunner/Mazel.

Kinsey, A., Pomeroy, W., & Martin, C. (1948). *Sexual Behavior in the Human Male*. Philadelphia: W. B. Saunders.

Kinsey, A., Pomeroy, W., Martin, C., & Gebhard, P. (1953). *Sexual Behavior in the Human Female*. Philadelphia: W. B. Saunders.

Lauman, E., Gagnon, J., Michael, R., & Michaels, S. (1994). *The Social Organization of Sexuality: Sexuality Practices in the United States*. Chicago: University of Chicago Press.

Leiblum, S. R., & Rosen, R. C. (2000). *Principles and Practice of Sex Therapy* (3rd ed.). New York: Guilford.

Levine, S. B., Risen, C. B., & Althof, S. E. (2003). *Handbook of Clinical Sexuality for Mental Health Professionals*. New York: Brunner-Routledge.

Lewis, S., & Bor, R. (1994, August). Nurses' knowledge of and attitudes towards sexuality and the relationship of these with nursing practice. *Journal of Nursing, 20*(2), 251-259.

Lief, H. I. (1977). Inhibited sexual desire. *Medical Aspects of Human Sexuality, 11*(7), 94-95.

LoPiccolo, J., & Friedman, J. M. (1988). Broad-spectrum treatment of low desire: Integration of cognitive, behavioral and systemic therapy. In S. Leiblum & R. Rosen (Eds.), *Sexual Desire Disorders*. New York: Plenum.

Masters, W., & Johnson, V. (1966). *Human Sexual Response*. Boston: Little, Brown.

Masters, W., & Johnson, V. (1970). *Human Sexual Inadequacy*. Boston: Little, Brown.

Masters, W. H., Johnson, V. E., & Kolodny, R. C. (1995). *Human Sexuality* (5th ed.). New York: HarperCollins College Publishers.

Money, J. (1985). *The Destroying Angel*. Buffalo, NY: Prometheus Books.

Montague, D. (1998). Erectile dysfunction: The rational utilization of diagnostic testing. *Journal of Sex Education and Therapy, 23*(3), 194-196.

Moynihan, R. (2003). The making of a disease: Female sexual dysfunction. *British Medical Journal, 326*, 45-47. Retrieved October 26, 2005, from http://bmj.bmjjournals.com/cgi/content/full/326/7379/45

Muller, W. R., & Lief, H. I. (1976, September). Masturbatory attitudes, knowledge, and experience: Data from the Sex Knowledge & Attitude Test (SKAT). *Archives of Sexual Behavior, 5*(5), 447-467.

Mutrux, G. (Producer), & Condon, B. (Director). (2004). *Kinsey* [Film]. Los Angeles: Fox Studios.

O'Donohue, W., & Kitchener, R. (1999). *Handbook of Behaviorism*. San Diego: Academia Press.

Peterson, F. L., Jr. (1999, March 11). Sexual myths. *Impact Weekly*, pp. 10-13.

Peterson, F. L., Jr. (2000). The assessment and treatment of erection dysfunction. In L. VandeCreek & T. L. Jackson (Eds.), *Innovations in Clinical Practice: A Source Book* (Vol. 18, pp. 57-71). Sarasota, FL: Professional Resource Press.

Pridal, C., & LoPiccolo, J. (2000). Multi-element treatment of desire disorders: Integration of cognitive, behavioral and systemic therapy. In S. Leiblum & R. Rosen (Eds.), *Principles and Practice of Sex Therapy* (3rd ed., pp. 57-81). New York: Guilford.

Process of Care Panel of the University of Medicine and Dentistry, New Jersey. (1998). *The Process of Care Model for the Evaluation and Treatment of Erection Dysfunction*. Unpublished manuscript used for continuing education, UMDNJ-Center for Continuing Education, Princeton, NJ.

Reinisch, J., & Beasley, R. (1990). What you must know to be sexually literate. *The Kinsey Institute New Report on Sex*. New York: St. Martin's Press.

Robinson, W. J. (1934). *Sexual Impotence* (19th ed.). New York: Eugenics Publishing Company.

Rosen, R. (2000). Medical and psychological interventions for erectile dysfunction: Toward a combined treatment approach. In S. Leiblum & R. Rosen (Eds.), *Principles and Practice of Sex Therapy* (3rd ed., pp. 276-304). New York: Guilford.

Schnarch, D. M. (1991). *Constructing the Sexual Crucible: An Integration of Sexual and Marital Therapy*. New York: W. W. Norton.

The Society for the Scientific Study of Sexuality. (2003). *Educational Opportunities in Human Sexuality: A Sourcebook*. Retrieved June 30, 2004, from www.sexscience.org

Stayton, W., Angelo, M., & Kaye, S. (2005, May). *Erotic Stimulus Pathways: The New Sexual Response Cycle*. Paper presented at the annual meeting of the American Association of Sexuality Educators, Counselors, and Therapists, Portland, OR.

U. S. Surgeon General. (2001). *The Surgeon General's Call to Action to Promote Sexual Health and Responsible Sexual Behavior* [A letter from the Surgeon General, U.S. Department of Health and Human Services]. Washington, DC: U.S. Government Printing Office.

Weeks, G. R. (2005). The emergence of a new paradigm in sex therapy: Integration. *Sexual and Relationship Therapy, 20*(1), 89-103.

Whipple, B. (2002). Women's sexual pleasure and satisfaction: A new view of female sexual function. *The Female Patient, 27*, 39-44.

World Health Organization. (2001). *Promotion of Sexual Health: Recommendations for Action*. Proceedings from a regional consultation convened by Pan American Health Organization and the World Health Organization in collaboration with the World Association for Sexology, Antigua Guatemala, Guatemala.

World Health Organization. (2004). *Progress in Reproductive Health Research: Sexual Health – A New Focus for WHO* [Pamphlet, No. 67]. Geneva: Author.

Zilbergeld, B. (1978). *Male Sexuality*. New York: Little, Brown.

Zilbergeld, B. (1992). *The New Male Sexuality* (rev. ed.). New York: Bantam.

How to Do a Sexual Health Assessment

Candace B. Risen

Never before has society been so aware of and so concerned about the myriad of sexual health problems that exist in the world. In 2001, the U.S. Surgeon General published a document entitled: *The Surgeon General's Call to Action to Promote Sexual Health and Responsible Sexual Behavior* as a "call to arms" for leadership in the health and mental health care sector in promoting and advancing education, intervention, and research in matters related to sexual health. In 2002 the World Health Organization revised its original definition of sexual health and defined it as

> a state of physical, emotional, mental, and social well-being related to sexuality; it is not merely the absence of disease, dysfunction, or infirmity. Sexual health requires a positive and respectful approach to sexuality and sexual relationships, as well as the possibility of having pleasurable and safe sexual experiences, free of coercion, discrimination, and violence. For sexual health to be attained and maintained, the sexual rights of all persons must be respected, protected, and fulfilled. (http://www.who.int/reproductive-health/gender/sexual_health.html

If mental health clinicians are to take on this leadership role in promoting and advancing sexual health, they must have the knowledge of the components and complexity of sexual health, the communication and interpersonal skills to use that knowledge, and the comfort and confidence that will enable them to do so. But what do we mean when we speak of promoting and advancing sexual health? I maintain that mental health clinicians are responsible for introducing, promoting, and facilitating a guided discussion of the topic as a significant aspect of physical and mental well-being, and not just when the client has a sexual concern. This is no easy task, especially because we come from a culture where sexuality is not discussed unless something bad happens and we are forced to. Even then, we are much more comfortable talking about it in global terms – homosexuality in the military, child abuse in the Catholic church, the AIDS epidemic – than we are about what we or our neighbors are thinking, feeling, or doing.

My task is to help you become more comfortable and more knowledgeable about assessing the sexual health issues in your clients' lives. I will devote the first half of this contribution to the process of conducting a sexual health assessment – that is, the why, when, with whom, and how – and the mental obstacles clinicians place in the way of engaging in that process. In the second half of this contribution, I will focus on a conceptual framework for understanding what should be included in a sexual health assessment. Remember, however, that a sexual health assessment is not something that must or even can be conducted in one sitting. It has many components that will be more or less relevant to the particular client or situation at hand. In real life, it will weave itself throughout the therapy, popping up from time to time, taking center stage at various points along the way, and then perhaps receding into the background until a future date.

THE PROCESS OF CONDUCTING A SEXUAL HEALTH ASSESSMENT

Why Conduct a Sexual Health Assessment?

Clinical practitioners are occasionally presented with specific questions about some aspect of sexual health, such as contraception, safe sexual practice, and changes in functioning. Taking a sexual history in these situations is clearly indicated. More often, clinical practitioners are called upon to engage with a client over some other aspect of concern or distress in his or her life. This distress may or may not be in the realm of sexuality; often it is not. Thus, taking a sexual health assessment may not be directly relevant to the situation at hand. Should the skill in doing one be learned and then tucked away in the far recesses of one's mental filing system to be brought up on the rare occasion that a sexual complaint appears front and center? I say no. Let me give you my two main reasons.

Everyone has sexual thoughts, feelings, and experiences that are integral to their sense of who they are and how they relate to the world. Sexual issues often manifest and mask themselves in two major problem areas that bring clients to a clinical practitioner: depression and anxiety related to either low self-esteem, relationship failures, or both. Yet, clients are shy about revealing their sexual issues. It feels so private, so awkward, so potentially embarrassing, that many are reduced to paralyzing inarticulateness. They dread being asked and they long to be asked. They know for sure that they need to be asked if it is ever to come out.

Secondly, this is a sexual health assessment we are talking about, not a sexual disease assessment. If we believe that sexual health is a vital aspect of physical and emotional health overall, we must be interested in and knowledgeable about what goes right for our clients, not just what goes wrong. We want to know about their strengths and sources of fulfillment as well as their weaknesses and areas of distress. We want to know about the events, experiences, and relationships in their lives, good and bad, that have shaped and molded who they are and how they relate to us and the world. How can we not ask about their sexual lives? Why would we not ask about their sexual lives?

Some might say, "Because I don't want to." Face it. We clinical practitioners are the products of the same inhibiting culture our clients are. We are supposed to be comfortable talking about anything in our professional role, including sex. But we are not. And we are not likely to get much help overcoming this particular hurdle in our professional education and training. So our unspoken anxiety sits in the room like a big boulder smack between our chair and our client's. Can we articulate it?

1. I'm not used to talking about sex; my discomfort and awkwardness will be obvious.
2. I don't exactly know why I am asking or what I want to know.
3. I won't know how to respond to what I hear back.
4. I may be unfamiliar with and/or not understand something my client tells me.
5. I may offend, embarrass, or sexually "interest" my client.
6. I may be perceived as nosy, provocative, or sexually "interested" in my client.
7. I won't know how to treat any problem I hear.
8. I'll be too embarrassed to consult with my colleagues.

Clinicians are often embarrassed to admit how anxious they feel about actually saying out loud sexual terms such as "penis, vagina, clitoris, and orgasm." All of a sudden we are confronted with how infrequently we actually vocalize these words, although we read them all the time. Am I pronouncing this right? Is it "cli**tor**is" or "**clit**oris"? Nevertheless, it is up to us to go first (i.e., to say the words out loud so that the client can follow suit). Sometimes we may use a word that is confusing or foreign to our client. Sometimes they will use words we don't understand. Over time one can build up knowledge of a large repertoire of expressions: some clinical and formal, others slang and street talk. It helps to gain a working familiarity with both kinds.

Beyond the awkwardness of sexual language, the many concerns about being perceived as nosy or intrusive may be more or less present depending on the particular client's ease in sharing sexual information. If the client seems uncomfortable and/or unable to respond to a simple question, it is natural to want to run for the hills. However, a little persistence can pay off.

Therapist:* We've been talking about your wife's unhappiness with your relationship to the children and being laid off for the past 3 months. How has that affected your sexual life together?
Tom: What do you mean (looks uncomfortable)?
Therapist: Sometimes marital conflict spills over into the bedroom. It can have a negative impact on the sexual part of the relationship.
Tom: We haven't been sexual in a while . . . a long while. We don't talk about it. I'm afraid to bring it up.
Therapist: Tell me more about your fear.

Tom is a little taken aback by the initial question. He doesn't know how to respond because he is not used to articulating aspects of his sexual life. A simple statement by his therapist about sexual intimacy helps get Tom started.

You may feel particularly uncomfortable or resistant when the topic is something you have never experienced and know nothing about. How will you appear knowledgeable about what the patient is talking about? What if the patient senses your ignorance and thinks you are too naïve or stupid to be of much help?

If you have no clue as to what someone is talking about, you have the choice of either being honest about your ignorance or covering it by asking further questions in a way that will illuminate the patient's response. Let's take a look at an example of each. Both are situations that actually happened to me.

Mr. A: I'm here because I've lost my nature.
Therapist: (Oh, my goodness! What is a nature? How does one lose it?) Tell me more about that.
Mr. A: You know, my nature. I just haven't had it in awhile.
Therapist: I don't really know what that word means, but if you can describe it, I'll probably understand what you are experiencing.

In this case, I first tried to bluff my way through by asking the tried and true "Tell me more." When that didn't work, I came clean but did it in such a way that invited more information and at the same time suggested that I would still be able to help. (By the way, I later learned that some patients used this term to describe libido and others used it to describe erectile capacity.)

In the next example, I managed to cover my ignorance by inviting a more personalized response. In this case, I did not want to profess total ignorance of the subject because the patient was counting on my being someone experienced and knowledgeable in all areas of sexuality. In truth, I was relatively new to the field and woefully deficient in my knowledge of unconventional sexual behaviors.

---

* Names and identifying characteristics have been changed to protect confidentiality.

Ray: So, you know, I've been attending these swinging parties and, lately, it's been bothering me.

Therapist: What is bothering you about them?

Ray: Well, you know what goes on there. You know all about these parties, right?

Therapist: But I don't know *your* experience of these parties. I don't want to assume anything. Tell me what they are like through your eyes. Then I will know better what is bothering you.

In this case, I thought the patient's concerns about being viewed as weird would be exacerbated by my lack of knowledge and perceived naivete, so I chose to dodge the question and focus on learning more about him.

Sometimes it is not our ignorance that gets in the way but our distress when we hear about a behavior or situation we disapprove of. We all have values and moral standards that we live by, and we may be tempted to react by taking a strong judgmental stance. Although clients may be looking to us to model those values and standards, imposing them or even sharing them prematurely will more often than not shame the client and shut down all further communication.

Jennifer: I want to get married some day and have children. I'm so afraid I'll be alone for the rest of my life. I keep meeting these guys at bars and they tell me they think I'm hot, but after one or two nights of "hooking up," they disappear. What's wrong with me? Why don't they like me?

Therapist: How can you think a guy will respect you if you "hook up" right away? What kind of guys do you think you're going to meet at a bar anyway?"

This may be what the therapist is thinking and it may even be true, but expressing it is likely to shut the patient down and discourage any future sharing. Had the therapist responded like this. . . .

Therapist: Tell me about your expectations when you go to bars and hook up with guys.

. . . the patient would have felt invited to explore her feelings about what she is doing.

Self-awareness and reflection are invaluable tools. Being consciously aware of your own ambivalence or discomfort when talking about sexual matters will help you not give in to it. Reflecting back on what you have explored will help you identify what you missed and need to revisit. As with most things, practice pays off. Remember that you are likely to do more harm by never broaching the subject than you are by broaching it awkwardly. With experience, your increasing comfort and expanding knowledge will make the job that much easier. In the meantime, patience, persistence, and a sense of humor will help you get through the processes of gaining experience. It helps to know that although patients may initially react as though you had intruded into territory too personal to be shared, they are usually settled by a simple explanation as to the relevance of the question and ultimately grateful for your interest.

DO *recognize the meaning and value of sexual expression in people's lives.*

DON'T *let your own inhibitions prevent you from inquiring about sexual matters.*

When Should I Do This?

Conducting a sexual health assessment when someone shows up in a crisis about something else is not particularly relevant or helpful. Early and abrupt questions about sexuality will be off-putting unless the chief complaint is of a sexual nature. On the other hand, putting it off indefinitely or waiting until the client brings it up may reinforce the idea that it is a taboo subject. Because sexuality is a topic that is difficult for patients to bring up, the therapist must assume responsibility for introducing it as an area of possible relevance.

The situation that offers the most natural segue into the topic is the gathering of psychosocial and developmental information early on in the counseling process. As one is inquiring about childhood history, significant events, issues, and problems, there can be a natural lead-in to inquiring about sexual matters. Examples of such transitional questions are:

- We've been talking a lot about your marriage today. Tell me something about the sexual relationship between you and your spouse.
- I have asked you a lot of questions about your childhood and family of origin. How and what did you learn about sex growing up?
- Has your low self-esteem affected your sexual life as well as the other areas you have mentioned?

The advantage of conducting a sexual health assessment early on is that it gives the client permission to speak of sexual issues at any time. If, however, you've forgotten to do this, introducing the topic at a later time won't hurt.

- I realize that, in our focus on your marital struggles around finances and the children, I've neglected to ask you about your sexual relationship with your spouse.

Whether you introduce questions about sexual health early on or after a period of work together, you may be met with openness and even relief on one hand or momentary discomfort on the other. Don't be dissuaded by the latter. If nothing else, the inquiry tells the patient "This is OK to talk about. I'm interested in hearing about it if you want to tell me. I'll even help you talk about it by taking the lead."

DO *go first. You must be the one to introduce the topic.*

DON'T *assume sexuality is not an important area of inquiry just because the client hasn't mentioned it.*

With Whom Should I Do This?

Unless the chief complaint is so specific and narrow in focus or the time spent together so short or crisis oriented, every client from preadolescence on up should be offered the opportunity to address sexual concerns. Younger children are generally not asked unless there is a specific sexual concern. You might worry that bringing up the subject of sex is inappropriate when talking with a preadolescent. In today's world, preadolescents have already been exposed to a myriad of sexual messages, images, and terminology, much of which they may be confused about or have concerns. Many of them have already had sexual experiences, wanted or unwanted. Most of them have questions about contraception, safe sex, and pregnancy that will not be cleared up by attending a sexual education class. It is naïve and irresponsible to think that they do not need a format for discussing their sexual concerns. If your initial interest in their sexual life is met with resistance, it may be easier for them to talk first about what their peers are saying or doing rather than what their own sexual experiences have been. At the other end of the spectrum, the elderly must be included as well. Therapists are often reluctant to inquire about the sexual feelings and activities of the elderly (often defined as anyone as old or older than one's parents!). Our culture emphasizes youth and beauty, and there is a tendency to see aging people as asexual or, even worse, to make fun of their displays of sexual interest. Older adults, in turn, may be embarrassed to admit that they still have needs for physical affection, closeness, intimacy, and sexual gratification. I will never forget a man in his eighties who called our intake line and asked rather tentatively, "Am I too old to talk to someone about my sexual problem?" He later told us that he had first gone to talk to his primary care physician about his erectile problems and was told he was "lucky to be alive" and shouldn't be worrying about sex (this was in the early 1980s, long before the advent of Viagra).

DO *include a sexual health assessment in your gathering of information unless there is a good reason not to.*

DON'T *assume someone is too young or too old to have sexual concerns.*

How Do I Do This Well?

Taking a sexual health assessment is not just about asking a series of questions in order to elicit a series of answers. Although clearly there are questions to be asked and answers to be told, it might be more helpful to think of it as inviting clients to tell their "sexual story." Open-ended questions that encourage clients to tell their sexual story using their own language are ideal, but many clients are too inhibited or unsure of what to say and require more direction. Patience and calm encouragement, along with the guidance of more specific questions, will usually get the ball rolling.

Sexual stories, as with any story, have a pattern of flow and a combination of plots and subplots, characters, and meaning. Here is a partial list of components of a sexual story:

1. Family/religious messages about sex during childhood
2. Sexual experiences, wanted or unwanted, in childhood
3. Discovery of sexual feelings/masturbation
4. Timing and experience of puberty
5. Body image
6. Awareness of same-sex or opposite-sex attractions
7. Dating
8. First and subsequent partner sexual experiences
9. First and subsequent experiences of romance and love
10. Problems with any aspect of sexual functioning
11. Contraception/protection
12. Pregnancy/childbirth
13. Impact of aging or chronic illness on sexual identity/expression

Some stories unfold chronologically from beginning to end; others begin at the end and flash backwards to illustrate and highlight the significant determinants to the ending. Either way, the events, characters, and meanings are eventually interwoven into one or two major themes that constitute "the story." Whether or not you begin by asking about current sexual feelings and behaviors and then gather history or begin by taking a developmental history depends on two factors:

1. The absence or presence of a current sexual issue that requires direct attention
2. The client's comfort with addressing current sexual functioning as opposed to historical narrative

When clients have immediate sexual concerns, they won't appreciate your starting with historical questions such as what sexual messages they received as children, even if the history is relevant. The following example illustrates staying with the present.

Kathy: (6 months pregnant) Steve and I planned for this baby and I should be so happy but I'm not. I've been crying and so irritable with him. When I finally blurted out last week that I was sorry I ever got pregnant, he made me promise I would see someone.
Therapist: What do you think the problem might be?
Kathy: I don't know. I mean, I know Steve loves me and I love him, but. . . .
Therapist: What made you sorry you ever got pregnant?
Kathy: I don't know. I mean, I should be happy but I feel terrible.

There is a story to be told here but, so far, the therapist is clueless. The best thing to do is to keep gently pushing Kathy, using the words she uses to try to get at the source of her anguish.

Therapist: Terrible how? What is that feeling?
Kathy: Guilty! I feel guilty!
Therapist: What do you have to feel guilty about?
Kathy: I'm afraid to tell you. I've never told anyone. Even Steve doesn't know.
Therapist: Do you want to tell me now?
Kathy: When I was in college I was raped. I got pregnant and had an abortion. Steve doesn't know. We're both Catholic. I feel guilty about the rape, guilty about the abortion, and guilty about the secret. I thought having this baby would make it all go away. Instead, it's worse!

In this case, the therapist stayed with the client in the present, following her lead rather than asking a series of pointed questions. Kathy's anxiety and need to reveal her secret to someone won out.

On the other hand, when clients are embarrassed or uncomfortable talking about the present, they can often ease into it by talking about sexual issues growing up.

Therapist: What is your sexual life these days?
Joyce: I don't know what you mean . . . like, am I seeing anyone?
Therapist: Sure . . . we can start there.
Joyce: Well, I've been dating this guy, Richard, for 3 months. We have been sexual. . . . (long silence)
Therapist: How has that been for you? Are you enjoying the sexual relationship?
Joyce: It's OK. (silence)
Therapist: Is Richard your first sexual partner?
Joyce: No. (silence)
Therapist: Tell me about the first one.
Joyce: I was 15 and he was a year ahead of me in high school. My parents didn't approve of him because he smoked and hung out with a crowd they didn't like. But I wasn't having a good year and he was an escape for me. He had a car and we would go driving around after school. I told my mother I had to stay after school for one thing or another.

Therapist: What led up to your being sexual with him?

Joyce: I didn't really want to but he did and I didn't want to lose him. The first time was in his car. I didn't really get anything out of it. We went together until he graduated and went to work. We were sexual the whole time but I never really felt good about it. I didn't trust him. Later, after he broke up with me, I heard he had been with others and I felt stupid and really angry with myself. I think it warped me or something. Sex has never been all that good. I don't get much out of it. I think I just do it to stay in a relationship.

In this case, the therapist helped Joyce by being willing to start with whatever Joyce brought up, "Like am I seeing anyone?" Even so, Joyce was reticent and so, rather than push her beyond an initial question or two, the therapist switched gears and inquired about her earlier experiences. Joyce had an easier time responding to this question and was then able to relax enough to go back to talking about her current experience. Had she not been able to make that transition, the therapist would have been wise to keep the focus on past experiences and inquire about the present another time.

DO *be flexible in your approach to helping clients talk about their sexual lives.*

DON'T *let your concerns about getting the "right" information get in the way of letting the sexual story unfold.*

Sexual Health Assessments of Couples

Clinicians are often called upon to counsel couples around issues of interpersonal conflict. Whether or not the main concern is sexual in nature, understanding something about how the couple relates sexually seems intrinsic to understanding the essence of their relationship. Doing a sexual health assessment of a couple requires sensitivity to three additional issues:

1. Most partners communicate very little with each other about their sexual relationship. Being invited to do so in front of a therapist may be intimidating and uncomfortable in the beginning.
2. Partners often have very different viewpoints about their sexual relationship. They may or may not be willing to confront or correct each other.
3. Each partner has private sexual thoughts, experiences, and even secrets that he or she may not be willing to share. Often these include prerelationship sexual experiences, masturbation, and sexual fantasy. One must respect these private thoughts and experiences and address them only in an individual session.

When conducting a sexual health assessment with a couple, you may want to introduce the topic in a conjoint interview to get an overall sense of any sexual concerns and the ease with which they can talk about sexual issues together. However, it is wise to schedule at least one individual interview with each partner early in the assessment as a matter of "routine." That way they know that each will have some private time in which to discuss feelings or life experiences that cannot be discussed with as much candor in front of their partner.

DO *include a sexual health assessment when you are counseling couples.*

DON'T *inquire about private sexual matters in a couple's format.*

Overcoming the mental obstacles to taking a sexual health assessment and gaining confidence about your ability to discuss sexual matters will certainly offer your clients a much needed opportunity to come forward with their sexual concerns. This is a reward in and of itself. There is an additional bonus, however. You may well find an increased interest in and comfort with exploring your own sexual story, whether in the privacy of your own mind or shared with someone else. Now that's invaluable!

THE COMPONENTS OF A SEXUAL HEALTH ASSESSMENT

Overcoming inhibition, initiating discussion, and being interested and nonjudgmental will go a long way toward helping clients talk about their sexual lives. Clients, however, may not be readily able to describe their sexual thoughts, feelings, or behaviors without being guided through a series of questions that reflect the clinician's knowledge about the subject. So, what do we mean when we ask our clients about their "sexual lives"? What are we really asking them to describe? I propose the following conceptual framework that addresses that question.

The term "sexuality" can be thought of as comprising three distinct components: identity, function, and relational meaning.

Sexual Identity

Sexual identity has to do with the core of one's sexual "being." The two major features of a sexual identity are gender identity and orientation. Gender identity refers to both biologic sex – that is, male or female and the more subjective sense of self as either masculine or feminine. A small number of people are distressed about their biologic gender and are confused by their strong persistent wishes to be the opposite sex. Most people, however, are comfortable with the fact of their biologic gender. They may or may not feel, however, that they live up to some yardstick of femininity or masculinity. Issues of body image, personality characteristics, interests, and sexual desirability may be a source of conflict or shame when they don't fit with the image of an "ideal" masculine or feminine persona. Some people struggle with a lifelong feeling of inadequacy because of one or more of these issues.

Mark: (a residential house manager) I've been doing a painting job at our best friend's house. It's really made me feel bad about myself. They have such a traditional life. He goes off to work every day and she takes care of their two kids. He makes a lot more money than I do. I'm painting on the side just to make ends meet. I know Mary wants to work full time but still. . . . I mean, I love being the one home when our kids get off the bus, but I feel ashamed.

Therapist: What is the shame about?

Mark: My father and three brothers all make big money. I've always been different. I like to cook and take care of the house and kids. I like the flexibility of my schedule. But I haven't been successful the way they have, and every time I go home to visit, I'm reminded of it. Sometimes they even tease me and call me "Marcie."

Others struggle only when certain life events create changes that threaten their sense of gender identity.

Sarah: I've felt great during the pregnancy and we are so looking forward to the baby! I'm just worried that I've gained so much weight. I feel like a whale even though the doctor says I'm fine. I'm afraid of what Michael will think if I can't lose it quickly.

Therapist: What might he think?

Sarah: Well, Michael has always said that he was attracted to me from across the room because I was tall and thin and beautiful. I know he loves me but I think looks are very important to him. I guess I've relied on my body to keep his attention.

A persistent negative gender identity sense can lead to low self-esteem, avoidance of partner-related sex and intimacy, and social and emotional isolation. Gentle inquiry about body image, comfort with gender roles, and gender preferences may reveal areas of gender conflict.

Orientation refers to the linkage of sexual feelings with an attraction to another person. It includes both a subjective sense of attraction to a same- or opposite-sex partner as well as actual or objective behavior with a partner. Therapists need to be clear that the subjective and objective aspects of orientation are not always congruent and cannot be assumed from each other. For example, a man may be engaging in sex with his wife while fantasizing about another man. His subjective orientation is homoerotic at the same time that he is engaging in heterosexual behavior.

The following use of language may help differentiate the objective and subjective components of orientation:

Objective	**Subjective**
Contact with opposite sex (heterosexual)	Fantasy about opposite sex (heteroerotic)
Contact with same sex (homosexual)	Fantasy about same sex (homoerotic)
Contact with both sexes (bisexual)	Fantasy about both sexes (bierotic)
Contact with neither sex (asexual)	Fantasy about neither sex (anerotic)

It is important to remember not to assume heterosexuality because of your own heterosexist bias or because of certain client characteristics such as marital status, appearance, age, or religious background. Try to ask orientation-neutral questions such as "Who was your first sexual partner?" rather than "Who was your first boy(girl)friend?" When you have learned about one set of experiences, whether heterosexual or homosexual, ask about the other. A simple question such as, "How about same- (or opposite-) sex experiences; have you ever had any or thought you might like to?" will introduce the subject. If your client expresses surprise or even dismay, you can simply reply "Well, many people do," and move on. The goal is to encourage clients to speak about *all* of their sexual feelings and behaviors, including those that they may be reluctant to reveal.

Sexual Functioning

Sexual functioning refers to the actual process of engaging in sexual behavior. Clients often present with complaints about some aspect of their or their partner's ability to function sexually. A list of frequently heard complaints about sexual functioning can be found on page 32. Enhancing male sexual functioning via a drug such as Viagra has become a huge marketing phenomenon in the past half decade. In the privacy of a clinician's office, however, clients often have trouble articulating what aspect of functioning is bothering them. They lack the language to make the distinctions among libido, drive, desire, arousal, ejaculation, and orgasm.

Their attempts to describe what is happening can be confusing and often misleading unless the clinician can guide the discussion.

Sexual functioning can be most easily described if one breaks it down into three separate but related components: desire, arousal, and orgasm. Sexual desire is composed of the interaction of three elements: (a) a biologic urge referred to as drive or libido, (b) a cognitive wish to engage in sexual behavior, and (c) an emotional willingness to allow one's body to respond to a sexual experience. For example, one could have a biological urge to be sexual and an emotional longing for a specific person, but the cognitive wish *not* to engage in sexual behavior because of religious or moral prohibitions. Although men's desire, especially young men, is most often determined by drive, women's desire is more often experienced as a receptivity to an external sexual overture (Basson, 2000). Sexual desire is complex and cannot be understood based on any one question. Asking several questions such as the following will help you understand better:

1. How often do you feel like having sex?
2. How often would you have sex if you could?
3. How do you feel when your partner initiates sexual contact?
4. What makes you want to have sex?
5. What gets in the way of your wanting to have sex?

Sexual arousal is easier to describe. It is a "horniness" or bodily excitement, a warm, tingling, and increasingly pleasurable sensation. Arousal is usually in response to an external stimulus such as touch or a visual image, but it can also happen in response to a thought or fantasy or, in a young male, absolutely nothing! It is usually but not always accompanied by increased blood flow to the pelvic area resulting in an erection in males and vulvar swelling and lubrication in females. Questions about arousal might include:

1. Do you have any trouble getting or staying aroused?
2. How does it feel when your breasts or genitals are touched?
3. Does your arousal build up as the stimulation continues?
4. What kinds of stimulation are you most (least) aroused by?

Orgasm, also known as "climax" or the more colloquial expression "to come," refers to the rhythmic contractions and accompanying pleasurable sensations that culminate the build-up of arousal. Male complaints about orgasm usually center on their inability to control the timing of it. Either they climax too quickly to suit their or their partner's needs (referred to as premature ejaculation) or they find orgasm very difficult or impossible to achieve. The latter is often the result of certain drugs that interfere with or delay orgasm such as many of the antidepressants and antihypertensive medications. Female complaints typically center on their inability to build up enough arousal to reach orgasm, especially during intercourse. Some women may not be sure they have ever had an orgasm. They may even ask you how they can be sure! It's tempting but not useful to respond by saying, "If you're not sure, you probably haven't." I have found that comparing arousal and orgasm to a sneeze is helpful. Sexual arousal is akin to the tingly sensation you feel in your nasal passages when a sneeze is coming on. Orgasm is the sneeze. I had one woman respond by saying, "Oh, I get it. I've never sneezed!"

Problems with desire, arousal, or orgasm are referred to as sexual dysfunctions. For some people, the problem has been lifelong; for others a problem is "acquired" during the course of their sexual life. Some problems are global: experienced all the time, with partners and during self-stimulation. Others are more situational: that is, with only certain partners or with a partner but not during self-stimulation.

Linda is a happily married 35-year-old mother of two. Her husband complains that she has no desire for sex and rebuffs his advances. Except for briefly during their courtship, Linda has never been interested in sex. She reports that she never understood what her high school girlfriends were giggling about, nor did she feel the urge to masturbate. Her husband has been her only sexual partner. *(lifelong, global lack of desire)*

Jake is a 50-year-old male whose year-long affair ended abruptly 6 months ago after he had a mild heart attack. Jake knows that the affair had to end anyway and he is both sad and relieved. He is attempting to put the pieces of his life back together. He was afraid to be sexual for several months after the heart attack, but he has resumed masturbation successfully. However he is not able to sustain an erection when he attempts sex with his wife. *(acquired, situational erectile dysfunction)*

Lifelong sexual dysfunctions usually signal that something went awry in the developmental process of becoming a comfortable sexual being. It may make more sense for the clinician, therefore, to explore childhood and familial sexual experiences, attitudes, messages, and beliefs that may have negatively impacted that process. On the other hand, acquired sexual dysfunctions reflect a negative change in something that worked well before. That change may be a physical change such as illness, injury, medication, or surgery; an emotional change as a result of personal, partner, or familial discord; or both. The emotions that most often interfere with sexual functioning are anxiety, guilt, fear, anger, and sadness.

If we go back to the example of Linda, it appears that Linda's lack of interest in sex has little if anything to do with her relationship with her husband or her satisfaction in life. She reports never having much interest in the topic of sexuality nor was she aware of sexual feelings in her body. It may be fruitful to explore the sexual messages she received from her family, church, and others during childhood and adolescence; whether or not she suffered any negative or unwanted sexual experiences; and anything else we or she can think of that may have predisposed her to shut down sexual interest.

Jake, on the other hand, enjoyed sex and was able to function for a good part of his life. We might speculate that Jake's current inability to sustain an erection with his wife may be a reflection of (a) anxiety about the impact of sexual arousal on his heart, (b) depression about the loss of youth and vitality as he knew it, (c) grief over the abrupt ending of his affair, (d) guilt about the affair, or (e) negative feelings about his wife and marriage. All of these will require careful exploration.

We must remember that any attempt to explore a client's sexual functioning should include an understanding of the partner's functioning as well. The sexual functioning of one partner always has an impact on the other. Each partner's component characteristics – desire, arousal, orgasm – impact on the other whether the components are positive or problematic. His erectile difficulties may negatively impact her desire; her lack of desire may negatively impact his ability to get an erection. On a more positive note, his excitement may positively augment her desire; her arousal may facilitate his orgasm. Levine (1998) refers to this balancing act as the "sexual equilibrium." It continually occurs and accounts for the different outcomes from partner to partner and from episode to episode with the same partner. Although Linda identifies her lack of interest in sex as a lifelong problem, her husband's reaction to this problem may make it better or worse. If he is critical, angry, and demanding of her, she is unlikely to be able to effect much positive change. Her problem may even lead to his developing a sexual problem such as loss of desire or anxiety about being sexually adequate.

Relational Meaning

The decision to be sexual, whether made on impulse or carefully thought out, almost always has some relational meaning. It conveys something about how one person feels about the other and the role sexual behavior will play in conveying that feeling. The feelings can range from "I'm horny and you're available" to "We're both lonely" to "I like you and want to know you better" to "I love you" or a myriad of other meanings. When taking a sexual health assessment, it is important to elicit the role or meaning that sexual expression plays in your client's life. This is especially critical when you are dealing with adolescents and single young adults who are often struggling with how sexual behavior fits in to their view of their sexual identity and value system. Are they seeking sexual behavior in order to gain experience, develop skill, find out what they like and don't like, and have fun? This group might see sex as recreational and won't attach significant relational meaning to it. Others may see sexual behavior as a way to get to know someone better and discover whether the person will be a suitable partner. They are using sexual behavior as one of many activities in the process of seeking an intimate and hopefully permanent, or at least long-standing, commitment. A third group, ever shrinking in today's world, reserve engaging in sexual behavior until they find this partner. For them, sexual behavior is the culmination of an emotional commitment they have already felt and given to their partner. With clients of all ages, however, significant values, morals, and beliefs about sexual identity and behavior will emerge in response to your questioning and help you get a sense of the essence of this person.

Sometimes the urges to be sexual are less benign and reflect a need to control, humiliate, dominate, or use another person for personal gratification. When the meaning or purpose of engaging in sexual behavior is unusual, hostile, dehumanizing, or coercive, the American Psychiatric Association (2000) terms these urges "paraphilias." The term is actually of Greek origin; "para" means on the side, of "philia," or love. Included in these are exhibitionism, voyeurism, fetishism, pedophilia, and sadomasochism. These are more difficult to share, and even the gentlest of approaches may not elicit an honest, accurate response. Often, they will come to the attention of a clinician only after a spouse or partner discovers the particular preoccupation through actual experience of it or discovery of pornography or other sources depicting these unusual themes. Years ago, clinicians were rarely confronted with paraphilias. Today, access to a wide variety of unusual sexual interests via the Internet has rapidly brought these problems to the forefront. Although you may never want to treat these types of problems, taking a good sexual health assessment requires that you inquire about them and be willing to discuss them in a helpful manner. At the very least, you can increase the likelihood that your client will accept a referral to a specialist for ongoing care.

A FINAL NOTE

Guiding someone through a sexual health assessment can be a rewarding experience for both client and clinician. Your client will benefit from having the unique opportunity to explore the complexity of his or her sexual life in a safe, nonjudgmental, and thoughtful manner. You will benefit by acquiring an ever-growing comfort and skill in talking intelligently about a subject that is often deemed taboo in this culture. Hopefully, both of you will walk away feeling privileged to have had this experience.

Frequently Heard Complaints About Sexual Function

Desire

- I have no desire. (absent)
- I hate the thought of sex. (aversive)
- I have too little desire. (hypoactive)
- I have too much desire. (hyperactive)
- My partner and I are incompatible in our desire for sex.

Arousal

- Male
    1. I cannot obtain and/or maintain an erection under any circumstances (i.e., masturbation, early morning awakening, or with a partner).
    2. When I am with a partner, I cannot obtain and/or maintain an erection sufficient for penetration.
    3. When I am with a partner, I lose my erection shortly after penetration.

- Female
    1. I cannot become aroused and/or maintain arousal under any circumstances. I feel little or nothing when I touch or my partner touches my breasts or genitals.
    2. I am never aroused enough to achieve orgasm.
    3. I can become aroused/maintain arousal with masturbation but never with a partner.

Orgasm

- Male
    1. I ejaculate too quickly (premature ejaculation) when I am with a partner.
    2. I cannot ejaculate in the vagina.
    3. I cannot ejaculate when I am with a partner.
    4. I get little/no physical pleasure from orgasm.
    5. Ejaculation is painful.
    6. I have an orgasm but do not ejaculate.

- Female
    1. I find it too difficult to achieve orgasm under any circumstances and infrequently or never do.
    2. I cannot achieve orgasm with intercourse.
    3. I cannot achieve orgasm when I am with a partner.
    4. I get little/no physical pleasure from orgasm.

Penetration

- Male
    1. My erection is bent, making penetration and thrusting painful and/or difficult.
    2. I have no feeling in my penis during intercourse.
    3. My erection and/or penetration are painful.

- Female
    1. Penetration is impossible: I tighten up so much that nothing can penetrate my vagina. (vaginismus)
    2. I have no feeling in my vagina during intercourse.
    3. Penetration and thrusting are painful. (dyspareunia)

Satisfaction

- Because of a sexual problem, I am not satisfied.
- We have no sexual problem, yet I am not satisfied.
- My partner's sexual response is not satisfying.

CONTRIBUTOR

Candace B. Risen, LISW, is the Co-Director of the Center for Marital and Sexual Health in Beachwood, Ohio, an internationally recognized training center in the field of human sexuality. Her clinical specialty lies in the areas of sexual deviance disorders, sexual functioning, and sexual identity. She is the Associate Editor of the *Handbook of Clinical Sexuality for Mental Health Professionals*, published in 2003. In 2005, Mrs. Risen was the Co-Recipient of the Masters and Johnson Award for outstanding contribution to the field of human sexuality. Mrs. Risen may be contacted at 23230 Chagrin Boulevard, #350, Beachwood, OH 44122. E-Mail: candace.risen@case.edu

RESOURCES

Cited Resources

American Psychiatric Association. (2000). *Diagnostic and Statistical Manual of Mental Disorders* (4th ed. text rev.). Washington, DC: Author.

Basson, R. (2000). The female sexual response: A different model. *Journal of Sex and Marital Therapy, 26,* 51-65.

Levine, S. (1998). *Sexuality in Mid-Life.* New York: Plenum.

U.S. Surgeon General. (2001). *The Surgeon General's Call to Action to Promote Sexual Health and Responsible Sexual Behavior.* Retrieved March 23, 2002, from http://www.surgeongeneral.gov/library/sexualhealth/

World Health Organization. (2002). *Gender and Reproductive Rights, Glossary, Sexual Health.* Retrieved July 11, 2003, from http://www.who.int/reproductive-health/gender/glossary.html

Additional Resources

Levine, S., Risen, C., & Althof, S. (Eds.). (2003). *Handbook of Clinical Sexuality for Mental Health Professionals.* New York: Brunner-Routledge.

Maurice, W. (1999). *Sexual Medicine in Primary Care.* St. Louis, MO: Mosby.

Senior Sexual Health:
The Effects of Aging on Sexuality

Andrea Bradford and Cindy M. Meston

By the year 2030, nearly 20% of people in the United States will be 65 years of age or older. This group will consist of an estimated 71 million individuals, 19.5 million of whom will exceed the age of 80 (Centers for Disease Control and Prevention [CDC], 2003). This trend is not restricted to Americans; worldwide, adults aged 60 and older comprise the most rapidly growing segment of the population (World Health Organization, 2002). Increasing longevity is partly responsible for this demographic shift, suggesting a need for focus on sustaining health and quality of life into old age. The maintenance of good health and general well-being in later life has meaningful implications for sexual relationships and behaviors. Although the average adult age is clearly on the rise, sexuality in older adults is often misunderstood, misrepresented, or simply invisible. The purpose of this contribution is to provide an overview of the influence of aging on the sexual lives of men and women and to describe potentially important aspects of assessment and treatment of older adults with sexual concerns.

SEXUALITY ACROSS THE LIFE SPAN: WHAT IS "NORMAL"?

Normative information about sexuality can be both educational and therapeutic to clients who are concerned about their own sexual lives as they grow older (Leiblum & Segraves, 2000). Although information on sexuality in midlife and old age has been limited compared to the available data on younger adults, the growth of the older adult population has contributed to recent interest in the scientific study of sexual feelings and behaviors in this age group. The precedent for including mature adults in studies of sexual behavior extends back a number of decades (e.g., Kinsey, Pomeroy, & Martin, 1948), but many of the most comprehensive examinations of sexuality in this population have been conducted more recently (e.g., American Association of Retired Persons [AARP], 2005; Laumann et al., 2005; National Council on Aging [NCOA], 2005).

A consistent finding from multiple studies is that sexuality continues to be an important aspect of life for many adults throughout midlife and into old age. The American Association of Retired Persons reported that 62% of men and 51% of women between ages 60 and 69 believed sexual activity is an important component of a good relationship; these figures declined slightly after age 70 (AARP, 2005). The National Council on Aging (2005) reported that 71% of men in their 60s and 57% of men in their 70s engaged in sexual activity at least once per month. These percentages were somewhat lower for women (51% and 30%, respectively).

Less is known about sexuality in very old age (e.g., 80 years of age or older), but the available data suggest that sexuality is significant for many people in this age range as well. Bretschneider and McCoy's (1988) survey of 202 men and women over the age of 80 concluded that the majority of these individuals continued to fantasize about intimate contact with a partner. The NCOA (2005) study reported that 27% of men and 18% of women in their 80s engaged in sexual activity at least once a month.

Men

Although erectile functioning tends to decline progressively beginning in midlife (Araujo, Mohr, & McKinlay, 2004; Laumann, Paik, & Rosen, 1999), it should not be inferred that erectile failure is an inevitable consequence of aging. Although some degree of change in sexual response is normal for middle-aged and older men, there is considerable variability in the extent to which these changes affect the ability to engage in satisfying sexual activity. Typical changes in erectile function include a lengthier delay in attaining a full erection, less distension or rigidity of the erect penis, fewer erections during sleep, and a decline in penile sensitivity (Rowland, 1998; Schiavi, 1999; Wespes, 2002). Adapting to these changes may require some variation from the sexual routines of years past, including, for example, the addition or prolonging of foreplay, greater emphasis on direct physical stimulation of the penis, and adjustment to sexual intercourse positions that are more feasible when some rigidity of the erection is lost.

Men may also experience change in orgasmic responses with age. Latency to ejaculation may be increased, and consequently the amount of time and stimulation required to reach orgasm may be greater. Typically the orgasmic response itself is shorter in older men, with a less forceful ejaculation and a lower volume of semen expelled at each ejaculation. The refractory period following ejaculation is also lengthened; whereas a young man may be able to become aroused to orgasm within minutes of a previous ejaculation, in older men this delay can be considerably longer, spanning as long as a few days (Masters & Johnson, 1966; Schiavi, 1999).

Androgen production gradually wanes in men beginning around age 50 and is often implicated in the decline of libido and sexual responsiveness. In a longitudinal study of aging men, nearly half of men aged 80 and older could be classified as "hypogonadal" on the basis of norms for testosterone levels in younger men (Harman et al., 2001). However, testosterone treatment for sexual problems and the concept of a "testosterone deficiency" or "andropause" syndrome in older men are controversial. The available clinical evidence to date suggests that the benefits of testosterone for sexual function are limited to those men whose natural testosterone levels fall below a relatively low "threshold" value that seems to be necessary to maintain adequate sexual function. Thus, men who are near or within a normal range of androgen production are unlikely to enjoy substantial benefit from the use of testosterone (Isidori et al., 2005).

Women

Unlike men, whose capacities for sexual responsiveness generally peak in early adulthood and slowly change over time, women's sexual responding does not show such a consistent pattern over the life span. The incidence of some sexual problems in women may actually decrease after early adulthood (Laumann et al., 1999). However, women experience a steeper decline in sexual interest than men in later life (DeLamater & Sill, 2005). Interestingly, this trend does not parallel sexual satisfaction among older women, which may remain somewhat higher in women than in men (AARP, 2005).

Menopause typically occurs in midlife around the age of 50 and is marked by a dramatic reduction in estrogen, progesterone, and androgen levels. Menopause, more so than age *per se*, seems to be critically associated with sexual changes in women (Dennerstein, Alexander, & Kotz, 2003). Following menopause, a number of physiological changes secondary to the loss of estrogen affect the appearance and functioning of the genitals. The lining of the vaginal wall thins, and vaginal secretions are reduced. The vagina also shortens and loses flexibility (Masters & Johnson, 1966). Atrophy of the genital tissues and vaginal dryness may lead to painful sexual intercourse. An increased risk of urethral irritation, urogenital infections, and urinary incontinence also accompanies postmenopausal changes in genital tissue (Butler et al., 1994; Masters & Johnson, 1966; Society of Obstetricians and Gynaecologists of Canada, 2004).

Age-related changes in women's sexual responses somewhat mirror those that occur in men. Vaginal lubrication is not only reduced but also takes longer to appear following the onset of sexual stimulation. Likewise, engorgement of the clitoral and vaginal tissue is slower and less robust. As in men, orgasm tends to be briefer and associated with fewer muscular contractions, although the capacity for multiple orgasms is not necessarily compromised. These declines in responsiveness may be attenuated somewhat by engaging in regular sexual activity, although the mechanism is not understood (Masters & Johnson, 1966).

Despite abundant interest in the effects of sex hormones on women's sexual desire, responsiveness, and satisfaction, the clinical efficacy of systemic hormone replacement therapy for sexual problems is unclear. The effects of estrogen treatment on the integrity of genital tissue are the best established. Speculation about the influence of androgens on sexual desire, on the other hand, has yielded numerous studies with clinically ambiguous outcomes (Alexander et al., 2004; Davis et al., 2005). The long-term safety of estrogen and androgen supplementation in women has also been called into question (e.g., Basaria & Dobs, 2004; Hickey, Davis, & Sturdee, 2005), and thus at present there is insufficient data to inform a clear risk-benefit calculation. Among women who cannot or choose not to take systemic estrogen, localized estrogen preparations (e.g., creams, vaginal suppositories) can be effective alternatives for treating vaginal dryness and irritation (for recommendations, see Society of Obstetricians and Gynaecologists of Canada, 2004). Although the loss of estrogen during menopause inevitably brings about physical changes, it should be noted that women's psychological and relational adjustment during the menopausal transition and beyond have a greater influence on sexuality than genital structure and function alone (Hartmann et al., 2004).

SEXUALITY AS AN ASPECT OF HEALTHY AGING

A number of chronic medical conditions are more prevalent in older adults, and the impact of poorer health on sexuality can be substantial. Clinical reports suggest that many elderly couples discontinue sexual activity due to illness, especially in the male partner (Leiblum & Segraves, 2000). Some of the most common chronic medical conditions among middle-aged and older adults, including cardiovascular disease, hypertension, and diabetes mellitus, are associated with various sexual problems in men and women (M. Burchardt et al., 2002; DeLamater & Sill, 2005; Doruk et al., 2005; Laumann et al., 2005). The impact of degenerative neurological disorders, such as multiple sclerosis (McCabe, 2004) and Parkinson's disease (Bronner et al., 2004), is also associated with a greater incidence of sexual problems and lower levels of sexual activity than in people without these conditions. In women, sexual problems can arise from pelvic pain and bleeding resulting from gynecological conditions such as uterine fibroids and endometriosis. Unfortunately, conventional treatment of these conditions with hysterectomy may not always result in improved sexual outcomes (Meston & Bradford, 2004).

Cancers involving the reproductive organs can be particularly devastating to sexual function due to the effects of treatment on overall health status, self-image, and psychological well-being. In addition, nerve damage following surgical procedures or radiation therapy can markedly alter genital function and sexual responses. In men, treatment of testicular and prostate cancer is frequently associated with erectile dysfunction (Kao, Jani, & Vijayakumar, 2002; Nazareth, Lewin, & King, 2001). Adverse sexual outcomes are also common after pelvic radiation and radical hysterectomy for cancers of the female reproductive organs (Andersen, Woods, & Copeland, 1997; Bergmark et al., 1999). Sexual problems in patients recovering from nonpelvic organ cancers are also common, but, with the exception of breast cancer in women (see Henson, 2002), are less emphasized in the clinical literature (Monga, 2002).

In addition to physical health complaints, psychiatric disorders can negatively affect sexual well-being. Depression and anxiety are notable risk factors for sexual problems (Dunn, Croft, & Hackett, 1999), although there are few indications that adults become more vulnerable to these disorders as they age (Henderson et al., 1998). The prevalence of cognitive impairment and dementia does increase with age, however (Graham et al., 1997), and this can present unique challenges for maintaining sexual health. Dementia can significantly change the dynamic of a sexual relationship, and concerns about the cognitively impaired partner's ability to consent to sexual activity are common. If the degree of cognitive impairment necessitates the use of residential care, maintaining a sexual relationship becomes especially difficult. Inappropriate sexual behavior occurs in some individuals with dementia, but this is relatively atypical (Benbow & Jagus, 2002; Jagus & Benbow, 2002).

Several types of drugs are commonly associated with sexual dysfunction in men and women. Selective serotonin reuptake inhibitors (SSRIs), used for the treatment of depression and related conditions, have a host of well-documented side effects, including decreased sexual interest, sexual arousal difficulties, and inhibited orgasm. Tricyclic antidepressants may have sexual side effects as well (Meston & Gorzalka, 1992). Other psychiatric drugs, including antipsychotics (Wirshing et al., 2002) and benzodiazepines (Segraves, 1988), are also associated with an increased risk of sexual problems. Other classes of drugs frequently associated with sexual problems include beta blockers and some diuretics (Leiblum & Segraves, 2000). Finally, the long-term use of recreational drugs (including alcohol and nicotine as well as many illicit drugs) can interfere with sexual function (for review see Huws & Sampson, 1993). Although these are some of the most commonly reported drugs involved in sexual complaints, other drugs may have similar effects as well. The effects of current medication use, therefore, should be considered in the sexual health assessment.

There is a growing body of evidence that suggests that lifestyle factors, particularly physical activity, may offer some protection against sexual problems that are frequently associated with health concerns. Several studies have investigated the benefit of physical activity on erectile function and other aspects of sexual response among older men. Derby et al. (2000) followed a cohort of men between the ages of 40 and 70 over a period of about a decade. Their findings indicated that smoking, obesity, alcohol use, and a sedentary lifestyle were all associated with an increased risk of erectile dysfunction. However, the effects of inactivity on erectile function appeared to be somewhat reversible with the adoption of regular exercise during the course of the study. In another study, middle-aged chronic heart failure patients who received 8 weeks of exercise training showed significant improvement on a questionnaire assessing the quality of their sexual relationships and erectile responses. This effect was attributed in part to improved endothelial function as a result of training (Belardinelli et al., 2005). Studies examining the contribution of physical activity to sexual function in women have been less comprehensive, but have so far been promising. Physical activity in menopausal women has been linked to frequency of sexual intercourse, overall sexual responsiveness (Dennerstein & Lehert, 2004), sexual satisfaction (Gerber et al., 2005), and orgasmic functioning (Penteado et al., 2003). The extent to which these effects are attributable to the impact of activity on physical or mental health remains to be seen.

SEXUALITY AND AGING
IN A PSYCHOSOCIAL CONTEXT

Across age groups, men and women are more likely to be sexually active if they have access to a regular sexual partner (i.e., married or otherwise in a long-term partnership). Because women tend to live longer than men, and often marry men who are older than themselves, they are more likely than men to be widowed and live alone in old age. This trend has important implications for understanding statistics on sexuality in older women, which often suggest a rapid deterioration of women's sexual function in old age. For women in midlife and old age, not only is the presence of a partner associated with levels of sexual desire, but sexual desire appears to be more dependent on the availability of a partner in women than in men (Baumeister, 2000; DeLamater & Sill, 2005). Indeed, it is not unheard of for women to express a loss of interest in sex coinciding with the disability or death of a spouse, suggesting that some older people, especially women, transition into a state of "sexual retirement" (Gott, 2005). This is compounded by the fact that the male-female ratio progressively decreases with advanced age; thus, finding a new partner seems a more viable option from the outset for older (heterosexual) men than for women. However, the urgency with which individuals seek a new sexual partner – if they do so at all – is highly variable. Voluntary celibacy should therefore be carefully distinguished from *problematic* deficits in sexual desire; this may be challenging if guilt or negative attitudes toward sexuality conflict with continued sexual interest after the loss of a partner.

A plausible and quite different reaction to the loss of a long-term partner is a sense of renewed sexual curiosity or "reawakening" of sexual desire. This may be particularly significant for individuals coming out of partnerships in which sexual expression was restricted due to the other partner's illness, disability, or lack of interest. However, older people who wish to seek out new sexual partners may understandably have some difficulty adjusting to dating. Concerns about the adequacy of one's own sexual performance may be activated with the prospect of a new and unfamiliar partner. In addition, unresolved feelings toward a previous partner (e.g., grief, guilt) may interfere with the development of new sexual relationships.

A potentially strong barrier to sexual expression among older people is a lack of broad social recognition and support for sexual relationships after midlife. This is fueled by myths and misperceptions about aging and sexuality (Hodson & Skeen, 1994). Although there is some evidence to suggest that attitudes toward sexuality in later life have improved over the past several decades (Gott, 2005), there remains little representation of later-life sexuality in popular culture and media. What is depicted often conveys the message that older people are or *should* be asexual. Walz (2002) noted that, among the relatively few representations of older adults' sexual lives in film or literature, a negative subtext is often present (e.g., the predatory conquests of a "dirty old man"). Some of these negative images are instantly recognizable character types from popular media, television, and film: the man in midlife crisis desperately clinging to the "glory days" of his youth; the promiscuous older woman dressed unflatteringly in provocative clothing. Perhaps more prominent, however, are images of chastity or sexual indifference among elders – their sexuality is invisible or nonexistent.

Lesbian, gay, bisexual, and transgender (LGBT) adults face unique challenges associated with aging. Heterosexuality is often assumed by society and caregivers, leaving many nonheterosexual elders with little social support for intimate relationships. Adults who live openly as gay, lesbian, or bisexual risk discrimination by health care providers (Brotman, Ryan, & Cormier, 2003; Gott, 2005), exposure to violence or neglect, and economic inequalities in countries that lack legal recognition of same-sex unions. Supplementary social services for LGBT persons may be limited or absent in many areas. Moreover, even within some sexual minority communities, older people may be marginalized. A study by Schope (2005) suggested that ageist attitudes pose a greater perceived threat to gay men than to lesbians. Although resources for sexual minority populations are not uniformly available, many LGBT community organizations offer special services and programming to older people.

Some stereotypes about sexuality in old age are based on the belief that older people are more conservative in their sexual behavior. This perception is not entirely inaccurate; older adults tend to report less permissive attitudes about sex, often having grown up in more restrictive environments than their children or grandchildren (Hartmann et al., 2004; Leiblum & Segraves, 2000). However, AARP's (2005) survey of adults over 45 indicated that approximately half of respondents were receptive to trying new sex-related activities (e.g., watching erotic films, role playing, using sex toys) with their partners, although men and younger adults were generally more willing to consider these activities. Differences in sexual attitudes and behaviors between older and younger adults are most likely due to generational differences rather than actual changes related to age *per se*, and within generations there exists considerable variability in sexual attitudes and mores. Negative attitudes toward sex are, not surprisingly, associated with lower levels of sexual desire and a greater risk of problems related to sexual arousal and orgasm (DeLamater & Sill, 2005; Laumann et al., 2005). However, sexuality education may be useful in challenging and modifying negative attitudes toward sexuality in older adults (White & Catania, 1982).

ASSESSMENT OF SEXUAL CONCERNS IN OLDER PERSONS

In evaluating the sexual well-being of older persons, the clinician is charged with the delicate task of *acknowledging* the client's advanced age while resisting assumptions about what that may entail for the individual's sexuality. On one hand, approaching the assessment of an 80-year-old client as one would a 30-year-old can appear disingenuous and may be perceived as insulting. Moreover, the "age-blind" approach may neglect information that is particularly relevant to people in later stages of life (e.g., health concerns, changes in living arrangement, ill health or death of sexual partners). On the other hand, clinicians are not immune to the belief that older peoples' sexual lives are less active, varied, or satisfying than those of their younger counterparts. This belief may manifest itself not only in the content of interactions with the client, but perhaps most often in what is *not* addressed during the assessment. For example, the assumption that an older client won't engage in casual sex may lead the clinician to entirely neglect the topic of protection against sexually transmitted infections (STIs). The clinician's negative attitudes toward sexuality in later life can subtly reinforce existing shame, discomfort, or self-doubt in a client who is reluctant to discuss sexual topics. Organizations that provide education about sexuality in old age and support for lifelong sexual health can help correct misinformed beliefs and may be appreciated by clinicians and clients alike; see Table 1 (p. 41) for a list of resources.

In addition to addressing one's own biases, the clinician should be sensitive to the possibility that clients may have internalized negative attitudes about sexuality in old age. For instance, the older client who dismisses the idea of sex at her age may be tacitly expressing shame, embarrassment, or hopelessness about her sexual life. Acquiescing to the client's dismissal of sexuality may neglect an opportunity to discuss ways in which her sexual situation might be changed. Regardless of whether sexual topics are discussed in depth, the clinician should be careful to avoid inadvertently confirming ageist attitudes by failing to inquire about sexuality at all. Because many older people hesitate to initiate conversations with health care providers about sexual topics (Gott, 2005), a sensitive but proactive approach is warranted.

TABLE 1: Recommended Organizations and Internet Resources for Clinicians and Clients

Title/Organization	Description	Contact Information	Website*
General Information			
American Association of Retired Persons	Major nonprofit organization devoted to advocacy and services for adults over the age of 50	201 E Street, N.W. Washington, DC 20049 (888) 687-2277	http://www.aarp.org
Sexuality Information and Education Council of the United States	Provides sexuality education on a wide range of topics; website offers comprehensive bibliographies of resources for older people	130 W. 42nd Street, Suite 350 New York, NY 10036-7802 (212) 819-9770	http://www.siecus.org
American Psychological Association, Aging and Human Sexuality Resource Guide	An online guide to books, articles, and other media on the topic of aging and sexuality; especially appropriate for professionals	American Psychological Association 750 First Street, N.E. Washington, DC 20002-4242 (202) 336-5500	http://www.apa.org/pi/aging/sexuality.html
Elder Abuse			
National Center on Elder Abuse	Organization devoted to education, research, and advocacy related to elder abuse and neglect	1201 15th Street, N.W., Suite 350 Washington, DC 20005-2800 (202) 898-2586	http://www.elderabusecenter.org
Disability and Illness			
Sexual Health Network	An Internet resource for general sexuality information and information targeted to people with disabilities and chronic illnesses	3 Mayflower Lane Shelton, CT 06484	http://www.sexualhealth.org
Disability Resources Monthly WebWatcher	Provides a list of Internet sites related to sexual topics of interest to people with disabilities	Disability Resources, Inc. 4 Glatter Lane Centereach, NY 11720-1032 (631) 585-0290	http://www.disabilityresources.org
Association of Cancer Online Resources	Guide to online cancer support resources; also hosts a mailing list dedicated to discussion of sexuality after cancer diagnosis	173 Duane Street, Suite 3A New York, NY 10013-3334 (212) 226-5525	http://www.acor.org
Menopause			
North American Menopause Society	Scientific organization promoting menopause research and education for professionals and consumers	P.O. Box 94527 Cleveland, OH 44101 (440) 442-7550	http://www.menopause.org
Lesbian, Gay, Bisexual, and Transgender Issues			
American Society on Aging: Lesbian and Gay Aging Issues Network	Organization devoted to education and advocacy in support of LGBT elders; professional development is a major focus	833 Market Street, Suite 511 San Francisco, CA 94103 (415) 974-0300	http://www.asaging.org/lgain
Transgender Aging Network	Promotes awareness and support of issues relevant to older transgender adults; also offers a mailing list	6990 N. Rockledge Avenue Glendale, WI 53209 (414) 540-6456	http://www.forge-forward.org/tan

* Although all contact information and websites in this contribution were correct at the time of publication, they are subject to change at any time.

Beyond the details of the presenting problem, the assessment of sexual concerns in an older client should include a sexual history, or a discussion of how sexuality has been experienced over time. Past experience, enjoyment, and perceived importance of sex are natural antecedents to sexuality in later life. Similarly, sexual disturbances due to primary sexual dysfunction, relationship maladjustment, sexual abuse history, health conditions, or other factors may have long-lasting implications for sexual function even after their acute impact has passed. Other important considerations include current or recent life stress, physical and mental health status, relationship satisfaction, sexual risk behaviors, and the partner's sexual functioning. If the client is not able to live independently, his or her living environment should also be assessed to determine whether he or she is able to pursue sexual activities with privacy and dignity, and whether he or she may be at risk of abuse or neglect.

TREATMENT STRATEGIES FOR OLDER ADULTS

The differentiation of a sexual problem and a "dysfunction" in need of treatment (i.e., an attempt to change) should be approached with caution and with respect to the client's appraisal of the problem. Sexual dysfunctions as defined by the *Diagnostic and Statistical Manual of Mental Disorders* (*DSM-IV-TR*; American Psychiatric Association, 2000) are diagnosed only when sexual functioning is a source of interpersonal difficulty or personal distress. Sexual problems and sexual distress are not inherently linked. For example, Bancroft, Loftus, and Long (2003) reported that even as older women tended to report less frequent sexual interest than younger women, younger women were more likely to endorse distress about low sexual interest. At times it may be appropriate to help a client appreciate the impact of a sexual problem on his or her life, but in other circumstances it may be to the client's benefit to normalize rather than pathologize a change in sexuality.

There is some evidence to suggest that knowledge of sexuality in later life is associated with more positive attitudes about sexuality among older people (for review, see Hillman & Stricker, 1994); thus it is worthwhile to consider the potential usefulness of sexuality education in modifying clients' attitudes toward sex. Educating clients about typical age-related bodily changes may help to normalize their experiences and reduce distress about the meaning of their symptoms. Suggesting alternative sexual techniques (e.g., sexual positions or activities that maximize direct genital stimulation) or sexual aids (e.g., lubricants for women with vaginal dryness) may also be an appropriate aspect of education.

Understandably, changes in health and body functions with advancing age may not always be met with full acceptance. How the individual interprets and copes with these changes, however, may transform a relatively benign event into a significant sexual dysfunction. For example, a man who experiences erectile failure during sexual intercourse with his partner may interpret the event as a signal of impending sexual impotence and react catastrophically, creating expectations of future disappointing sexual experiences. Performance anxiety can lead to avoidance of sex as well as arousal difficulties during sexual activity (Barlow, 1986). Thus, expectations of failure can have a powerful effect on future sexual encounters, especially when combined with an "all-or-nothing" attitude toward sexual performance. Cognitive restructuring may be useful in modifying pessimistic or overly rigid beliefs about sexuality that hinder adjustment to normal aging (Schiavi, 1999).

Advances in medical treatments for sexual problems, particularly for men, may be of interest to older clients who present with sexual dysfunction. The availability of phosphodiesterase type 5 (PDE-5) inhibitors such as sildenafil (Viagra) for erectile dysfunction may be especially appealing. However, medical treatments for sexual dysfunction entail some degree of risk and may not be appropriate for all clients. A thorough assessment that includes screening for physical and psychiatric health problems should inform appropriate referrals for medical management when a medical condition is a suspected etiological factor in sexual problems. Targets for medical intervention may include sexual problems that co-occur with changes in health status, persistent sexual problems that develop in the absence of relational or psychosocial changes, changes in genital function that occur despite sexual interest and desire for sexual activity, and sexual changes that arise with medication use. Even when medical treatments for sexual problems are not indicated, counseling about lifestyle modification may be worthwhile. Adopting or increasing regular physical activity may be beneficial to sexuality by improving fatigue, mood, self-image, and cardiovascular fitness, and it may also help prevent future sexual dysfunctions.

CONCLUSION

Aging typically entails some degree of change in men's and women's capacities for sexual "performance" from a strictly physiological standpoint, yet research data suggest that a large proportion of people find sex in later life equally satisfying, if not more so, than in their youth. Their "secret" seems to lie not in the pursuit of a sexuality left behind in early adulthood, but in a positive, adaptive attitude toward aging that includes entitlement to sexual well-being. Continued sexual enjoyment into later life requires a degree of adjustment to changes in the body, the mind, relationships, and life circumstances. This does not preclude, and may even enhance, continued sexual expression and pleasure late into life.

There is no mysterious threshold separating the sexual concerns and difficulties of older people from those of younger people, and it is reasonable to conclude that there is no one event or quality that characterizes "old-age sexuality." On the other hand, it is important to recognize that older people are at risk for several health-related, psychosocial, and environmental circumstances that can hinder sexual expression and functioning. Although some of these barriers cannot be prevented entirely, education, advocacy, and adaptive coping strategies can soften their impact considerably. Clinicians who work with older clients should be aware of the ageist context in which many of their clients' social interactions take place and take action, when possible, to counter cultural and societal myths about sexuality in old age.

CONTRIBUTORS

Andrea Bradford, MA, received a master's degree in clinical psychology from the University of Texas at Austin in 2004. Her research interests include behavioral and psychosomatic aspects of women's health. Ms. Bradford is a member of the American Psychological Association, the International Society for the Study of Women's Sexual Health, and the American Medical Writers Association. Ms. Bradford may be contacted at 1 University Station A8000, Austin, TX 78712. E-mail: annie@alumni.utexas.edu

Cindy M. Meston, PhD, is currently Associate Professor of Clinical Psychology at the University of Texas at Austin. Dr. Meston was the 2003 President of the International Society for the Study of Women's Sexual Health, is a Full Member of the International Academy of Sex Research, and is a member of the American Psychological Association, the Canadian Psychological Association, and the Society for the Scientific Study of Sexuality. Her research has appeared in numerous peer-reviewed academic journals. Dr. Meston can be reached at 1 University Station A8000, Austin, TX 78712. E-mail: meston@psy.utexas.edu

RESOURCES

Alexander, J. L., Kotz, K., Dennerstein, L., Kutner, S. J., Wallen, K., & Notelovitz, M. (2004). The effects of postmenopausal hormone therapies on female sexual functioning: A review of double-blind, randomized controlled trials. *Menopause, 11*, 749-765.

American Association of Retired Persons. (2005). *Sexuality at Midlife and Beyond: 2004 Update of Attitudes and Behaviors.* Retrieved November 2005, from http://www.aarp.org/research/family/lifestyles/2004_sexuality.html

American Psychiatric Association. (2000). *Diagnostic and Statistical Manual of Mental Disorders* (4th ed. text rev.). Washington, DC: Author.

Andersen, B. L., Woods, X. A., & Copeland, L. J. (1997). Sexual self-schema and sexual morbidity among gynecologic cancer survivors. *Journal of Consulting and Clinical Psychology, 65*, 221-229.

Araujo, A. B., Mohr, B. A., & McKinlay, J. B. (2004). Changes in sexual function in middle-aged and older men: Longitudinal data from the Massachusetts Male Aging Study. *Journal of the American Geriatrics Society, 52*, 1502-1509.

Bancroft, J., Loftus, J., & Long, J. S. (2003). Distress about sex: A national survey of women in heterosexual relationships. *Archives of Sexual Behavior, 32*, 193-208.

Barlow, D. H. (1986). Causes of sexual dysfunction: The role of anxiety and cognitive interference. *Journal of Consulting and Clinical Psychology, 54*, 140-148.

Basaria, S., & Dobs, A. S. (2004). Safety and adverse effects of androgens: How to counsel patients. *Mayo Clinic Proceedings, 79*, S25-S32.

Baumeister, R. F. (2000). Gender differences in erotic plasticity: The female sex drive as socially flexible and responsive. *Psychological Bulletin, 126*, 347-374.

Belardinelli, R., Lacalaprice, F., Faccenda, E., Purcaro, A., & Perna, G. (2005). Effects of short-term moderate exercise training on sexual function in male patients with chronic stable heart failure. *International Journal of Cardiology, 101*, 83-90.

Benbow, S. M., & Jagus, C. E. (2002). Sexuality in older women with mental health problems. *Sexual and Relationship Therapy, 17*, 261-270.

Bergmark, K., Avall-Lunqvist, E., Dickman, P. W., Henningsohn, L., & Steineck, G. (1999). Vaginal changes and sexuality in women with a history of cervical cancer. *New England Journal of Medicine, 340*, 1383-1389.

Bretschneider, J. G., & McCoy, N. L. (1988). Sexual interest and behavior in healthy 80- to 102-year-olds. *Archives of Sexual Behavior, 17*, 109-129.

Bronner, G., Royter, V., Korczyn, A. D., & Giladi, N. (2004). Sexual dysfunction in Parkinson's disease. *Journal of Sex and Marital Therapy, 30*, 95-105.

Brotman, S., Ryan, B., & Cormier, R. (2003). The health and social service needs of gay and lesbian elders and their families in Canada. *Gerontologist, 43*, 192-202.

Burchardt, M., Burchardt, T., Anastasiadis, A. G., Kiss, A. J., Baer, L., Pawar, R. V., de la Taille, A., Shabsigh, A., Ghafar, M. A., & Shabsigh, R. (2002). Sexual dysfunction is common and overlooked in female patients with hypertension. *Journal of Sex and Marital Therapy, 28*, 17-26.

Butler, R. N., Lewis, M. I., Hoffman, E., & Whitehead, E. D. (1994). Love and sex after 60: How to evaluate and treat the sexually-active woman. *Geriatrics, 49*(11), 33-42.

Centers for Disease Control and Prevention. (2003). Public health and aging: Trends in aging – United States and worldwide. *Morbidity and Mortality Weekly Report, 52*, 101-106.

Davis, S. R., Davison, S. L., Donath, S., & Bell, R. J. (2005). Circulating androgen levels and self-reported sexual function in women. *Journal of the American Medical Association, 294*, 91-96.

DeLamater, J. D., & Sill, M. (2005). Sexual desire in later life. *Journal of Sex Research, 42*, 138-149.

Dennerstein, L., Alexander, J. L., & Kotz, K. (2003). The menopause and sexual functioning: A review of the population-based studies. *Annual Review of Sex Research, 14*, 64-82.

Dennerstein, L., & Lehert, P. (2004). Women's sexual functioning, lifestyle, mid-age, and menopause in 12 European countries. *Menopause, 11*, 778-785.

Derby, C. A., Mohr, B. A., Goldstein, I., Feldman, H. A., Johannes, C. B., & McKinlay, J. B. (2000). Modifiable risk factors and erectile dysfunction: Can lifestyle changes modify risk? *Urology, 56*, 302-306.

Doruk, H., Akbay, E., Cayan, S., Akbay, E., Bozlu, M., & Acar, D. (2005). Effect of diabetes mellitus on female sexual function and risk factors. *Archives of Andrology, 51*, 1-6.

Dunn, K. M., Croft, P. R., & Hackett, G. I. (1999). Association of sexual problems with social, psychological, and physical problems in men and women: A cross sectional population survey. *Journal of Epidemiology and Community Health, 53*, 144-148.

Gerber, J. R., Johnson, J. V., Bunn, J. Y., & O'Brien, S. L. (2005). A longitudinal study of the effects of free testosterone and other psychosocial variables on sexual function during the natural traverse of menopause. *Fertility and Sterility, 83*, 643-648.

Gott, M. (2005). *Sexuality, Sexual Health and Ageing.* New York: Open University Press.

Graham, J. E., Rockwood, K., Beattie, B. L., Eastwood, R., Gauthier, S., Tuokko, H., & McDowell, I. (1997). Prevalence and severity of cognitive impairment with and without dementia in an elderly population. *Lancet, 349*, 1793-1796.

Harman, S. M., Metter, E. K., Tobin, J. D., Pearson, J., & Blackman, M. R. (2001). Longitudinal effects of aging in serum total and free testosterone levels in healthy men. *Journal of Clinical Endocrinology and Metabolism, 86*, 724-731.

Hartmann, W., Philippsohn, S., Heiser, K., & Rüffer-Hesse, C. (2004). Low sexual desire in midlife and older women: Personality factors, psychosocial development, present sexuality. *Menopause, 11*, 726-740.

Henderson, A. S., Jorm, A. F., Korten, A. E., Jacomb, P., Christensen, H., & Rodgers, B. (1998). Symptoms of depression and anxiety during adult life: Evidence for a decline in prevalence with age. *Psychological Medicine, 28*, 1321-1328.

Henson, H. K. (2002). Breast cancer and sexuality. *Sexuality and Disability, 20*, 261-275.

Hickey, M., Davis, S. R., & Sturdee, D. W. (2005). Treatment of menopausal symptoms: What shall we do now? *Lancet, 366*, 409-421.

Hillman, J. L., & Stricker, G. (1994). A linkage of knowledge and attitudes toward elderly sexuality: Not necessarily a uniform relationship. *Gerontologist, 34*, 256-260.

Hodson, D. S., & Skeen, P. (1994). Sexuality and aging: The hammerlock of myths. *Journal of Applied Gerontology, 13*, 219-235.

Huws, R., & Sampson, G. (1993). Recreational drugs and sexuality. In A. J. Riley, M. Peet, & C. Wilson (Eds.), *Sexual Pharmacology* (pp. 197-210). New York: Oxford University Press.

Isidori, A. M., Giannetta, E., Gianfrilli, D., Greco, E. A., Bonifacio, V., Aversa, A., Isidori, A., Fabbri, A., & Lenzi, A. (2005). Effects of testosterone on sexual function in men: Results of a meta-analysis. *Clinical Endocrinology, 63*, 381-394.

Jagus, C. E., & Benbow, S. M. (2002). Sexuality in older men with mental health problems. *Sexual and Relationship Therapy, 17*, 271-279.

Kao, J., Jani, A., & Vijayakumar, S. (2002). Sexual functioning after treatment for early stage prostate cancer. *Sexuality and Disability, 20*, 239-260.

Kinsey, A. C., Pomeroy, W. B., & Martin, C. E. (1948). *Sexual Behavior in the Human Male.* Philadelphia: W. B. Saunders.

Laumann, E. O., Nicolosi, A., Glasser, D. B., Paik, A., Gingell, C., Moreira, E., & Wang, T. (2005). Sexual problems among women and men aged 40-80 y: Prevalence and correlates identified in the Global Study of Sexual Attitudes and Behaviors. *International Journal of Impotence Research, 17*, 39-57.

Laumann, E. O., Paik, A., & Rosen, R. C. (1999). Sexual dysfunction in the United States: Prevalence and predictors. *Journal of the American Medical Association, 281*, 537-544.

Leiblum, S. R., & Segraves, R. T. (2000). Sex therapy with aging adults. In S. R. Leiblum & R. Rosen (Eds.), *Principles and Practice of Sex Therapy* (3rd ed., pp. 423-448). New York: Guilford.

Masters, W. H., & Johnson, V. E. (1966). *Human Sexual Response.* Boston: Little, Brown.

McCabe, M. P. (2004). Exacerbation of symptoms among people with multiple sclerosis: Impact on sexuality and relationships over time. *Archives of Sexual Behavior, 33*, 593-601.

Meston, C. M., & Bradford, A. (2004). A brief review of the factors influencing sexuality after hysterectomy. *Sexual and Relationship Therapy, 19*, 5-14.

Meston, C. M., & Gorzalka, B. B. (1992). Psychoactive drugs and human sexual behavior: The role of serotonergic activity. *Journal of Psychoactive Drugs, 24*, 1-40.

Monga, U. (2002). Sexual functioning in cancer patients. *Sexuality and Disability, 20*, 277-295.

National Council on Aging. (2005). *Sex after 60: A Natural Part of Life.* Retrieved November 2005, from http://www.ncoa.org/content.cfm?sectionID=109&detail=134

Nazareth, I., Lewin, J., & King, M. (2001). Sexual dysfunction after treatment for testicular cancer: A systematic review. *Journal of Psychosomatic Research, 51*, 735-743.

Penteado, S. R. L., Fonseca, A. M., Bagnoli, V. R., Assis, J. S., & Pinotti, J. A. (2003). Sexuality in healthy postmenopausal women. *Climacteric, 6*, 321-329.

Rowland, D. L. (1998). Penile sensitivity in men: A composite of recent findings. *Urology, 52*, 1101-1105.

Schiavi, R. C. (1999). *Aging and Male Sexuality.* Cambridge, UK: Cambridge University Press.

Schope, R. D. (2005). Who's afraid of growing old? Gay and lesbian perceptions of aging. *Journal of Gerontological Social Work, 45*, 23-38.

Segraves, R. T. (1988). Sexual side effects of psychiatric drugs. *International Journal of Psychiatry in Medicine, 18*, 243-252.

Society of Obstetricians and Gynaecologists of Canada. (2004). The detection and management of vaginal atrophy. *International Journal of Gynaecology and Obstetrics, 88*, 222-228.

Walz, T. (2002). Crones, dirty old men, sexy seniors: Representations of the sexuality of older persons. *Journal of Aging and Identity, 7*, 99-112.

Wespes, E. (2002). The ageing penis. *World Journal of Urology, 20*, 36-39.

White, C. B., & Catania, J. A. (1982). Psychoeducational intervention for sexuality with the aged, family members of the aged, and people who work with the aged. *International Journal of Aging and Human Development, 15*, 121-138.

Wirshing, D. A., Pierre, J. M., Marder, S. R., Saunders, C. S., & Wirshing, W. C. (2002). Sexual side effects of novel antipsychotic medications. *Schizophrenia Research, 56*, 25-30.

World Health Organization. (2002). *Active Ageing: A Policy Framework.* Retrieved November 2005, from http://www.who.int/ageing/publications/en/

Medications and Sexual Health

William W. Finger

Historically, a psychoanalytic paradigm was used to explain our sexual maladies, with much of the blame placed on deep-seated psychic conflict. More contemporary explanations for sexual concerns focused on interpersonal anxiety, emotional turmoil, early life experiences, and relationship concerns. However, as more has been learned about the complexity of sexual desire and function, the impact of physiology and pharmacology has begun to play a larger role in our conceptual frameworks. Today, most sexual disorders are believed to be at least partially physical in nature, either as a direct result of medical conditions or as a result of the medications used to treat these conditions.

More than 3.3 billion prescriptions are written every year in the United States (Gebhart, 2006). This figure has increased by nearly 1 billion prescriptions in the last 5 years alone, resulting in more than 10 prescriptions written each year for every man, woman, and child living in the U.S. today. The positive side of this trend is that medications are available to treat many of the medical and psychiatric concerns often associated with sexual problems. The impact of high cholesterol, diabetes, heart disease, and other medical conditions on vascular or neurological function necessary for good sexual health can be slowed or even stopped through pharmacological interventions. Psychiatric conditions, including anxiety, depression, and psychoses, which are likely to impact sexual health directly through symptoms such as anhedonia and social withdrawal, or indirectly through effects on interpersonal interactions, can often be effectively treated with medications.

The downside of this trend is that many of the medications in use today have undesired side effects, including sexual side effects (Micromedex Healthcare Series, 2005). In fact, 10 of the top 20 medications prescribed in 2005 have sexual side effects, as do all of the 10 most frequently prescribed psychiatric medications (Micromedex Healthcare Series, 2005; Rx300, 2006). It is essential that sexual health professionals consider the potential impact of these medications when assessing sexual concerns.

MEDICATIONS AFFECTING SEXUAL FUNCTION

The medications reviewed below are only some of the hundreds of medications noted to cause changes in sexual function. Although these classes of medications are frequently associated with sexual problems, controlled studies remain sparse. If a medication is in a class known to have sexual side effects, but is not identified here, it can be assumed to have the potential for causing changes in sexual function. When a medication is suspected, but is not in a class known to cause sexual problems, information from the patient, including onset, dosing, and timing, can assist in determining any possible association. Advice on assessing potential sexual side effects is included in a subsequent section.

Antidepressant Medications

Three antidepressant medications were listed among the top 30 most prescribed medications in the U.S. in 2005 (Rx300, 2006). Use of these medications is on the rise, partially because kinder, less toxic medications have been developed, and partially because of increased recognition and treatment of psychiatric concerns. Antidepressants are also being prescribed for a wider range of symptoms and disorders, including anxiety, panic attacks, obsessive-compulsive disorder, and posttraumatic stress disorder. With a proliferation of new antidepressants in the last two decades, adverse effects profiles, tolerability, and quality of life issues have become of primary concern to patients and a primary marketing strategy (Gregorian et al., 2002).

Although most classes of antidepressant medications have been associated with sexual concerns, the very nature of depression complicates the picture. Anhedonia, or lack of interest in pleasurable activities, is a primary symptom of most affective disorders and may include loss of desire for sex (Kanaly & Berman, 2002). Researchers have found that as many as 50% of nontreated depressed individuals report some type of sexual problem, compared to only half that number for nondepressed people (Angst, 1998).

Selective Serotonin, Norepinephrine, And Noradrenaline Reuptake Inhibitors

Selective serotonin reuptake inhibitors (SSRIs) and, more recently, serotonin/norepinephrine and noradrenaline reuptake inhibitors have replaced tricyclics as the most commonly prescribed antidepressant medications. Initial reports indicated that these medications had fewer side effects than older antidepressants such as tricyclics. Early studies relied on spontaneous reporting of sexual side effects and generally found rates in the single digits. However, patients are unlikely to report these side effects on their own, perhaps because they do not attribute these changes to the medication or because they may be embarrassed to discuss sexual problems. When patients are specifically asked about sexual side effects, rates increase significantly. Although these newer medications probably do have lower rates of erectile disorder than older medications, delayed or absent orgasm is commonly reported. Prozac, Zoloft, and Paxil, the earliest SSRIs, delay orgasm significantly, with rates approaching 75% (Gregorian et al., 2002; Kennedy et al., 2000; Landen, Hogberg, & Thase, 2005). Newer SSRIs, such as Celexa, Luvox, and Lexapro, may have lower rates of delayed orgasm, but these rates are still quite substantial (Clayton et al., 2002; Kennedy et al., 2000; Montejo et al., 2001), and the paucity of controlled trials makes a clear distinction of rates of side effects difficult (Gregorian et al., 2002).

In addition to the high incidence of delayed or absent orgasm reported with SSRIs, arousal problems, including erectile disorder, have also been reported, although the association has not been as consistent (Montejo et al., 2001). Decreased desire has been associated with SSRIs as well, but this association is confounded by the high rate of this problem in untreated and treatment-resistant depression (Angst, 1998).

The mixed serotonin/norepinephrine reuptake inhibitors (SNRIs) such as Cymbalta, Remeron, and Effexor may impact sexual function to a lesser extent than traditional SSRIs (Hirschfeld & Vornik, 2004; Hudson et al., 2005; Saiz-Ruiz et al., 2005), but rates of treatment-emergent sexual dysfunction with these medications are generally higher than placebo (Delgado et al., 2005; Detke et al., 2002). However, studies also suggest that switching from traditional SSRIs to these medications may actually alleviate medication-induced anorgasmia (e.g., Gelenberg et al., 2000; Koutouvidis, Pratikakis, & Fotiadou, 1999), suggesting that, at least for some patients, sexual side effects are less likely to occur with these medications.

Tricyclics

Tricyclic antidepressants were one of the first classes of antidepressants developed and had many side effects, including sexual side effects. With the advent of antidepressants with safer side effect profiles, these medications have fallen out of favor but are still used for some cases of depression, as well as for sleep disturbance and neuropathic pain.

Tricyclics are commonly associated with decreased sexual desire, arousal difficulties, decreased ejaculatory volume, and delayed or absent orgasm (Balon et al., 1993; Monteiro et al., 1987). Of the tricyclics, clomipramine, doxepin, amitriptyline, and imipramine may have the highest rate of sexual side effects. Sexual side effects of clomipramine are especially common, even at relatively low doses. A 15% rate of erectile disorder has been reported with clomipramine use; lack of orgasm and ejaculation occurs at a rate as high as 70% and delayed orgasm as high as 92% (DeVeaugh-Geiss, Landau, & Katz, 1989; Monteiro et al., 1987).

Other Antidepressants

Monoamine oxidase inhibitors are rarely prescribed today, mainly due to side effects and interactions with other drugs and certain foods. When they were in common use, various sexual side effects were reported, including impaired sexual desire, erectile function, and orgasmic disorder (Ghadirian, Annable, & Belanger, 1992; Kowalski et al., 1985). Lithium is still in common use for bipolar disorder and also has been reported to cause impaired sexual desire and problems with erections (Vinarova et al., 1972).

Some classes of antidepressants appear to have less impact on sexual function. The phenylpiperazine class of antidepressants, which includes trazodone and nefazodone, has occasionally been associated with priapism (a painful erection that persists without sexual stimulation) but is less likely to impair desire, erection, or orgasmic response (Saenz de Tejada et al., 1991). Bupropion, an aminoketone antidepressant, also seems to have limited or absent effects on sexual function (Ginzburg, Wong, & Fader, 2005).

Other Psychiatric Medications

Both antianxiety medications and antipsychotic medications are frequently associated with sexual side effects. Many antipsychotic medications, especially the older antipsychotics such as phenothiazines (e.g., Thorazine, Prolixin, and Haldol) have been reported to cause erectile disorder and delay of ejaculation and orgasm (Segraves, 1988). Disorders of desire and cases of priapism have also been reported with these antipsychotics (Micromedex Healthcare Series, 2005; Segraves, 1988). Newer, atypical antipsychotic medications may have fewer effects on sexual function (e.g., Clozaril, Geodon, Risperdal, Seroquel, and Zyprexa; Seeman, 2002). Limited studies suggest that approximately 5% of patients taking Risperdal experience erectile dysfunction and ejaculatory dysfunction. Although this is higher than those taking placebo, it is considerably lower than those taking phenothiazines. Rare cases of priapism have been reported with Zyprexa and Seroquel, although no causative link has been found.

Benzodiazepines (e.g., alprazolam, clonazepam, diazepam, lorazepam, temazepam) are commonly prescribed for anxiety and alcohol withdrawal and have been associated with decreased sexual desire and the ability to attain orgasm (Lydiard et al., 1987; Micromedex Healthcare Series, 2005). Buspirone is another commonly prescribed anxiolytic, unrelated to the benzodiazepines, and has a low incidence of sexual side effects.

Antihypertensive Medications

Antihypertensive medications are widely prescribed in developed nations. Five of the 10 most frequently prescribed medications in the U.S. in 2005 were antihypertensive medications (Rx300, 2006). In 1999, only one of the top 10 medications was an antihypertensive (Rx300, 2006). These medications are gaining favor due to increased incidence and recognition of hypertension, as well as recognition of the need for more aggressive treatment of this potentially debilitating condition. Fortunately, new medications make avoiding sexual problems easier than in the past, when most available choices carried a significant risk of sexual side effects.

Alpha Blockers

Alpha-1 adronergic blockers, including doxazosin, prazosin, tamsulosin, and terazosin, have a low incidence of erectile dysfunction and ejaculatory changes (Lowe, 2005). Complicating this finding, alpha blockers are often used in men with benign prostatic hyperplagia (BPH), and this condition is associated with sexual problems, including increased erectile dysfunction, ejaculatory changes, and pain with ejaculation. A newer, uroselective alpha blocker, alfuzosin, has actually been found to reduce the rate of sexual concerns, including erection problems, in men with lower urinary tract symptoms (van Moorselaar et al., 2005), so the actual relationship of alpha blockers to sexual problems remains unclear.

Angiotensin II Receptor Blockers

Angiotensin II receptor blockers (e.g., Avapro, Benicar, Cozaar, and Diovan, among many) are a relatively new class of antihypertensive medication with few sexual side effects reported to date. Prescribing literature indicates a rate of desire and erection problems comparable to the rate reported with placebo. In fact, recent placebo-controlled studies suggest that Diovan has no negative effect on sexual function, does not decrease testosterone level, and actually may improve overall sexual function in hypertensive men when compared to beta blockers (atenolol and carvedilol) or placebo (Fogari et al., 2001, 2002, 2004; Fogari & Zoppi, 2004).

Angiotensin-Converting Enzyme (ACE) Inhibitors

Angiotensin-converting enzyme (ACE) inhibitors have relatively little documented impact on sexual function. ACE inhibitors, including benazepril, captopril, enalapril, fosinopril, and lisinopril, to name a few, do not appear to cause any significant change in sexual desire or response, although a low incidence of erectile dysfunction has been reported in some uncontrolled studies (Grimm et al., 1997).

Beta Blockers

Propranolol, the first beta blocker commercially available, has been associated with a high incidence of erection problems in men and decreased sexual desire in both sexes (Due, Giguere, & Plachetka, 1986; Fogari & Zoppi, 2004; Stevenson & Umstead, 1984). The incidence of sexual problems may be lower with more cardioselective beta blockers such as atenolol, carvedilol, and metoprolol, but erection problems and decreased desire are reported with these medications as well (Fogari et al., 2001; Stevenson & Umstead, 1984). Labetalol, which has both beta- and alpha-blocking effects, has been reported to cause fewer sexual side effects than the traditional beta blockers, and no sexual side effects have been reported with bisoprolol to date (Broekman et al., 1992; E. L. Michelson et al., 1983). Timolol, an eye drop used to treat glaucoma, has a surprisingly high rate of erectile dysfunction in men and decreased sexual desire in men and women, which may be alleviated if timolol is replaced by a newer ophthalmic beta blocker, betoxolol (Lynch et al., 1988).

Central Antiadrenergic Agents

Reserpine is a rauwolfia alkaloid that has lost considerable popularity because of a number of severe side effects, including severe depression. However, this medication is still used commonly in developing countries and less frequently in the elderly in the U.S. Sexual side effects from reserpine are common and include erection problems, decreased desire, and changes in orgasm. These side effects are likely to develop slowly. The incidence of these problems has varied considerably in studies, ranging from 1% to as high as 36% (Aldridge, 1982; Buffum, 1982; Horowitz & Goble, 1979; Papadopoulos, 1980) and are likely to occur with other medications in this class (e.g., deserpidine, rescinnamine; Micromedex Healthcare Series, 2005).

Methyldopa is a centrally acting sympatholytic. As with many other medications, initial reports of low incidence of sexual side effects was most likely due to poor methodology. More recent studies, relying on direct questioning of patients, found a high rate of erectile dysfunction (14%-36%), ejaculatory disorders (7%-19%), desire disorders (7%-14%), and gynecomastia (Aldridge, 1982; Duncan & Bateman, 1993; Hogan, Wallin, & Baer, 1980). Clonidine is another centrally acting sympatholytic, with therapeutic action and sexual side effects similar to methyldopa. Decreased sexual desire, erectile dysfunction, and delayed orgasm have all been reported with clonidine, at rates comparable to those found with methyldopa (Hogan et al., 1980; Stevenson & Umstead, 1984). Rates of sexual dysfunction appear to be related to dosage and mode of administration. Lower doses and transdermal delivery have resulted in considerably lower levels of sexual problems with clonidine (Langley & Heel, 1988). Guanabenz, guanadrel, and guanethidine have somewhat different mechanisms of action than clonidine and methyldopa, but have also been associated with significant rates of decreased desire, erection problems, and ejaculatory disturbance (Palmer & Nugent, 1983; Stevenson & Umstead, 1984).

Calcium Channel Antagonists

Calcium channel antagonists (or calcium channel blockers) have relatively low rates of sexual side effects. Medications in this class include amlodipine, diltiazem, felodipine, nifedipine, and verapamil, among others. Although research is scarce, calcium channel blockers may occasionally cause ejaculatory problems, decreased sexual desire, and erectile disorder (Barksdale & Gardner, 1999; Morrissette et al., 1993).

Diuretics

Two of the five most prescribed medications in the U.S. in 2005 were diuretics (Rx300, 2006). Nearly 80 million prescriptions were filled, either alone or in combination with other antihypertensive medications. Unfortunately, diuretics have been associated with decreased sexual desire, erectile disorders, and ejaculatory dysfunction (Fogari & Zoppi, 2004). Thiazide diuretics appear to have the greatest impact on sexual function. Chlorthalidone, which has a particularly long duration of action, may be the most likely to cause sexual problems, especially erectile disorder (Wassertheil-Smoller et al., 1991). Spironolactone, a potassium-sparing diuretic, has been associated with erectile dysfunction and gynecomastia in men, decreased vaginal lubrication in women, and decreased sexual desire in both sexes (Aldridge, 1982; Buffum, 1982; Greenblatt & Koch-Weser, 1973; Stevenson & Umstead, 1984). Hydrochlorothiazide may be a safer alternative at doses commonly prescribed for hypertension (12.5-25 mg), but at higher doses may cause decreased sexual desire and erectile dysfunction at rates similar to chlorthalidone (Chang et al., 1991). Furosemide (a loop diuretic), indapamide (a thiazide diuretic), and triamterene (a potassium-sparing diuretic) may be less effective at controlling hypertension than the previous diuretics, but may have fewer sexual side effects. Substitution of these diuretics for other antihypertensive medications has resulted in improvement in sexual function (Lacourciere, 1988).

Miscellaneous Medications

Over 100 million prescriptions were written for hydrocodone in 2005, making it the most frequently prescribed medication in the U.S. for the last 5 years (Rx300, 2006). Chronic use of hydrocodone and other opioids (e.g., codeine, fentanyl, methadone, oxycodone, tramadol) results in reduced sexual desire and erectile disorder at rates approaching 90% (Daniell, 2002).

Recognition of high cholesterol as a major contributor to heart disease, combined with the development of effective drugs to lower cholesterol levels, has resulted in a cholesterol-lowering medication becoming the second most frequently prescribed medication in the U.S., a position also held for the last 5 years (Rx300, 2006). Lipitor is an HMG-CoA reductase inhibitor and is only one of many lipid-lowering agents to be developed and widely prescribed in the last 20 years. Although controlled studies have not been conducted, case reports and prescribing literature have shown a regular association of these medications with sexual disorders, particularly disorders of arousal (Rizvi, Hampson, & Harvey, 2002). Men treated with cholesterol-lowering medications (e.g., pravastatin, simvastatin, fenofibrate, ciprofibrate, bezafibrate, or gemfibrozil) are nearly twice as likely to report erectile disorder as men not taking these medications (Bruckert et al., 1996). In this retrospective, naturalistic study, statin medications (e.g., pravastatin, simvastatin) were just as likely to result in this problem as fibrate medications (e.g., bezafibrate, ciprofibrate, fenofibrate, gemfibrozil).

Many medications are sold with and without prescription to treat heartburn, peptic ulcer, and other gastrointestinal concerns. One of the most common, Tagamet, has long been associated with decreased sexual desire and erectile dysfunction (Aldridge, 1982; Buffum, 1982; Horowitz & Goble, 1979). Similar medications such as famotidine, nizatidine, and ranitidine have not been associated with sexual problems, but given their similarities, it seems likely that the potential is there (Corinaldesi et al., 1987). Other gastrointestinal agents that may be related to sexual problems include atropine, clidinium, dicyclomine, glycopyrrolate, hyoscyamine, methscopolamine, omeprazole, propantheline, scopolamine, and sulfasalazine (Micromedex Healthcare Series, 2005).

Medications used in the treatment of cancer may impact sexual function as well. Antineoplastic agents (e.g., amsacrine, chlorambucil, megestrol, lonidamine, methotrexate, procarbazine) may impact sperm concentration, testosterone production, menstruation, sexual desire, and erections (Micromedex Healthcare Series, 2005). Antiandrogens (e.g., bicalutamide, nilutamide), antiestrogens (e.g., tamoxifen), and leutenizing hormone releasing hormone (LHRH) agonists (e.g., goserelin, leuprolide, nafarelin) may impact sexual desire and erectile function (Micromedex Healthcare Series, 2005).

ASSESSMENT OF SEXUAL SIDE EFFECTS

Given the complexity of sexual response; the numerous potential physical, psychological and pharmacological contributors to disrupted function; and the paucity of good research, the evaluation of sexual side effects may seem daunting. However, failure to undertake this task poses potential risk. Although physicians often underestimate both the prevalence of sexual concerns and the extent to which these concerns are bothersome to patients, sexual side effects are very common and distressing to patients (Hu et al., 2004). Failure to address these concerns poses a substantial risk of poor adherence and consequently exacerbation of or delayed recovery from medical or psychiatric concerns, and may negatively impact the overall relationship with the provider.

Although no guaranteed method exists, some simple guidelines can improve the likelihood that a medication side effect will be accurately identified or appropriately ruled out as the cause of a change in sexual function. For providers who prescribe medications, a baseline sexual function is often crucial to later identifying sexual concerns. Not only does this establish the level of premedication sexual function, it also gives patients permission to discuss sexual concerns as they arise.

For providers who do not have the advantage of contact with patients prior to the start of medications, a retrospective assessment can be helpful. Clearly documenting the start of the sexual concern and the initiation of new medications or new doses of medications can help identify medications that remain in contention. Any medication that was started after the onset of the sexual problem can be ruled out as the primary cause. Beyond that, temporal relations between medications and sexual side effects become less clear. Some medications are likely to have rather sudden effects on sexual response. Delayed orgasm from SSRIs is a good example of this. Other medications may have very delayed effects on sexual function and may develop gradually, mimicking a physiological or organic cause of the disorder. Opioids, which impact testosterone production only with chronic use, tend to have this type of effect on sexual desire and function. Finally, some medications have been shown to impact sexual function in a very dose-dependent manner, so being aware of changes in dose, in addition to initiation of medication, can often help identify the medication causing sexual problems.

Once established, most sexual side effects of medications remain fairly constant. That is to say, the problem will occur across time and across situations. Medication-induced erectile disorder will most likely impact erections with a partner, erections with masturbation, and erections during sleep (nocturnal penile tumescence and rigidity, or NPTR). Lack of NPTR may indicate physiological or pharmacologic involvement. A reduction in NPTR has been documented for various drugs including tricyclic antidepressants and cimetidine (Jensen et al., 1983; Kowalski et al., 1985). Although complicated and expensive methods exist for evaluating NPTR, patient self-reports of morning erections have been shown to be closely associated with more technical assessments (Ackerman et al., 1991).

Sexual problems that are less consistent may be more likely attributable to psychological causes or transient factors such as alcohol. Some exceptions to this exist, however. Some medications are active for relatively short periods of time, and the impact on sexual function will likewise be brief. With other medications, sexual side effects may resolve over time. With other patients, medications that do not initially impact sexual function may do so later, as the development or progression of an independent risk factor such as diabetes occurs. Other risk factors may increase the fragility of the sexual response and increase the susceptibility to a sexual side effect. In these cases, the medication may not be the only cause, but is a contributing factor.

TREATMENT OF SEXUAL SIDE EFFECTS

Identifying a sexual side effect is not enough. In most cases, simple reassurance is insufficient, and the expectation that patients will simply live with the problem is short-sighted. Holistic care requires consideration of sexual health as part of overall health and quality of life, and patients have come to expect this. Fortunately, many avenues exist for addressing sexual side effects. In most cases, an effective alternative can be found. Including patients' input in the assessment and treatment phase is the most effective way to maintain patient adherence and ensure an effective treatment outcome.

Spontaneous Remission or Accommodation

A simple solution to medication side effects is to wait for them to go away. For some medications, side effects are temporary, and spontaneous remission is common. However, for others, the rate of complete remission is low and may take many weeks or months. For example, delayed orgasm secondary to SSRIs occurs commonly, and the rate of total remission varies from close to zero to 30% and may take as long as 6 months (Croft et al., 1999; Haberfellner & Rittsmannsberger, 2004; Montejo et al., 2001). Long-term follow-up suggests that additional accommodation does not occur, even after more than 3 years (Ashton & Rosen, 1998). There is some indication that partial improvement is more likely than complete remission, and that the more severe the side effect is initially, the less likely significant remission will occur (Haberfellner & Rittsmannsberger, 2004). A moderate rate of remission from sexual side effects caused by antihypertensive medications has also been documented (Grimm et al., 1997).

Significant drawbacks of this approach exist. If remission takes a considerable period of time, quality of life is impacted, and this may have a negative effect on other factors, including mood and relationship health. If the patient is being treated for depression, not addressing sexual problems quickly may delay recovery from depression or even worsen existing depression. Failure to address sexual side effects quickly may also result in reduced adherence (Gregorian et al., 2002; Kanaly & Berman, 2002). Patients experiencing significant side effects are more likely to stop taking the medication and less likely to take the medication as prescribed.

No Treatment or No Medication

Providing no intervention for sexual side effects may be an option for some patients. If the problem is mild, or is not distressing to the patient, no intervention is warranted. However, this approach carries some risk as well. Physicians often underestimate how bothersome sexual side effects are to patients (Hu et al., 2004). Providers must not assume that a side effect is tolerable, because an error in judgment may lead to lack of medication adherence.

Other patients may be reassured to know that a sexual problem is caused by a medication and may not have any desire to address the issue. This may be the case when the patient is not sexually active, when the medication's benefit outweighs the side effect, or when the sexual change does not impact sexual performance (e.g., reduced volume of ejaculate or retrograde ejaculation).

Stopping a medication entirely is rarely an option. However, sexual side effects may provide a great motivation for patients to find alternative means of controlling medical problems or psychological concerns. Patients with high blood pressure or high cholesterol may have new incentive to begin exercising, dieting, and losing weight. Patients with mild anxiety or depression may opt for nonpharmacological interventions such as psychotherapy.

Dosage and Drug Holidays

Many sexual side effects are strongly dose related, and lowering the dose of a medication may alleviate the sexual concern without reducing therapeutic effectiveness. However, reducing doses carries the risk of loss of effectiveness, and there is no assurance that the side effect will remit (Gregorian et al., 2002).

Another option for treating medication sexual side effects is the use of "drug holidays," or skipping a medication for a day or two. For many medications, such as those used to treat hypertension, such an approach is not indicated. However, with others, in which loss of therapeutic effectiveness will not occur immediately, this approach may be indicated. A number of studies have found this intervention to be effective for SSRI-induced sexual side effects without eliciting a relapse of depression (Hirschfeld, 1999; Rothschild, 2000). However, this approach requires significant motivation and planning on the part of the patient and removes much of the spontaneity of sexual activity. Frequency of sexual activity is limited, as drug holidays should not occur closely together. This approach also works only with medications with relatively shorter half-lives. Patients taking sertraline and paroxetine report benefits from this approach, but those taking fluoxetine, with a relatively longer half-life, report no improvement (Rothschild, 2000).

Changing Medications

When other interventions are ill-advised, impractical, or ineffective, changing the medication may be an option. An approach that minimizes disruption of the patient's therapy is to switch to another medication in the same therapeutic class. There is evidence that some medications are more selective than others and may not carry as high an incidence of side effects. For example, although strong empirical support is lacking, there has been some indication that the beta blocker atenolol is less likely to cause erectile dysfunction than propranolol, secondary to lower lipid solubility and higher cardioselectivity. Similarly, citalopram and escitalopram may be less likely to cause sexual problems than older SSRIs such as fluoxetine, paroxetine, and sertraline (Ashton, Mahmood, & Iqbal, 2005; Waldinger, Zwinderman, & Olivier, 2001). The reason for this is not clearly elucidated, but may be due to higher selectivity or greater therapeutic response at lower doses (Ashton et al., 2005; Waldinger et al., 2001).

Unfortunately, many medications within the same therapeutic class have common rates of sexual side effects. Although it is possible that this approach will be effective, other cases may require consideration of an alternate class of medication, preferably one with a lower incidence of sexual problems. For example, switching from a beta blocker to an alpha blocker for hypertension may alleviate erectile disorder; changing from an SSRI to bupropion has been found to restore orgasmic response (Walker et al., 1993); and patients restarting nefazodone were less likely to experience sexual dysfunction than those restarting sertraline (Ferguson et al., 2001).

Pharmacological Antidotes

At times, changing a medication may not be an alternative, may not be clinically indicated, or may not be effective at alleviating the sexual side effect. Numerous "antidote" approaches have been suggested, but most lack sound empirical support. Some of the more common approaches are reviewed here.

Amantadine

Amantadine is a dopaminergic agent thought to improve sexual function by increasing dopamine availability (Kanaly & Berman, 2002). Although anecdotal and case studies have shown a positive response in SSRI side effects, a placebo-controlled trial found no effect (D. Michelson et al., 2000).

Antidepressants

Bupropion, used alone or as a substitute for an SSRI, has been shown to improve sexual function significantly. However, when used as an augmentation for SSRI-induced sexual dysfunction, the results are not as straightforward. Some studies have found a modest improvement in some measures of sexual function (Ashton & Rosen, 1998; Clayton et al., 2004; DeBattista et al., 2003), but others have found no such improvement (DeBattista et al., 2005; Masand et al., 2001). Mirtazapine has also been shown to have a lower rate of sexual side effects but has not been shown to alleviate sexual side effects caused by other antidepressants (D. Michelson et al., 2002).

Antihistamines

Cyproheptadine and loratadine have both been used in the treatment of SSRI-induced sexual dysfunction. A small, open-label study of loratadine found an improvement in erection scores after 2 weeks of treatment but did not evaluate orgasmic response (Aukst-Margetic & Margetic, 2005). Cyproheptadine has not been thoroughly tested, but case reports have found it effective at alleviating medication-induced anorgasmia (De Castro, 1985; A. J. Riley & E. J. Riley, 1986).

Buspirone

Buspirone, an antianxiety medication, has been used to treat antidepressant-induced sexual dysfunctions. Studies that used placebo-control designs found no significant remission in sexual dysfunction with the addition of buspirone, but one showed a trend in that direction (Landen et al., 1999; D. Michelson et al., 2000).

Ginkgo Biloba

Ginkgo biloba is an extract from the leaf of the Ginkgo tree, and is sold over the counter for various homeopathic treatments. Open trials using Ginkgo biloba have shown positive effects for sexual problems associated with antidepressants (Cohen & Bartlik, 1998). However, a placebo-controlled trial of Ginkgo biloba showed strong responses to both placebo and Ginkgo biloba, underscoring the necessity of including placebo-control groups in research on medication side effects (Kang et al., 2002).

Phosphodiesterase Type 5 Inhibitors (PDE5)

Viagra is a PDE5 inhibitor that has been shown to be an effective treatment for erectile dysfunction. Treatment of medication-induced erectile dysfunction with Viagra has not been independently studied, except for SSRIs. In these studies, Viagra does result in improved erectile function. Improvement in other areas of function, including orgasmic delay, are less significant, but likely (Nurnberg et al., 2003; Seidman, Pesce, & Roose, 2003).

Yohimbine

Yohimbine, a presynaptic a2-blocker, has been used for decreased desire and anorgasmia secondary to SSRIs. Similar to Ginkgo biloba, uncontrolled trials consistently show a positive response (Woodrum & Brown, 1998). However, studies using placebo groups have found just as positive a response to placebo as to yohimbine (D. Michelson et al., 2002).

CASE EXAMPLE*

George is 62 and has been married to Linda for 27 years. He always considered their sex life to be "healthy." Although he noticed some decreased desire for sex over the years, he attributed this to the stress of his work (George is a shift manager at a factory), family life (Linda and George have three children), and perhaps even some boredom with the sexual relationship. And, although he had noticed some changes in his erections, namely taking a bit longer to get firm and not being quite as firm as in the past, his erections were always sufficient for penetration. He simply attributed these changes to getting older.

Six months ago, George experienced sudden weakness on the right side of his body and was unable to speak clearly. George had been a heavy smoker for years, and his blood pressure and cholesterol had been on the rise, along with his weight. Following the stroke, George's doctor put him on medication for his blood pressure and his high cholesterol, as well as recommending some significant changes in his diet and exercise. He was also strongly encouraged to quit smoking, but found this very difficult.

In some ways, George was lucky. Following the stroke, he recovered all of the use of his right leg and most of the use of his right arm and hand. However, he was not able to return to work. This was quite distressing to George, as he always viewed working as a primary responsibility of a husband and father. To make matters worse, Linda continued to work full time at the local supermarket. George became withdrawn, moody, and irritable and, at the urging of his wife, discussed these changes with his doctor. His doctor started him on an antidepressant.

Two months later, George's mood and energy level had improved, and he was engaging in more activities with Linda. Having avoided sex since the stroke (no one had discussed whether sex would be safe for George, and when), they attempted intercourse. Much to George's dismay, he found it very difficult to obtain sufficient rigidity for penetration. When he did finally manage to, he was unable to reach orgasm before becoming too tired to continue. Frustrated and embarrassed, George began to avoid Linda sexually. Not used to talking about sex, and not wanting to make George uncomfortable, Linda avoided the topic as well. Also somewhat

---

* Names and identifying characteristics in this case example have been changed to protect privacy.

uncomfortable with this topic was George's doctor, and, at a loss for what to do, he referred George to a sexual health clinic.

As George, Linda, and their therapist discussed these issues, it became apparent that their initial reluctance to resume sexual activity was driven by fear and anxiety. Linda was afraid that George might have another stroke, and George was unsure how well he would be able to perform sexually; no one had told him what to expect following the stroke. George also acknowledged that feeling useless and depressed in the weeks immediately following the stroke had left him with little interest in anything, including sex.

With the provision of some accurate information, and some time discussing their concerns, George and Linda's fears and anxieties seemed to dissipate. George's depression seemed to lift almost entirely. George acknowledged that his desire for sex was returning but that he remained somewhat reluctant to initiate sex secondary to his concerns about his performance, both firmness of erections and lack of orgasm and ejaculation. His inability to climax left him feeling somewhat frustrated, and Linda felt inadequate, as she blamed herself for his weaker erections and inability to reach orgasm. George was concerned that Linda, nearly 10 years his junior, would seek sex elsewhere. In their therapy sessions, Linda was able to reassure George that this was not the case, and was also able to convince him that erections weren't that important to her sexual satisfaction. In fact, with their increasing comfort discussing sexual issues, George and Linda found new ways to enjoy their intimate time together and reported more satisfaction than ever with their sex lives. However, although George's erections were consistently functional, he continued to report difficulty reaching orgasm.

In addition to the stroke, anxieties, fears, and depression, it was clear that another possible contributor to the sexual concerns was the addition of medications prescribed after the stroke. George was prescribed a low dose of atenolol, a beta blocker, for his blood pressure; simvastatin, for his high cholesterol; and an SSRI, Celexa, for the depression. In reviewing the new medications and their potential sexual side effects, it became clear that all three could be contributing to the sexual concerns, but that the SSRI was most likely contributing to the most serious problem, the anorgasmia. Because there are no empirically validated adjunct treatments for SSRI-induced anorgasmia, and because his depression seemed resolved, he agreed with his primary medical provider's recommendation to taper off of this medication. They discussed the possibility that this might not restore the erections to their pre-stroke level, but agreed that they could deal with that problem as needed. He also understood that if his depression returned, he would need to consider another antidepressant or psychotherapy.

Within a few weeks of stopping the antidepressant entirely, George was happy to report that he was able to reach orgasm consistently. He and Linda were not avoiding sex, and while his erections were not perfect, they were consistently functional. As his erections had not returned to pre-stroke firmness, he discussed the beta blocker with his medical provider, who was reluctant to stop this medication. He suggested that George use a PDE5 Inhibitor (e.g., Cialis, Levitra, or Viagra). George found this helpful, and he and Linda used this at times, but typically found that it was not necessary.

CONCLUSIONS

Sexual side effects of medication are extremely prevalent and pose a substantial risk to medication adherence, treatment effectiveness, and overall quality of life. Ignoring these problems is not an option. In most cases, treatments exist that will alleviate the sexual concern. Being sensitive to the importance of sexual function, including the patient in the assessment and treatment process, and providing adequate follow-up can result in effective treatment.

CONTRIBUTOR

William W. Finger, PhD, is a psychologist at the James H. Quillen Veteran Affairs Medical Center in Johnson City, Tennessee and Professor in the Department of Psychiatry and Behavorial Sciences at the James H. Quillen College of Medicine, East Tennessee State University. Dr. Finger received a Bachelor of Arts from the University of Virginia and an MA and PhD in clinical psychology from the University of Missouri-Columbia. He is certified as a Sex Therapist by the American Association of Sexuality Educators, Counselors, and Therapists and has been awarded Diplomate status by that organization. He has published a number of articles on medication effects on sexual function and has presented on the topic locally, regionally, and nationally. Dr. Finger may be contacted at Psychology Service 116B2, James H. Quillen VAMC, P.O. Box 4000, Mountain Home, TN 37684-4000. E-mail: william.finger@med.va.gov

RESOURCES

Ackerman, M. D., D'Attilio, J. P., Antoni, M. H., Weinstein, D., Rhamy, R. K., & Politano, V. A. (1991). The predictive significance of patient-reported sexual functioning in RigiScan sleep evaluations. *Journal of Urology, 146,* 1559-1563.

Aldridge, S. A. (1982). Drug-induced sexual dysfunction. *Clinical Pharmacy, 1,* 141-147.

Angst, J. (1998). Sexual problems in healthy and depressed persons. *International Clinical Psychopharmacology, 13*(Suppl. 6), S1-S4.

Ashton, A. K., Mahmood, A., & Iqbal, F. (2005). Improvements in SSRI/SNRI-induced sexual dysfunction by switching to escitalopram. *Journal of Sex and Marital Therapy, 31,* 257-262.

Ashton, A. K., & Rosen, R. C. (1998). Bupropion as an antidote for serotonin reuptake inhibitor-induced sexual dysfunction. *Journal of Clinical Psychiatry, 59,* 112-115.

Aukst-Margetic, B., & Margetic, B. (2005). An open-label series using loratadine for the treatment of sexual dysfunction associated with selective serotonin reuptake inhibitors. *Progress in Neuropsychopharmacology and Biological Psychiatry, 29,* 754-756.

Balon, R., Yeragani, V. K., Pohl, R., & Ramesh, C. (1993). Sexual dysfunction during antidepressant treatment. *Journal of Clinical Psychiatry, 54,* 209-212.

Barksdale, J. D., & Gardner, S. F. (1999). The impact of first-line antihypertensive drugs on erectile dysfunction. *Pharmacotherapy, 19,* 573-581.

Broekman, C. P., Haensel, S. M., Van de Ven, L. L., & Slob, A. K. (1992). Bisoprolol and hypertension: Effect on sexual functioning in men. *Journal of Sex and Marital Therapy, 18,* 325-331.

Bruckert, E., Giral, P., Heshmati, H. M., & Turpin, G. (1996). Men treated with hypolipidaemic drugs complain more frequently of erectile dysfunction. *Journal of Clinical Pharmacy and Therapeutics, 21,* 89-94.

Buffum, J. (1982). Pharmacosexology: The effects of drugs on sexual function. A review. *Journal of Psychoactive Drugs, 14,* 5-44.

Chang, S. W., Fine, R., Siegel, D., Chesney, M., Black, D., & Hulley, S. B. (1991). The impact of diuretic therapy on reported sexual function. *Archives of Internal Medicine, 151,* 2402-2408.

Clayton, A. H., Pradko, J. F., Croft, H. A., Montano, C. B., Leadbetter, R. A., Bolden-Watson, C., Bass, K. I., Donahue, R. M., Jamerson, B. D., & Metz, A. (2002). Prevalence of sexual dysfunction among newer antidepressants. *Journal of Clinical Psychiatry, 63,* 357-366.

Clayton, A. H., Warnock, J. K., Kornstein, S. G., Pinkerton, R., Sheldon-Keller, A., & McGarvey, E. L. (2004). A placebo-controlled trial of bupropion SR as an antidote for selective serotonin reuptake inhibitor-induced sexual dysfunction. *Journal of Clinical Psychiatry, 65,* 62-67.

Cohen, A. J., & Bartlik, B. (1998). Ginkgo biloba for antidepressant-induced sexual dysfunction. *Journal of Sex and Marital Therapy, 24,* 139-143.

Corinaldesi, R., Pasquali, R., Paternico, A., Stanghellini, V., Paparo, G. F., Ricci Maccarini, M., & Barbara, L. (1987). Effects of short- and long-term administrations of famotidine and ranitidine on some pituitary, sexual and thyroid hormones. *Drugs Under Experimental and Clinical Research, 13,* 647-654.

Croft, H., Settle, E., Houser, T., Batey, S. R., Donahue, R. M., & Ascher, J. A. (1999). A placebo-controlled comparison of the antidepressant efficacy and effects on sexual functioning of sustained-release bupropion and sertraline. *Clinical Therapeutics, 4,* 643-658.

Daniell, H. W. (2002). Hypogonadism in men consuming sustained-action oral opioids. *Journal of Pain, 3,* 377-384.

DeBattista, C., Solvason, H. B., Poirier, J., Kendrick, E., & Loraas, E. (2005). A placebo-controlled, randomized, double-blind study of adjunctive bupropion sustained release in the treatment of SSRI-induced sexual dysfunction. *Journal of Clinical Psychiatry, 66,* 844-848.

DeBattista, C., Solvason, H. B., Poirier, J., Kendrick, E., & Schatzberg, A. F. (2003). A prospective trial of bupropion SR augmentation of partial and non-responders to serotonergic antidepressants. *Journal of Clinical Psychopharmacology, 23,* 27-30.

De Castro, R. M. (1985). Reversal of MAOI-induced anorgasmia with cyproheptadine [Letter to the editor]. *American Journal of Psychiatry, 142*, 783.

Delgado, P. L., Brannan, S. K., Mallinckrodt, C. H., Tran, P. V., McNamara, R. K., Wang, F., Watkin, J. G., & Detke, M. J. (2005). Sexual functioning assessed in 4 double-blind placebo- and paroxetine-controlled trials of duloxetine for major depressive disorder. *Journal of Clinical Psychiatry, 66*, 686-692.

Detke, M. J., Lu, Y., Goldstein, D. J., McNamara, R. K., & Demitrack, M. A. (2002). Duloxetine 60 mg once daily dosing versus placebo in the acute treatment of major depression. *Journal of Psychiatric Research, 36*, 383-390.

DeVeaugh-Geiss, J., Landau, P., & Katz, R. (1989). Preliminary results from a multi-center trial of clomipramine in obsessive-compulsive disorder. *Psychopharmacology Bulletin, 25*, 36-40.

Due, D. L., Giguere, G. C., & Plachetka, J. R. (1986). Postmarketing comparison of labetalol and propranolol in hypertensive patients. *Clinical Therapy, 8*, 624-631.

Duncan, L., & Bateman, D. N. (1993). Sexual function in women. Do antihypertensive drugs have an impact? *Drug Safety, 8*, 225-234.

Ferguson, J. M., Shrivastava, R. K., Stahl, S. M., Hartford, J. T., Borian, F., Ieni, J., McQuade, R. D., & Jody, D. (2001). Reemergence of sexual dysfunction in patients with major depressive disorder: Double-blind comparison of nefazodone and sertraline. *Journal of Clinical Psychiatry, 62*, 24-29.

Fogari, R., Preti, P., Derosa, G., Marasi, G., Zoppi, A., Rinaldi, A., & Mugellini, A. (2002). Effect of antihypertensive treatment with valsartan or atenolol on sexual activity and plasma testosterone in hypertensive men. *European Journal of Clinical Pharmacology, 58*, 177-180.

Fogari, R., Preti, P., Zoppi, A., Corradi, L., Pasotti, C., Rinaldi, A., & Mugellini, A. (2004). Effect of valsartan and atenolol on sexual behavior in hypertensive postmenopausal women. *American Journal of Hypertension, 17*, 77-81.

Fogari, R., & Zoppi, A. (2004). Effect of antihypertensive agents on quality of life in the elderly. *Drugs and Aging, 21*, 377-393.

Fogari, R., Zoppi, A., Poletti, L., Marasi, G., Mugellini, A., & Corradi, L. (2001). Sexual activity in hypertensive men treated with valsartan or carvedilol: A crossover study. *American Journal of Hypertension, 14*, 27-31.

Gebhart, F. (2006, March 20). *2005 Rx Market: The Highs and Lows. Lack of Blockbuster Launches Makes for Uneventful Year; Still, Scripts Rise 3%.* Retrieved July 21, 2006, from http://www.drugtopics.com/drugtopics/article/article Detail.jsp?id=312505

Gelenberg, A. J., McGahuey, C., Laukes, C., Okayli, G., Moreno, F., Zentner, L., & Delgado, P. (2000). Mirtazapine substitution in SSRI-induced sexual dysfunction. *Journal of Clinical Psychiatry, 61*, 356-360.

Ghadirian, A. M., Annable, L., & Belanger, M. C. (1992). Lithium, benzodiazepines and sexual function in bipolar patients. *American Journal of Psychiatry, 149*, 801-805.

Ginzburg, R., Wong, Y., & Fader, J. S. (2005). Effect of bupropion on sexual dysfunction. *Annals of Pharmacotherapy, 39*, 2096-2099.

Greenblatt, D. J., & Koch-Weser, J. (1973). Gynecomastia and impotence: Complications of spironolactone therapy. *Journal of the American Medical Association, 223*, 82.

Gregorian, R. S., Golden, K. A., Bahce, A., Goodman, C., Kwong, W. J., & Khan, Z. M. (2002). Antidepressant-induced sexual dysfunction. *Annals of Pharmacotherapy, 36*, 1577-1589.

Grimm, R. H., Jr., Grandits, G. A., Prineas, R. J., McDonald, R. H., Lewis, C. E., Flack, J. M., Yunis, C., & Svendsen, K. (1997). Long-term effects on sexual function of five antihypertensive drugs and nutritional hygienic treatment in hypertensive men and women. Treatment of Mild Hypertension Study (TOMHS). *Hypertension, 29*, 8-14.

Haberfellner, E. M., & Rittmannsberger, H. (2004). Spontaneous remission of SSRI-induced orgasm delay. *Pharmacopsychiatry, 37*(3), 127-130.

Hirschfeld, R. M. (1999). Management of sexual side effects of antidepressant therapy. *Journal of Clinical Psychiatry, 60*(Suppl. 14), 27-30.

Hirschfeld, R. M., & Vornik, L. A. (2004). Newer antidepressants: Review of efficacy and safety of escitalopram and duloxetine. *Journal of Clinical Psychiatry, 65*(Suppl. 4), 46-52.

Hogan, M. J., Wallin, J. D., & Baer, R. M. (1980). Antihypertensive therapy and male sexual dysfunction. *Psychosomatics, 21*, 234-237.

Horowitz, J. D., & Goble, A. J. (1979). Drugs and impaired male sexual function. *Drugs, 18*, 206-217.

Hu, X. H., Bull, S. A., Hunkeler, E. M., Ming, E., Lee, J. Y., Fireman, B., & Markson, L. E. (2004). Incidence and duration of side effects and those rated as bothersome with selective serotonin reuptake inhibitor treatment for depression: Patient report versus physician estimate. *Clinical Psychiatry, 65*, 959-965.

Hudson, J. I., Wohlreich, M. M., Kajdasz, D. K., Mallinckrodt, C. H., Watkin, J. G., & Martynov, O. V. (2005). Safety and tolerability of duloxetine in the treatment of major depressive disorder: Analysis of pooled data from eight placebo-controlled clinical trials. *Human Psychopharmacology, 20*, 327-341.

Jensen, R. T., Collen, M. J., Pandol, S. J., Allende, H. D., Raufman, J. P., Bissonnette, B. M., Duncan, W. C., Durgin, P. L., Gillin, J. C., & Gardner, J. D. (1983). Cimetidine-induced impotence and breast changes in patients with gastric hypersecretory states. *New England Journal of Medicine, 308*, 883-887.

Kanaly, K. A., & Berman, J. R. (2002). Sexual side effects of SSRI medications: Potential treatment strategies for SSRI-induced female sexual dysfunction. *Current Women's Health Reports, 2*, 409-416.

Kang, B. J., Lee, S. J., Kim, M. D., & Cho, M. J. (2002). A placebo-controlled, double-blind trial of Ginkgo biloba for antidepressant-induced sexual dysfunction. *Human Psychopharmacology, 17*, 279-284.

Kennedy, S. H., Eisfeld, B. S., Dickens, S. E., Bacchiochi, J. R., & Bagby, R. M. (2000). Antidepressant-induced sexual dysfunction during treatment with moclobemide, paroxetine, sertraline, and venlafaxine. *Journal of Clinical Psychiatry, 61*, 276-281.

Koutouvidis, N., Pratikakis, M., & Fotiadou, A. (1999). The use of mirtazapine in a group of 11 patients following poor compliance to selective serotonin reuptake inhibitor treatment due to sexual dysfunction. *International Clinical Psychopharmacology, 14*, 253-255.

Kowalski, A., Stanley, R. O., Dennerstein, L., Burrows, G., & Maguire, K. P. (1985). The sexual side-effects of antidepressant medication: A double-blind comparison of two antidepressants in a non-psychiatric population. *British Journal of Psychiatry, 147*, 413-418.

Lacourciere, Y. (1988). Analysis of well-being and 24-hour blood pressure recording in a comparative study between indapamide and captopril. *American Journal of Medicine, 84*(Suppl. 1B), 47-52.

Landen, M., Eriksson, E., Agren, H., & Fahlen, T. (1999). Effect of buspirone on sexual dysfunction in depressed patients treated with selective serotonin reuptake inhibitors. *Journal of Clinical Psychopharmacology, 19*, 268-271.

Landen, M., Hogberg, P., & Thase, M. E. (2005). Incidence of sexual side effects in refractory depression during treatment with citalopram or paroxetine. *Journal of Clinical Psychiatry, 66*(1), 100-106.

Langley, M. S., & Heel, R. C. (1988). Transdermal clonidine: A preliminary review of its pharmacodynamic properties and therapeutic efficacy. *Drugs, 35*, 123-142.

Lowe, F. C. (2005). Treatment of lower urinary tract symptoms suggestive of benign prostatic hyperplasia: Sexual function. *British Journal of Urology International, 95*(Suppl. 4), 12-18.

Lydiard, R. B., Howell, E. F., Laraia, M. T., & Ballenger, J. C. (1987). Sexual side effects of alprazolam. *American Journal of Psychiatry, 2*, 254-255.

Lynch, M. G., Whitson, J. T., Brown, R. H., Nguyen, H., & Drake, M. M. (1988). Topical beta-blocker therapy and central nervous system side effects. A preliminary study comparing betaxolol and timolol. *Archives of Ophthalmology, 106*, 908-911.

Masand, P. S., Ashton, A. K., Gupta, S., & Frank, B. (2001). Sustained-release bupropion for selective serotonin reuptake inhibitor-induced sexual dysfunction: A randomized, double-blind, placebo-controlled, parallel-group study. *American Journal of Psychiatry, 158*, 805-807.

Michelson, D., Bancroft, J., Targum, S., Kim, Y., & Tepner, R. (2000). Female sexual dysfunction associated with antidepressant administration: A randomized, placebo-controlled study of pharmacologic intervention. *American Journal of Psychiatry, 157*, 239-243.

Michelson, D., Kociban, K., Tamura, R., & Morrison, M. F. (2002). Mirtazapine, yohimbine or olanzapine augmentation therapy for serotonin reuptake-associated female sexual dysfunction: A randomized, placebo controlled trial. *Journal of Psychiatric Research, 36*, 147-152.

Michelson, E. L., Frishman, W. H., Lewis, J. E., Edwards, W. T., Flanigan, W. J., Bloomfield, S. S., Johnson, B. F., Lucas, C., Freis, E. D., Finnerty, F. A., et al. (1983). Multicenter clinical evaluation of long-term efficacy and safety of labetalol in treatment of hypertension. *American Journal of Medicine, 75*(Suppl. 4A), 68-80.

Micromedex Healthcare Series. (Edition expires 12/2005). Greenwood Village, CO: Thomson Micromedex.

Monteiro, W. O., Noshirvani, H. F., Marks, I. M., & Lelliot, P. T. (1987). Anorgasmia from clomipramine in obsessive-compulsive disorder. A controlled trial. *British Journal of Psychiatry, 151*, 107-112.

Montejo, A. L., Llorca, G., Isquierdo, J. A., & Rico-Villademoros, F. (2001). Incidence of sexual dysfunction associated with antidepressant agents: A prospective multicenter study of 1022 outpatients. *Journal of Clinical Psychiatry, 62*(Suppl. 3), 10-21.

Morrissette, D. L., Skinner, M. H., Hoffman, B. B., Levine, R. E., & Davidson, J. M. (1993). Effects of antihypertensive drugs atenolol and nifedipine on sexual function in older men: A placebo-controlled, crossover study. *Archives of Sexual Behavior, 22*, 99-109.

Nurnberg, H. G., Hensley, P. L., Gelenberg, A. J., Fava, M., Lauriello, J., & Paine, S. (2003). Treatment of antidepressant-associated sexual dysfunction with sildenafil: A randomized controlled trial. *Journal of the American Medical Association, 289*, 56-64.

Palmer, J. D., & Nugent, C. A. (1983). Guanadrel sulfate: A postganglonic sympathetic inhibitor for the treatment of mild to moderate hypertension. *Pharmacotherapy, 3*, 220-229.

Papadopoulos, C. (1980). Cardiovascular drugs and sexuality: A cardiologist's review. *Archives of Internal Medicine, 140*, 1341-1345.

Riley, A. J., & Riley. E. J. (1986). Cyproheptadine and antidepressant-induced anorgasmia. *British Journal of Psychiatry, 148*, 217-218.

Rizvi, K., Hampson, J. P., & Harvey, J. N. (2002). Do lipid-lowering drugs cause erectile dysfunction? A systematic review. *Family Practice, 19*, 95-98.

Rothschild, A. J. (2000). New directions in the treatment of antidepressant-induced sexual dysfunction. *Clinical Therapeutics, 22*(Suppl. A), A42-A61.

Rx300. (2006). *The Top 300 Prescriptions for 2005 by Number of US Prescriptions Dispensed.* Retrieved July 21, 2006, from http://www.rxlist.com/top200.htm

Saenz de Tejada, I., Ware, J. C., Blanco, R., Pittard, J. T., Nadig, P. W., Azadzoi, K. M., Krane, R. J. & Goldstein, I. (1991). Pathophysiology of prolonged penile erection associated with trazodone use. *Journal of Urology, 145*, 60-64.

Saiz-Ruiz, J., Montes, J. M., Ibanez, A., Diaz, M., Vicente, F., Pelegrin, C., Vinas, R., Arias, F., Carrasco, J. L., & Ferrando, L. (2005). Assessment of sexual functioning in depressed patients treated with mirtazapine: A naturalistic 6-month study. *Human Psychopharmacology: Clinical and Experimental, 20*, 435-440.

Seeman, P. (2002). Atypical antipsychotics: Mechanism of action. *Canadian Journal of Psychiatry, 1*, 27-38.

Segraves, R. T. (1988). Sexual side-effects of psychiatric drugs. *International Journal of Psychiatry in Medicine, 18*, 243-252.

Seidman, S. N., Pesce, V. C., & Roose, S. P. (2003). High-dose sildenafil citrate for selective serotonin reuptake inhibitor-associated ejaculatory delay: Open clinical trial. *Journal of Clinical Psychiatry, 64*, 721-725.

Stevenson, J. G., & Umstead, G. S. (1984). Sexual dysfunction due to antihypertensive agents. *Drug Intelligence and Clinical Pharmacy, 18*, 113-121.

van Moorselaar, R. J., Hartung, R., Emberton, M., Harving, N., Matzkin, H., Elhilali, M., Alcaraz, A., & Vallancien, G. (2005). Alfuzosin 10 mg once daily improves sexual function in men with lower urinary tract symptoms and concomitant sexual dysfunction. *British Journal of Urology International, 95*, 603-608.

Vinarova, E., Uhlir, O., Stika, L., & Vinar, O. (1972). Side effects of lithium administration. *Activitas Nervosa Superior, 14*, 105-107.

Waldinger, M. D., Zwinderman, A. H., & Olivier, B. (2001). SSRIs and ejaculation: A double-blind, randomized, fixed-dose study with paroxetine and citalopram. *Journal of Clinical Psychopharmacology, 21*, 556-560.

Walker, P. W., Cole, J. O., Gardner, E. A., Hughes, A. R., Johnston, J. A., Batey, S. R., & Lineberry, C. G. (1993). Improvement in fluoxetine-associated sexual dysfunction in patients switched to bupropion. *Journal of Clinical Psychiatry, 54*, 459-465.

Wassertheil-Smoller, S., Blaufox, M. D., Oberman, A., Davis, B. R., Swencionis, C., Knerr, M. O., Hawkins, C. M., & Langford, H. G. (1991). Effects of antihypertensives on sexual function and QOL: The TAIM Study. *Annals of Internal Medicine, 114*, 613-620.

Woodrum, S. T., & Brown, C. S. (1998). Management of SSRI-induced sexual dysfunction. *The Annals of Pharmacotherapy, 32*, 1209-1215.

Ethics in Sex Therapy

Catherine Dailey Ravella

Ethics is a discipline dealing with obligations and moral duty, a set of values or moral principles of conduct that govern the behaviors of an individual or group. Who determines what is right or wrong, moral or immoral, good or bad, proper or improper, ethical or unethical? For each culture, values and moral principles are often the outgrowth of a religious tradition that occasionally is incorporated into law. "Sexual morality (should) stand up to reason. . . . This is not meant to imply that moral standards can be entirely rational" (Haeberle, 1978, p. 487).

In the United States it is suggested that our ethical standards are based in the Judeo-Christian tradition. Professional ethics are not necessarily law; they are "permissive and aspirational standards and guidelines for professional practice" (American Association of Sexuality Educators, Counselors, and Therapists [AASECT], 2004, p. 1). The General Principles A through F of the ethics code of the American Psychological Association broadly guide the clinician's practice to first do no harm to those seeking service, to practice within the limits of competence, to be truthful, to uphold the dignity of all people, and to not condone unjust practices and prejudice (APA, 2003). Virtue ethics, originally formulated by Aristotle as a response to the perennial question of how people are to lead flourishing and happy lives, "requires the clinician to offer possibilities for living good or worthwhile lives and take into account each individual's abilities, circumstances, interests and opportunities" (Ward & Stewart, 2003).

WHAT IS ETHICAL SEX THERAPY?

Who decides what is ethical practice or the correct observance of standards for professional interactions in the field of sex therapy, especially in our media-enhanced, frequently emotionally charged area of human sexuality? Issues regarding professionalism and ethical practice can arise unexpectedly, leaving clinicians in a confused and awkward situation. Ethical issues confront all therapists. This contribution highlights some ethical issues that are within the realm of sex therapy, but the basic principles may also be applied to practice issues in general therapy. Understanding and adhering to the code of ethics prescribed by your individual profession offers the soundest guide. No one single code will ever be a complete guide for the conscientious therapist. Regular peer consultation, in addition to referring to one's professional code of ethics, will help avoid many ethical pitfalls.

THE ROLE OF PROFESSIONAL ORGANIZATIONS

The American Association of Sexuality Educators, Counselors, and Therapists (AASECT) *Code of Ethics* is included in another section of this volume (see pp. 279-286). This organization certifies psychologists, psychiatrists, psychiatric nurse specialists, clinical social workers, marriage and family therapists, and counselors; in other words, clinicians in varied therapeutic disciplines that have accomplished the additional training and supervision for certification in sex therapy, sex counseling, or sex education. An individual who maintains several professional roles is bound by more than one code of ethics; therefore, it is advisable to abide by the more stringent or restrictive code or you risk exclusion from that professional organization. It may seem that some codes conflict with one another.

The AASECT *Code of Ethics* was revised in 2004 after 3 years of deliberation to make it educational rather than adjudicative. This action is a trend in many professional organizations, such as in several of the state organizations of the American Psychological Association. Clinicians have sued their organizations when an adjudicative action was taken against them with countercharges of "defamation of character" or "restraint of trade." This fact points to the litigious nature of our society but does not relieve a professional organization from dealing with infractions of the established ethical code or from promoting a currently educated and appropriately functioning clinician. Professional codes of ethics are evolving to provide increased guidance to practitioners rather than disciplinary action.

No code can offer a clear guideline in every possible clinical situation, just as no law can always foresee every possible situation where its relevance may come to bear. An education that is commensurate with the type of practice the sex therapist performs goes without saying, yet nothing stops individuals in some states from hanging up a shingle and calling themselves a Sex Therapist. What is unethical is not always against the law.

THE ETHICAL NATURE OF ANY THERAPEUTIC RELATIONSHIP

Fundamental to the therapeutic contract is the issue of the expected vulnerability of the patient in the task of restoring the patient to a higher level of functioning and relieving symptoms of distress. The sex therapist may have special moral and ethical obligations that go beyond the care provided by general therapists.

The ethical delivery of service primarily focuses on the patient/client-therapist relationship. The use of the terms patient, client, and sometimes consumer provides an interesting and somewhat diverse view of the clinical relationship. The term patient is used most frequently by those who come from a medical model. The Scribner-Bantam dictionary tells us the patient is "one that is expectantly hopeful," while client is the term applied to "those who engage a lawyer, or one who is *dependent*" [italics added]. The consumer is one who "uses up or destroys, goods or services." Each term may suggest a view of the clinical relationship. Dependency issues, which are acknowledged in sex therapy for the "encouragement of positive transference of parental authority" (V. E. Johnson, personal communication, October 10, 1983) may also be misused when the patient or couple are damaged by the therapist's use of the therapeutic relationship to gratify his or her own emotional, financial, or sexual needs (Blackshaw & Patterson, 1992).

The following vignette* should stimulate some thoughtful consideration for understanding and establishing your own personal boundaries in clinical practice:

> Bill is a 48-year-old, divorced, Catholic psychologist in private practice. He presented for treatment in a sex therapy practice with a chief complaint of erectile dysfunction with his present partner, Nancy, age 44, who was divorced and also a psychologist.

---

* Names and characteristics in all case examples have been changed to protect privacy.

Nancy's former husband, Sean, had been a partner of Bill's and also was the individual who reported the unethical sexual behavior of Bill to his psychology licensing board. Nancy and Sean were divorcing during this period, and Nancy was receiving support from their mutual friend, Bill.

Bill's ethical infraction was with Alyssa, a patient in treatment for depression. Alyssa had announced she was quitting therapy because she had lost her job and her health insurance. Bill had been wishing to hire a transcriptionist/secretary. The position was offered and accepted by Alyssa. She discontinued therapy and began work in Sean and Bill's office. Alyssa, as employee, was rewarded with gifts from Bill, including shopping trips for clothing that was more "professional" in appearance. Bill suggested she "seduced (him) into sexual liaisons" in the office. Bill's license was suspended for 2 years for sexual misconduct with a client. The partnership with Sean ended and so did the relationship with Alyssa.

The treatment issues in the present relationship between Nancy and Bill were intertwined with Bill's understanding of his role as a therapist, his self-perception as a "rescuer" for both Alyssa the patient and Nancy the girlfriend, and his lack of boundaries in choices concerning his personal gratification. Bill sought and previously received the suggested counseling recommended for his ethical infraction.

What role does the sex therapist have, if any, to further rehabilitate this patient as a psychologist? Should Bill's role as therapist be considered part of the present couple treatment? Bill made personal gains with Nancy in sex therapy. Understanding his own sexual needs and gender role socialization helped provide him with increased awareness of his patient issues, as well as his own countertransference issues. His basic caring, warm, and sensitive personality was encouraged to incorporate respect for trustworthiness, honesty, and prudence in his professional as well as personal dealings. Ongoing peer supervision was recommended with a colleague as a way of dealing with his sexualized views of dependent, vulnerable female patients. The underlying issue, sexual activity with a patient, underscored the role and treatment focus of the sex therapist.

In a discussion of a similar case in *The Pennsylvania Psychologist* (Wallach, 2001), the rhetorical question was raised if a "profession that helps people change apparently believes that newly-acquired cognitions and behaviors can be induced in other people, (can this be the case for) psychologists?" (p. 6). The author suggested that the then newly formed Pennsylvania Psychological Association Colleague Assistance Committee might be a step in the right direction. Following this line, ongoing supervision in practice offers a broader safety net for what has been labeled a "slippery slope."

Acting on sexual attraction toward patients is strictly forbidden; "talking about any counter transference (including erotic counter transference) is definitely encouraged . . . 'desensitization' and greater openness [with a supervisor] are essential if the current situation is ever to change" (Blackshaw & Patterson, 1992, p. 3).

Jack Annon, former AASECT Ethics committee chair and Hawaii Psychological Association Ethics chair, recommends: "consult with colleagues. Seek one, two or even three opinions from others in the field but avoid the obvious choice of friends. . . . You are more likely to get an objective answer" (Melby, 2005, p. 4). A peer supervisor may have helped Bill in those first questionable choices: hiring an ex-patient (which was a questionable act for his colleague, Sean, as well), buying personal gifts, and eventually becoming involved in a sexual relationship.

In a humorous, tongue-in-cheek "Informed Consent for Sex Between Health Professional and Patient or Client," Plaut outlines the various "risks and benefits" and how a patient may be harmed if a clinician is to begin a sexual relationship with a patient. He argues that "the possibility of 'successful' relationships notwithstanding, one may indeed question whether the consent given in such relationships is truly *informed*, even to the extent typically expected for medical procedures" (Plaut, 1995, p. 129).

Unlike the APA ethics code, in the AASECT *Code of Ethics* a therapeutic relationship is viewed as "continuing in perpetuity," not ending after 2 years or more, no exceptions. The therapist begins the relationship in a position of power and trust. We ask the patient to suspend the usual cultural defenses and reveal intensely personal material with the hope of being understood and helped. It is to be expected that some patients will develop intense feelings toward a therapist, which is the nature of transference. In sex therapy, the numerous, explicit sexual discussions may arouse sexual feelings commingled with the normal attachments that take place in a therapeutic relationship.

There is a blind spot in clinicians who argue that the patient is not harmed by sexual contact with a therapist or that it is the *right* of patients to choose whomever they wish. This blind spot points to the therapist's inability to move beyond the need for personal gratification by not recognizing that the change in the relationship is a betrayal of that initial trust and a misuse of the power inherent in the relationship. There is ample evidence that patients are harmed by sexual contact with a therapist (Schoener, Hofstee-Milgram, & Gonsiorek, 1985; Sonne et al., 1985).

Prohibited sexual behaviors are spelled out in the AASECT *Code of Ethics* and include kissing, sexual intercourse, and/or the touching by either party of breasts or genitals. Some therapists have even questioned if a "friendly hug" is ever allowed in the therapeutic relationship. A retiring sex therapist suggested a rough guideline in such areas: " Would you do 'it' in front of your clinical supervisor when you were a graduate student?" In other words, can your behavior stand up to another professional's scrutiny?

THERAPIST COMPETENCE AS A MEASURE OF SOCIAL RESPONSIBILITY

Understanding your own personal boundaries, including limits of expertise, is part of the role of a professional. In the *Conference Report: Ethical Guidelines for Research and Clinical Perspectives on Human Sexuality* developed in March 1978 by the Reproductive Biology Research Foundation (later known as the famed Masters and Johnson Institute), it is clearly stated that "it is unethical for the therapist to engage in sexual activity with a client" (Kolodny, 1978, p. 4). This paper was originally presented at a time when sex therapy was emerging as a separate, specialized area of treatment. The timeliness of this document is still evident. The task force outlined five major areas of ethical concern: (a) competence and integrity of sex therapists, (b) confidentiality in sex therapy, (c) welfare of the client, (d) welfare of students and trainees, and (e) welfare of research subjects. In an interview with Robert Woody (personal communication, February 10, 2006) he commented that in his service on several ethics boards and past chairmanship of the AASECT Board of Ethics, the most common complaints of these ethical guidelines were in the areas of Principle Three, Sections A and C. He cited state statutes that hold that no person may claim to possess a title or degree that is unaccredited. Confusion exists as to who may call themselves sex therapists.

The 1978 task force and the AASECT *Code of Ethics* clearly define "competence in another primary discipline such as psychology, psychiatry, and marriage counseling is not equivalent to competence in sex therapy." In order to claim to be an AASECT-certified sex therapist one must hold a valid license in another discipline first and then submit to additional training and supervision to achieve competence and certification. Holding a license in a therapeutic field is prerequisite. Those trained in these disciplines bring their professional experience and insights to provide the foundation upon which sex therapy training is added.

Individuals who offer sexual treatments and use titles such as sex coach, life director, and personal educator frequently are not licensed or do not hold membership in any organization that requires these individuals to be accountable to a prescribed code of ethics. These individuals may offer some valuable advice, but in seeking treatment for sexual problems the patient is wise to follow the "buyer beware" concept and seek services from a competent provider.

AASECT members that are certified as Educators or Counselors are advised to follow the PLISSIT model; this involves the clinician assessing the need for "Permission giving – Limited Information – the use of Specific Suggestions – or the move to Intensive Therapy" (Annon, 1974). At the point in a counseling or educational interaction when it is recognized that intensive therapy is required beyond the more straightforward suggestions and/or support that may be offered in such initial interactions, a referral to a more qualified professional is deemed appropriate (Principle Three, Section O, AASECT *Code of Ethics*).

THE USE OF SURROGATES AND SEX OFFENDER TREATMENT

The use of partner surrogates in sex therapy is a highly debated issue. It may be ethically permissible in establishing a therapeutic environment if conducted in a responsible manner. If a surrogate is to be used at all, it is understood that the partner surrogate is not a sex therapist. Surrogates should understand that their role is never as a sex therapist or psychotherapist.

A therapist who chooses to utilize the services of a surrogate must exercise caution in protecting the welfare of both the patient and the surrogate and be aware of the local laws governing this practice. The AASECT *Code of Ethics*, being national in scope, does not specifically prohibit the use of surrogates nor does it condone the practice. It states, "The member shall not enter into association for professional practice . . . or promote in any manner the practice of . . . any person . . .[who] does not adhere to the standards of AASECT or is in violation of any law" (p. 4). Several states and local attorneys have interpreted the use of surrogates as prostitution and therefore in violation of state law. Again, it is prudent to be aware of the local laws in the state in which a therapist is practicing.

The use of surrogates in couple therapy also is questioned for therapeutic value due to the nature of couple treatment and how therapy is viewed as assisting the couple to work out their interpersonal issues and achieve a more fulfilling relationship, including sexual functioning. Couple sex therapy is not limited to sexual functioning. In 1983, Virginia Johnson, of The Masters and Johnson Institute, one of the original couple Sex Therapist team, described couple sex therapy as a combination of sex education, communication skill training, and general marriage counseling. Introducing a third party into the sexual relationship may confound the issue (V. Johnson, personal communication, October 10, 1983).

Yet the use of surrogates has continued in this country for over 30 years. An interesting use of surrogate therapy for an individual was presented as a case conference at a national sex therapy meeting in the late 1970s.

A sex therapist working in a correctional facility reported treating a 28-year-old man, described as a pedophile. He was arrested and convicted as a sex offender and served an 8-year jail term. The man was evaluated by the sex therapist and continued in therapy throughout his incarceration. The therapist continued to follow this individual in treatment for 4 years postdischarge. He was convicted for molesting eight 12- to 14-year-old boys. He met them in a boy's club where he worked, befriended them, and engaged in mutual masturbation and oral sex. He had not been prosecuted for his previous sexual activities that had begun at age 19, and now confided these to the therapist. He had never engaged in an adult sexual experience. His history included sexual experiences with a male cousin, 2 years older than himself, at approximately 10 years of age.

During the course of his incarceration the therapist introduced an adult male surrogate to help the prisoner/patient gain comfort with his homosexuality and to provide adult socialization and sexual experience opportunities. At the time of the case presentation the individual had been out of prison more than 4 years. He lived in a gay community, experiencing sexual contact only with adult partners. He continued in voluntary weekly outpatient treatment. He claims to have not involved adolescent boys in his sexual activities since his discharge from prison.

The ethics of this case present some interesting considerations. The area of practice obviously did not prohibit the use of surrogates, since this was in a public facility, so we assume no actual laws were violated. Some will question the use of a male surrogate, since initially the prisoner denied his homosexuality. Was the therapist making assumptions? Little consideration is given to the patient's vulnerability as someone presenting for treatment against his will when the therapist is administering a state-ordered treatment, even though the therapist is attempting to restore some "normalcy" for the offender. The offender may not have perceived his behavior as maladaptive. This paradigm presents the sex therapist with a unique ethical role in treating a convicted sex offender.

The traditional patient-centered ethical guidelines may be breached when viewed in what has been called therapeutic jurisprudence (Glasser, 2003). In therapeutic jurisprudence the rights of the community trump the rights of the individual. We attempt to force the views of the community agencies on offenders to promote an effective intervention. Yet to many in the community the use of surrogates is not an acceptable practice even when the outcome for community safety may appear to be more desirable. In the *Ethical Guidelines Conference Report*, therapists are cautioned to "not condemn certain types of sexual practices, except those that are coercive or involve deceit" (Kolodny, 1978, p. 16).

The offense-free time of the preceding individual was offered as a symbol of success in an area that sees high recidivism. There was a suggestion that disregard for the offender's "autonomy and welfare" is not an exception to routine ethical guidelines (which would consider it a violation of his right to confidentiality when he self-incriminated by admitting past offenses) or his right to have his perceived "best interests" protected.

Sex offender treatment may not promote the offender's "well-being" if the offender senses a lack of congruent behavior on the part of the therapist. It may be difficult for sex offenders to learn the virtue of honesty and congruent behavior if we as therapists are ethically conflicted between the needs and interest of society and the therapeutic needs of the offender. A sex therapist whose conflicted ethical loyalties may be breached must be clear from the onset about what can be offered to the individual who has violated community sexual norms, to prevent erratic and inconsistent trust. Advising the patient at the onset of therapy of the limits of the patient/therapist relationship in these circumstances at least will clarify the parameters of informed consent.

REPARATIVE/CONVERSION THERAPY

It has been a relatively short period of time since the official stance of the American Psychiatric Association viewed homosexuality as an aberration (1968) and to suggest treatment for this former diagnosis. Now a clinician's effort to cure or change the orientation of a homosexual is labeled "reparative or conversion therapy." This type of therapy is viewed by most clinicians as unethical, yet some therapists are taking up the challenge to convert homosexuals to a heterosexual expression, seeing this practice as their moral imperative. This is not to be confused with a therapist offering counseling or therapy geared toward developing a better understanding of the discontent that may be experienced by a homosexual and subsequently assisting with the development of a congruent lifestyle.

In 1998 the Christian Coalition ran full-page advertisements in the *New York Times* and other major newspapers entitled "Truth in Love." *Newsweek* questioned one of the organization's spokesmen, asking where the facts were to base their claims of success for conversion. No data were ever published. Instead, many anecdotal stories of people that have successfully completed their conversion have been published (Besen, n.d.).

One cannot help but question the possibility that these "successful" individuals may be closer to the midrange on the Kinsey scale of human sexuality (Kinsey, Pomeroy, & Martin, 1948) and that their sex drive and/or orientation may be less of an issue in their self-concept than their spiritual motivation and affiliation. The majority of anecdotal stories of attempted conversion describe painful experiences of everything from rejection to physical abuse offered as aversive conditioning (Besen, n.d.).

The ethical question for the professional sex therapist remains, do you choose your religious affiliation over your professional affiliation when there is "no published scientific evidence for the efficacy of reparative therapy" (American Psychiatric Association, 1998)? Most codes of ethics are based on opinions, beliefs, notions, theories, and, sometimes, personal interests. When the question is based on the latter, which is the ethical principle that prevails?

FACILITATED SEX

The question of "facilitated sex" is not to be confused with the use of surrogates. Disabled individuals who are unable to satisfy their own sexual needs may request the services of a caretaker or personal assistant to set-up or assist with positioning and removing clothing to allow for partner activity or masturbation. The personal assistant facilitator is not actually participating in any sexual activity with the individual in treatment. For these disabled individuals this may be no different from requesting a set-up for feeding, bathing, toileting, or any activities of daily living.

According to Mitch Tepper, PhD, MPH, it is not easy assigning sexual preparation roles to personal assistants (Melby, 2003). Involving a sex therapist who is connected to a medical facility or who has a medical background may help with some of the preparation. Nursing facility staff members have long assumed maternalistic care of their patients and, as such, frequently do not see their charges as being independent adults with sexual needs.

Carolyn Livingston, ARNP, PhD, described the ethical questions regarding her role as a sex therapist for a cerebral palsy patient. She was told the woman wished to masturbate but needed assistance in removing her clothing, positioning her, and providing an apparatus that the patient was capable of using independently. Some caregivers refused to assist in these activities. After Livingston attempted to educate the nursing staff, instructing and assisting the willing staff members, the patient was placed on a specifically designed board with a control for a vibrator near the head of her bed. Livingston was clear that she "never touch my clients, I talk to my clients. I don't want anything to be misinterpreted" (Melby, 2003). This instance seemed to offer no conflict for Livingston, a registered nurse who, with the assistance of one of the caregivers, removed the clothing of the patient and helped position her, then left the patient alone.

In other instances personal assistants of disabled persons have refused to assist a patient to act on sexual needs. Because it is unethical for a sex therapist to engage in sexual activity with a patient, procedures generally involved with nudity or observation of sexual activity may go beyond the boundaries of established therapeutic practice, but when there is good evidence that the patient's best interests are being served and not the personal interests of the therapist, such activities fall within ethical practice. Nudity in a health care setting always has received more tolerance than from the community at large.

In the past, when I instructed nursing staff who would argue the appropriateness of asking patients about their sexual needs, claiming "too personal," I would remind them that as a health care provider they do not find it inappropriate to ask about the patient's bowel or bladder functioning, or to manually remove a fecal impaction from a rectum or place a catheter in a urethra. These acts are generally viewed as very personal, yet these acts are recognized as legitimate care provided by a trained individual for those not capable of providing for those needs for themselves.

Establishing legitimacy in performing any function requires knowledge of what is needed, development of personal comfort with the procedure, and the appropriate setting for the activity, all part of the purview of a skilled professional. Perhaps it is a misuse of ethical standards when we deny care to those who need assistance in providing sexual expression, a basic *need*, not just a *want*. Establishing legitimate functioning in our professional arena may be the most ethical behavior.

APPROPRIATE SETTING FOR SEX THERAPY: THE USE OF ELECTRONIC MEDIA

With the ever-increasing use of the Internet, the issue of online therapy via e-mail, web-cam, or other electronic media is a frequently explored subject. The APA has stated that it takes no specific position on the ethical delivery of services for online or telephone therapy and that it is reviewing the ramifications of this practice in a "rapidly evolving area of service" (APA, 1997).

The American Mental Health Counselors Association offers detailed guidelines in Principle 14, "Internet On-Line Counseling." Consideration is given to confidentiality and the difficulties ensuring complete client confidentiality of information transmitted through electronic communications. The requirement of a "client waiver" acknowledges the limitations inherent in the lack of a face-to-face setting in establishing the therapeutic relationship. The counselor is to "determine whether on-line counseling is appropriate for the needs of the client," assessing if the client is "intellectually, emotionally, and physically capable of using on-line services." If it is determined that it is not appropriate, the client is "encouraged to continue counseling through a traditional alternative method" (AMHCA, *Code of Ethics*, 2000, Principle 14).

The American Mental Health Counselors' *Code of Ethics* attempts to deal with the legal consideration of the client and clinician being in two different states, with two potentially distinct laws governing this activity. There is the unresolved question of where the therapeutic interaction actually is occurring: the therapist's or the patient's local area.

The inherent pitfalls of online counseling and therapy have arisen as a frequent discussion topic in the professional online list-serv of AASECT. The written AASECT Code does not specifically address the problems of online counseling or therapy.

It has been suggested that ethical care for patients who may request online services for a sexual problem may be simplified by again referring to the PLISSIT model put forth by Annon in 1974 for other therapeutic settings. Some online individuals may only be seeking information or clarification on a particular topic. There is recognition of the wish for anonymity in seeking sexual information; many individuals express discomfort in asking society's embarrassing questions.

At what point does giving information or providing simple suggestions such as to read an informative book or use "the squeeze technique" (Kaplan, 1995) become therapy, and who holds the therapist accountable for the information or simple suggestions given?

A Google search will provide the name, e-mail address, and website of any AASECT-certified sex therapist. Google also provides the name of many individuals who have self-identified as sex therapists or counselors. The range of information available to individuals surfing the web suggests that most people have learned a fair amount of information about their perceived sexual problem before they actually make contact with a therapist from this source.

If there is a consensus that can be gleaned from the recent correspondence of the contributing professionals on the AASECT list-serv, there is an acceptance of initial, broad information given to individuals online, information that may be considered similar to that which is found in available published sources.

Situations where patients who have begun face-to-face therapy and, for some reason, such as travel difficulties, wish to continue with online consultations, are viewed as appropriate if all the rules of local governance are adhered to, including issues of confidentiality. Additionally, a signed consent for the change in the mode of therapy is recommended. This may include limited telephone therapy sessions with established patients.

An additional burden is placed on the therapist to prove that other means of therapy have been explored when the issue of fees for online service is introduced. Fees are generally set in accord with a "standard allowable" (as set by an insurance company) or prevailing rate in the area of practice. What is the area when therapy is conducted in cyberspace? How does one compare time on the net to face-to-face office time?

There may be inherent problems with online sex therapy, but many sex therapists appear to benefit from using the AASECT list-serv for case discussion and general information exchange. This may illustrate a new form of peer consultation that hopefully can provide an opportunity to avoid some ethical entanglements.

CONCLUSIONS

Throughout history people have wrestled with the problem of sexual ethics, or whether their own or other people's behavior was good or bad. Our fundamental beliefs reflect our assumptions about the nature of sex. With the struggle for more self-determination and an increase in individual rights in the United States, our sexual rights as a society have changed. Our view of what is ethical practice as a therapist has also changed with the flow of history. The illustrations in this contribution offer only some of the ethical dilemmas that modern sex therapists encounter. The general psychotherapist may confront some of these issues in varied forms. The professional is expected to follow the code of ethics of the most restrictive field of practice.

In *The Sex Atlas*, Haeberle predicted, "both failure and success (of sexual practices) will increasingly be judged in practical terms. The final arbitrator will be experience, not some unquestioned religious dogma. . . . Science alone cannot tell us what we should do as sexual beings. At best, it can make us alert and critical, but it cannot by itself establish a code of ethics" (Haeberle, 1978, p. 485).

Again, the ethical professional therapist is required to follow the code of ethics as set out by the individual's professional organization. Sex therapists follow the AASECT code as well as their profession's codes for nursing, medicine, psychology, family therapy, and the like. Not every potential ethical dilemma will be covered in any written code, and the good therapist is wise to consult with respected colleagues.

The difficulty in the development of the dialogue needed for a practical, coherent sexual ethic and the subsequent development of a professional code of ethics is illustrated rather humorously by the comment in the 1980 bestseller, *Thy Neighbor's Wife*, by Talese: "Murder is a crime. Describing murder is not. Sex is not a crime. Describing it is" (p. 538).

CONTRIBUTOR

Catherine Dailey Ravella, RN, C, PhD, is a private practice sex therapist in Pittsburgh, Pennsylvania. She is certified by the American Association of Sexuality Educators, Counselors, and Therapists both as a supervisor and therapist. For the past 3 years she served on this organization's Ethics Committee, which rewrote the ethics code, changing it from adjudicative to educative in nature. In 2006, Dr. Ravella was appointed chairman of the Ethics Advisory Committee. Dr. Ravella also holds certification in psychiatric and mental health nursing by the American Nursing Credentialing Center. Prior to full-time private practice she managed a Pittsburgh hospital psychiatric unit. She frequently presents on sexual health topics and on her work with PhotoTherapy to various community educational and support groups. Dr. Ravella may be contacted at 1376 Freeport Road, Pittsburgh, PA 15238. E-mail: cravella@comcast.net

RESOURCES*

American Association of Sexuality Educators, Counselors, and Therapists [AASECT]. (2004). *Code of Ethics.* Retrieved February 2, 2006, from http://www.aasect.org/codeofethics.asp

American Mental Health Counselors Association. (2000). *Code of Ethics.* Retrieved February 2, 2003, from http://www.amhca.org/code/

American Psychiatric Association. (1968). *Diagnostic and Statistical Manual of Mental Disorders* (2nd ed.). Washington, DC: Author.

American Psychiatric Association. (1998, December). *Position Paper.* Washington, DC: Author.

American Psychological Association. (1997). *APA Statement on Services by Telephoning, Teleconferencing, and Internet.* Retrieved February 2, 2006, from http://www.apa.org/ethics/stmnt01.html

American Psychological Association. (2003). *Ethical Principles of Psychologists and Code of Conduct.* Retrieved February 2, 2006, from http://www.apa.org/ethics/code2002.html

Annon, J. S. (1974, November). *The PLISSIT Model: A Proposed Conceptual Scheme for the Behavioral Treatment of Sexual Problems.* Paper presented at the annual meeting of the Society for the Scientific Study of Sex, Las Vegas, NV.

Besen, W. (n.d.). *Finally Free.* Retrieved February 14, 2006, from http://www.hrc.org/Content/ContentGroups/Publications1/FinallyFREE.pdf

Blackshaw, S. L., & Patterson, P. G. R. (1992). The prevention of sexual exploitation of patients: Educational issue. *Canadian Psychiatric Association–Position Papers.* Retrieved February 14, 2006, from http://www.cpa-apc.org/Publications/Position_Papers/Exploitation.asp

Glasser, B. (2003). Therapeutic jurisprudence: An ethical paradigm for therapists in sex offender treatment programs. *Western Criminology Review, 4*(2), 143-154.

Haeberle, E. J. (1978). *The Sex Atlas.* New York: Seabury.

Kaplan, H. S. (1995). *The Sexual Desire Disorders: Dysfunctional Regulation of Sexual Motivation.* New York: Brunner/Mazel.

Kinsey, A. C., Pomeroy, W. P., & Martin, C. E. (1948). *Sexual Behavior in Human Male.* Philadelphia: W. B. Saunders.

Kolodny, R. C. (1978, March). *Ethical Guidelines for Research and Clinical Perspectives on Human Sexuality.* Reproductive Biology Research Foundation. Final Revision, Conference Report, St. Louis, MO.

Melby, T. (2003). Facilitated sex. *Contemporary Sexuality, 37*(11), 1-6.

Melby, T. (2005). How to avoid common ethical pitfalls. *Contemporary Sexuality, 39*(10), 1-6.

Plaut, S. M. (1995). Informed consent for sex between health professional and patient or client. *Journal of Sex Education and Therapy, 21*(2), 129-131.

Schoener, G., Hofstee-Milgram, J., & Gonsiorek, J., (1985). Sexual exploitation of clients by therapist. In C. T. Mowbray, S. Lanir, & M. Bulce (Eds.), *Women and Mental Health: New Directions for Change.* New York: Harrington Park Press.

Sonne, J. B., Meyer, C., Borys, D., & Marshall, V. (1985). Clients' reaction to sexual intimacy in therapy. *American Journal of Orthopsychiatry, 55*(2),183-189.

Talese, G. (1980). *Thy Neighbor's Wife.* New York: Dell.

Wallach, C. (2001, January). Letter to the editor. *The Pennsylvania Psychologist, 9,* 6.

Ward, T., & Stewart, C. A. (2003). Good lives and the rehabilitation of sex offenders. In T. Ward, D. R. Laws, & S. M. Hudson (Eds.), *Sexual Deviance: Issues and Controversies.* Thousand Oaks, CA: Sage.

---

* Although all websites in this contribution were correct at the time of publication, they are subject to change at any time.

Section II:
Sexual Dysfunctions
And Disorders

This section of *Innovations* includes contributions that update readers on each of the major types of sexual dysfunctions and disorders. Each contribution includes information about assessment, a summary of relevant research, and practical information for treatment. One or more case examples are used to highlight treatment principles.

In the first contribution, Katherine M. Hertlein, Gerald R. Weeks, and Nancy Gambescia discuss one of the most common problems appearing in the practice of couple and sex therapy – low sexual desire. While hypoactive sexual desire is prevalent, it is also among the most complex and difficult sexual problems to treat because several factors may be involved, including feelings and beliefs about sexual intimacy and relationship issues. It also occurs in conjunction with other sexual dysfunctions.

Sally A. Kope discusses the evolving model of female sexual response in the second contribution in this section. She describes the anatomy and physiology of arousal and orgasm along with treatment suggestions. The role of hormones is presented and a case example is explored in depth.

Female genital pain is one of the most disturbing sexual problems for patients. Jill W. Bley describes the debates about distinguishing between vaginismus and dyspareunia and offers treatment suggestions for both types of pain.

Perhaps no other area of sexual health has changed as much over the past decade as the treatment of erection dysfunction. In the next contribution, Frederick L. Peterson, Jr. and Donald E. Fuerst assist readers in developing a better understanding of how to respond to clients who complain of erection dysfunction. They review best practices for assessment and treatment and include three clinical vignettes.

Michael E. Metz and Barry W. McCarthy focus on ejaculatory problems in the next contribution. Ejaculatory dysfunction ranges from ejaculation before intercourse can begin to complete inability to ejaculate. Their contribution focuses on premature ejaculation and ejaculatory inhibition. They describe potential causes and effects, specific assessment and treatment strategies, and several case examples.

In the next contribution, Gene G. Abel, Markus Wiegel, and Candice A. Osborn discuss atypical sexual behaviors that pose significant problems for the person and for others, namely pedophilia and other paraphilias. Generally, paraphilias pose a problem because the person selects an inappropriate sexual target, such as is seen in pedophilia, fetishism, and bestiality, or because the person uses inappropriate courtship behaviors, as in voyeurism, stalking, and exhibitionism. Central to both categories is the absence of consent by the partner. The major focus of this contribution is on evaluations of clients who present with these sexual behaviors.

Many clients present with sexual complaints that are not found in the *DSM-IV-TR*, yet have a devastating impact on their health, career, and family life. Their sexual behavior is out of control. In some instances, clinicians may not agree on its causes or treatments, or even what to call the problem. Dennis P. Sugrue provides helpful information on how to think about and treat out-of-control sexual behavior.

In the final contribution of this section, Stephen L. Braveman discusses innovative treatment methods for clients who have experienced sexual trauma. Traditional psychotherapy methods have frequently been used with these clients, but the author states that many such clients report they do not reach full recovery through these methods alone. This contribution explores basic elements of sexual trauma, addresses traditional treatment approaches, and examines some innovative methods that can be added to help sexual abuse survivors to heal.

The Treatment of Hypoactive Sexual Desire Disorder: An Intersystem Approach

Katherine M. Hertlein, Gerald R. Weeks, and Nancy Gambescia

Hypoactive sexual desire disorder (HSDD) is considered to be one of the most common problems appearing in the practice of couples and sex therapy; approximately 20% of men and 33% of women are affected (Laumann, Palik, & Rosen, 1999). The incidence is higher in the clinical population; over 50% of couples will present in treatment with a complaint of insufficient sexual desire within their relationship (K. Segraves & R. Segraves, 1991).

Although HSD (hypoactive sexual desire) is prevalent, it is also among the most complex and difficult sexual problems to treat. That is, it is usually "caused" by several factors, arising from within the individual's feelings and beliefs about sexual intimacy as well as relationship issues. Further, HSD can occur in conjunction with other sexual dysfunctions in either partner.

There is also a wide disparity between clinicians in terms of definitions regarding HSD. In order to appropriately diagnose HSD, there are three criteria that must be met per the *DSM-IV-TR* (American Psychiatric Association [APA], 2000). First, there is a lack of sexual fantasy and desire to engage in sexual activity. This absence of fantasy and desire must produce marked personal or interpersonal distress. Finally, this condition cannot be met by another Axis I disorder or another sexual dysfunction, be a byproduct of a general medical condition, or be the result of substance abuse.

Another complication with HSD is the way in which this disorder is treated by the clinician. Specifically, sex, marital, and family therapy are often seen as distinct and separate entities (Weeks, 2004). Thus, treatment can be fragmented. In fact, some treatment models focus on the identified partner and overlook the contribution of the spouse in the development, maintenance, and treatment of the difficulty. In such cases, a treatment that is grounded by an individualistic perspective is inadequate and not systemic; sexual problems affect the couple and can be related to the couple in many ways.

The Intersystem approach is our preferred method for treating the complex systemic factors that are typically seen in HSD cases. This approach includes five different components (Weeks, 1994, 2004). First, each individual brings to the couple his or her own individual physiological perspective. It is essential to understand what biological, physiological, and genetic factors might be present and influencing HSD. The next component is the individual's psychological makeup. This includes one's values, attitudes, psychopathology, developmental information, and intelligence. This is an important area to assess in HSD cases, as one's values and attitudes regarding sexuality and sexual behavior often affect one's level of desire. The couple's relationship is the third component. The therapist must work from a systemic perspective, because numerous relational factors influence the extent of sexual problems within the couple. For example, we will discuss later that HSD might result from a fear of intimacy between partners. Family-of-origin is the fourth element. Our families have a profound impact on attitudes, values, and expectations toward sex. Some families, for example, might remain tight-lipped about sexuality, communicating to their children that sex is "bad." These feelings might often result in sex guilt and contribute to HSD. The last component of the model is environmental. This includes societal, cultural, religious, and historical factors that can influence decision making and judgments about behavior. Further, as times change, couples reinterpret their sexual behavior through other lenses (Weeks, 2004).

In this contribution, we will present an integrative approach to treating HSD in couples therapy. The foundation of this model is the Intersystem approach developed by Weeks (1994, 2004), in that we view this problem to have individual, interactional, and intergenerational components. Our treatment strategy reflects our belief that HSD typically results from a convergence of intersystemic factors and that it becomes embedded in the couple's dynamics.

ASSESSMENT OF HSD

Treating HSD first involves a thorough assessment. These assessment procedures are detailed in a handout on page 88. Additionally, there are certain conditions that are favorable for therapy as well as contraindications; these are also detailed in a handout on page 89.

Etiology

Certain psychological characteristics in individual partners can be expressed within the context of sexual intimacy, thus giving rise to the development of HSD. These involve anxiety, depression, negative cognitive distortions, inaccurate beliefs about sex, a poor body image, a tendency to fuse sex and affection, career overload, and related sexual problems. In such cases, the therapist may be tempted to turn the focus of treatment to the partner with the lack of desire, but it is imperative that therapists maintain a relational stance.

The fear of intimacy can also be a risk factor for developing HSD. Because emotional and physical intimacies are closely related, working on sexual desire may be hampered by one partner's fear of being emotionally vulnerable and intimate. Other fears in one or both partners could leave a couple at risk for the development of HSD, such as fear of anger, rejection, abandonment, exposure, feelings, or dependency. As noted previously, psychiatric factors such as anxiety, depression, obsessive-compulsive disorder, and sexual orientation conflicts can contribute to the development of HSD. Further, physical and emotional trauma can inhibit desire. It is important for the therapist to assess in all of these areas.

Many of the aforementioned risk factors, such as antisexual beliefs, are learned within the social and familial contexts of each partner. It is essential that the therapist explore intergenerational legacies and other environmental messages regarding sexual intimacy.

Interactional risk factors might overshadow the course of treatment, as research indicates that the extent to which people are satisfied with their marriage is related to their sexual satisfaction (Morokoff & Gilliland, 1993). Specifically, problems related to dyadic adjustment and HSD often coexist. For example, women with HSD tend to report greater degrees of marital distress and less relational cohesion (Trudel, Ravart, & Matte, 1993). For women, sexual satisfaction is related to factors such as the manner in which sex was initiated, the level of arousal, and the behaviors present in that interaction. Basson's (2000, 2001) model of female sexual response appears to support this interaction, in that she believes that women's sexual response cycles are connected to the amount of trust and intimacy in her relationship. Other relational risk factors include contemptuous feelings, criticism, defensiveness, power struggles, and toxic communication (Gottman, 1994).

TREATMENT OF HSD

Lowering Response Anxiety

When individuals notice that they are not feeling desire for sex with their partner, they experience anxiety. As anxiety increases, the likelihood that they will experience that desire decreases, thereby increasing anxiety, and so on. One critical component to the treatment of HSD is lowering the response anxiety. It is important to treat this component first, as it can be both a cause and an effect of HSD.

There are several techniques to help reduce response anxiety. First, the therapist educates the couple about response anxiety by explaining the concept. The partners are then asked to observe what happens to their anxiety levels when they force themselves to feel desire for their partner. Cognitive techniques such as thought-stopping and thought substitution are useful in treating response anxiety. Another technique is to confront irrational ideas that foster response anxiety, such as the equation of sex and intercourse. In this case, the definition of sex is broadened to include behaviors, such as noncoital sexual touching, that are less likely to cause response anxiety. Part of broadening this definition is to educate the client on ways to separate sex, intimacy, affection, and sensuality. Paradoxical interventions can also be used if the therapist is familiar with systemic techniques. One form is to intentionally prescribe a construct, such as the use of humor. The therapist can ask clients to generate an image that they would find entertaining, as the more humorous the image, the less likely they are to feel anxious. Finally, the therapist can educate the couple on ways to create a sensual environment. Through trial and error, they alter their setting to allow themselves to positively anticipate and enjoy the sensual aspects of sexual intimacy; thus they will become aroused by certain environmental factors.

Reframing

In couples who present with HSD, the symptom bearer is the partner who lacks desire, wants to have sexual desire, and feels the pressure to have sex in order to please their partner. In HSD treatment, however, it is critical that the partner with the higher desire be an active part in the therapy. Further, the couple must be educated to view the HSD as a relationship problem, not just the responsibility of the symptom bearer. Reframing is one technique the therapist can use to create the conceptual understanding of HSD as a couple issue. In reframing, the therapist works with each part of the system to help the clients identify what their role is in their involvement of the problem. The therapist asks focused questions that become more and more directed. In this way, the therapist is able to gain more information and present it back to the couple system. As couples begin to hear their own responses, they get a different picture of what is happening in the system. Once the couple is able to reframe their own perceptions and behaviors, the label of symptom bearer is dropped and HSD is viewed as a relational problem by both partners.

Attending to the Affective, Cognitive, and Behavioral Aspects of HSD

In a couple presenting with HSD, the therapist will need to continually assess the presence and influence of affect, behavior, and cognitions experienced by each partner throughout the course of treatment. For instance, the lower desire partner appears to have a lack of motivation for sex and a lack of affect, and the lack of motivation causes a response anxiety which becomes part of the cycle. The higher desire partner is often more emotional, frustrated, and pessimistic. In these instances, the therapist should direct the couple to explore, understand, and reassess their feelings over time. The therapist can then intervene by normalizing feelings for the couple as they learn to understand and support one another. In terms of addressing the cognitive components, the therapist should be aware that the partner with the HSD is thinking negative thoughts about sexuality. These thoughts, no matter how aware the client may be of them, can exert a powerful influence over affect and behavior.

TREATMENT PLAN

Treatment plans can be as focused as addressing only the presenting problem or as broad as addressing one's relational, vocational, behavioral, emotional, and cognitive functioning. In this treatment model, our goals are to examine the problem in context. In this way, the therapist connects the client's HSD to a larger concept in the relationship, such as maintaining a sense of control or avoiding the fear of rejection. Further, treatment should be collaborative, where the therapist presents an idea and seeks the couple's agreement before proceeding.

Elements of the Treatment Plan

There are several elements to the HSD treatment plan. The first is the focal point of the lack of desire. Because this is the problem that brought the couple into therapy, the treatment plan should reflect this issue. Second, it is the goal of treatment to improve the overall level of sexual functioning of the couple. A lack of sexual desire can be tied to other elements of the sexual relationship, specifically those that diminish the sexual experience. In establishing communication within the couple about their sex life, the global quality of one's sexual life can be improved. The final element of the treatment plan is to improve the overall quality of the couple's relationships. If couples can effectively work together to solve their sexual problem, it will relate to greater improvements in the marital relationship.

Setting Treatment Priorities

Once the goals for treatment are established, the therapist identifies which of those objectives takes precedence over the others. This is an important step, as some of the therapy goals may overlap or be addressed concurrently. As stated earlier, the therapist begins with the HSD prior to treating other sexual difficulties in either partner. If treating the HSD is ineffective because of the problems within the relationship, the therapist should address the relational issues that take precedence. Further, if the partners cannot work together in conjoint sessions, the format can be changed to concurrent individual sessions on a short-term basis, bringing the couple back together later to continue to work on the relational issues and the HSD. As the couple is able to work together constructively, the HSD and relational issues are addressed. The simplest problems are tackled first, moving gradually to the more difficult. The therapist and couple can begin to work on any other sexual difficulties once the presenting problem has been resolved to the couple's satisfaction. Finally, when the couple believes they have essentially eliminated their relational and sexual problems, the therapist can offer to assist with optimizing their sexual and couple relationship.

Homework and Incremental Change

Homework is an important component of the treatment of sexual difficulties. It increases the chances of success, lowers anxiety, and creates a safe environment in which the couple can try out new behaviors. Homework is intended as a way for the couple to take responsibility for creating positive changes in their relationship and to relearn how to function sexually. The therapist encourages the couple to proceed slowly, engaging only in activities that have been assigned.

There are several structural elements of homework. First, the therapist and clients discuss who will be responsible for initiating the completion of the homework assignment. The therapist generally prescribes the HSD client to be the one to initiate the homework in order to promote mental preparation for the activity. Scheduling is another element of homework. The therapist asks that the couple schedule the homework for two reasons. First, without the schedule, it is unlikely that the couple will complete the assignments. Second, when the couple schedules time to do the homework, they are intentionally setting aside time to do something meaningful with one another. Whenever the couple fails to complete the homework, the therapist must help them process and understand the reasons for noncompliance.

The therapist must remember that homework will gradually desensitize the couple, reduce anxiety, and promote enjoyment of sexual activity; therefore, many elements of homework must be structured for the couple and assigned in graduated increments. For instance, in the earlier stages of treatment, the duration of each exercise should be short and tailored to the needs of each couple; as the course of therapy continues, the therapist can extend the duration of each exercise. Initially, sensual touching is often assigned for a period of 5 to 10 minutes. As the couple is able to endure this activity, the therapist can extend the timeframe to 20 to 30 minutes. The decision about duration of an assignment should be underwritten by the couple's comfort level. The frequency of homework assignments is also an important consideration. The therapist must keep in mind that this couple likely has not had sexual experience with one another for months or longer. Nonetheless, the couple will need to have repeated assignments in order to become comfortable with sensual and sexual touch. Typically, homework frequency is at least three times per week, but this prescription is adapted to each couple and adjusted as needed. Finally, location is another aspect of the homework that must be addressed. Many couples connect sexual activity with the bedroom; it is likely that HSD couples might have negative connotations of the bedroom because of the association with problematic sexual activity. The therapist should explore with the couple various locations that would work best for them in terms of reducing their anxiety and increasing compliance with the assignment.

Promoting Compliance for Homework

There are a few ways in which the therapist can promote compliance for homework (Strong & Claiborn, 1982). First, the therapist has to respect the element of choice. Directing people to do something specific often removes the element of choice and creates psychological resistance. Therapists will fare better if they collaborate with the client in making decisions about homework. This collaboration can take the form of structuring the basics of the assignment for the couple and having the couple fill in the gaps. Couples need to have a vested interest in the process. Another important element of homework is what to call it. Clients might have negative connotations of the word "homework." In such instances, the therapist and/or couple can decide what to call these activities based on personal preference. The second way that therapists can promote compliance through homework is by the use of depersonalization. This means that the therapist assigns homework by explaining to the couple that this work is "standard," "typical," or "needed" at this stage in the therapy. This relieves the therapist of being in a position of ordering the clients to a certain activity, also reducing the likelihood of resistance. Finally, the therapist can use implicit rather than explicit directions to describe the homework. In this way, the therapist might say "You might try . . . " and allow the client room to feel whatever might occur.

Treating Other Sexual Dysfunctions

It is not unusual for an individual to have more than one sexual problem; thus, it is possible that HSD might be a part of another sexual difficulty such as physical discomfort during sex or trouble with orgasm. Sometimes, the non-HSD partner also has sexual difficulties, such as erectile dysfunction or premature ejaculation. Sexual difficulties in the partner can make intercourse less desirable, thereby increasing the possibility of HSD. The role of the therapist is to educate the couple in how other sexual dysfunctions might contribute to the development and maintenance of HSD. Further, the couple is encouraged to make a commitment to working on all elements of the dysfunction, not just the HSD.

Promoting Sexual Intimacy

In this treatment model, sexual intimacy is promoted in four stages. First, the therapist helps the couple to share their ideas about what it means to be intimate. In this stage, the partners discuss their views of intimacy, identify discrepancies in their definitions, and work toward a common definition. Next, the therapist helps the couple to understand that intimacy and sex are not distinct entities. The partners adopt attitudes and thoughts that will foster intimacy within their sexual relationship. Third, the therapist works with the couple to redefine sexuality by broadening their definition of sexuality to include more than intercourse. Finally, the couple needs to become aware of and identify the barriers that inhibit sexual desire and prevent them from gaining greater intimacy.

Relapse Prevention

The therapist should help the couple to understand that sexual desire is maintained through active sexual contact with one another. Thus, the therapist assists the couple in relapse prevention by including strategies in the repertoire that involve sensual touching and caressing. Also, the couple will need help in solving conflicts and anger not related to sexuality, as this can inhibit desire. One of the signs that a couple is relapsing is their noncompletion of the homework assignments. Therefore, the couple is reminded to plan regular times/sexual dates to spend with one another. Another strategy for preventing relapse is to generate an agreement for the couple on what is expected from the initiation to the completion of the sexual activity.

Paradoxical strategies can also prevent relapses (Weeks & L'Abate, 1982). One strategy is to ask the couple to identify the ways that they might sabotage their sexual relationship. The therapist also encourages the couple to seek more treatment if they have a continual dry spell in their sexual intimacy. Therapists can also ask the couple to predict the factors that might cause inhibited desire. Asking the couple to think about the ways that this therapy will be undone will increase the likelihood that these problems will not occur.

IMPLEMENTATION AND PROCESS

Implementation

A great deal of the work done with HSD couples addresses the relational problems that contribute to and maintain the sexual difficulties. It is essential that the therapist be qualified and knowledgeable about couples and sex therapy techniques. Also, the therapist should have enough experience to know the circumstances under which the techniques will be most effective. The implementation of techniques should be tailored to the specific problems of each couple, rather than utilizing a "one size fits all" method. Moreover, we suggest that when a technique is implemented in the course of treatment, the couple should be aware of why it is being used and what the outcome is expected to be. Clients are more likely to be compliant when they have an idea about how the technique fits into the scope of the treatment plan and when they are aware of any potential problems in implementing this technique. Again, couples must be active members of their treatment.

Process

The focus of treatment should be on the emotional processes that occur within the session. In this way, the couple will learn to communicate about feelings rather than staying fixed on content. For instance, they will learn to speak in terms of "I feel" rather than "you did." In treating HSD cases, the first process that should be addressed is that of the expectation of the couple. It is important for the partners to share their anticipations and beliefs about treatment and for the therapist to help them to come up with realistic expectations for the course of their therapy.

TREATING RISK FACTORS IN THE COUPLE

Intimacy-Based Approach to Treatment

Sternberg (1986) provides a model of love in adult relationships. This model is primarily composed of three elements: commitment, intimacy, and passion. Commitment refers to the cognitive component of love. It is the decision one makes to commit exclusively to another person. There are many ways that a couple can express commitment to each other, such as through marriage, cohabitation, and so on. Intimacy in Sternberg's model refers to the extent of closeness people feel toward their partner. It is characterized by the emotional support supplied to one another, being able to demonstrate vulnerability to one's partner, regarding the other in a positive light, being honest and empathetic with one's partner, and so forth. Passion signifies the aspect of Sternberg's triangle related to the physical attraction one feels for one's partner. It is this passion that Sternberg believes motivates people to come together physically.

In considering Sternberg's triangle model for describing love, we emphasize that in cases of HSD, passion, intimacy, and commitment are all related. We believe that passion does occur within the context of an intimate and committed relationship. In this way, our treatment approach includes not only revitalizing the passion through sex therapy behavioral techniques, but also addressing the intimacy and/or commitment needs within the relationship.

STAGES OF TREATMENT

Defining the Relationship

Defining relationships is an important component of relationships. It allows us to know what is expected of us and what our roles are, and can provide a framework for understanding behaviors, emotions, and cognitions within a context. As such, one of the first stages of treatment is to help the couple to define their relationship through the Sternberg (1986) model. Thus, the therapist must provide a brief overview of this model and demonstrate how each side of the triangle is interconnected to other parts.

The therapist then moves forward to solicit information from the couple about their fit within this model. One question is to ask whether both partners desire all three components as described in the triangle. Discussing this question can reveal where couples agree, but also where they disagree. This question also sets the stage for a conversation about how love and intimacy are identified in their relationship. The next part of this conversation is the therapist asking whether each phase of this triangle is needed in the couple's relationship. You simply ask the couple if they are committed to each other, if they want to have an intimate relationship with one another, and if they desire passion in their relationship. Again, it is important to assess the discrepancies in the responses. For example, one partner may feel that he or she wants passion and intimacy, but is not certain that he or she wants to commit to the relationship. This would indicate another issue in the relationship that would need to be resolved. It is also at this phase that the therapist assesses for any underlying intimacy fears. Intimacy fears can be disguised as commitment fears and can occur in one or both partners. It is imperative that the therapist distinguish whether fears of commitment are truly the result of fear of intimacy.

Once the partners are able to establish whether they want or need certain aspects of the Sternberg model, the therapist can ask whether each partner wants the same level of intensity for each of the three components. It is possible that couples may agree that they want commitment, intimacy, and passion in their relationship but disagree on the degree to which they want it. In some couples, one partner wants to be closer than another. The partner who does not want to be as close may engage in strategies to distance, of which one strategy may be removing himself or herself from sexual encounters. The result of this distancing can leave the partner who wants greater closeness and intimacy feeling hurt and angry, thereby reducing this partner's desire.

As relationships progress, partners may determine that they need to balance the time they spend together with time spent on their own. Therefore, it is important that the therapist ask the couple about the amount of togetherness and individuation each partner wants in the relationship. Typically, it is easier for couples to talk about ways to spend more time together rather than ways where they can spend more time apart. Couples may avoid talking to one another about needs for individual time for fear of hurting one another's feelings. They instead find ways to take this time, whether it be working late, losing oneself in the computer all evening, and so on. Couples should be encouraged to discuss how they will balance their individual and togetherness needs within their relationship.

Couples are typically able to understand Sternberg's (1986) model from a cognitive standpoint, yet they may have difficulty being able to conceptualize how to express these dimensions in a real-world way. It is important for the therapist to understand what prevents the partners from being able to freely express themselves. These difficulties may be related to socialization and upbringing. Men, for example, are not typically socialized in the same way as women regarding emotional expression. As a result, they may be unable to demonstrate intimacy. It is also possible that partners have come from families that were detached from one another or cold. In such cases, it may behoove the therapist to employ a focused genogram depicting the manner in which love was expressed in each partner's family of origin.

Couples also come into a relationship with expectations of themselves, each other, and what it means to be in a loving relationship. Some of these expectations might be mismatched, and partners are left feeling disappointed and sad upon the realization that these expectations will not come to fruition. There are also those expectations that are unrealistic from the start, such as believing that if your partner loved you, he or she would know automatically what you want. In cases where expectations are not met, one partner may misattribute this to their partner not caring about them enough and, as a result, withhold sex or desire. The therapist should help the couple to develop realistic perceptions of themselves, what each can offer, and a realistic perception of love and all that it involves.

Creating Greater Intimacy

Once the couple has appropriately defined their relationship and has come to an agreement about what is meant by developing/maintaining intimacy in their relationship, it is time to combine it with action. The therapist instructs each member of the couple to make a list of actions they can do that will develop intimacy in the aforementioned areas. It is important that the actions they choose be of value to their partner because if the partner does not view it as being valuable, the couple will not become closer. Partners are expected to check their list at the end of each day to determine how successful they were in performing the tasks on the list and to consider reasons that they may not have been successful.

We also suggest the three A's exercise. In this exercise, the A's stand for affection, appreciation, and affirmation. In this activity, we encourage the couple to show how much they like and value one another (affection), to show how much they appreciate one another (appreciation), and to make an expression of affirming the relationship, such as "I love you" (affirmation).

Couples also need to talk to one another on a process rather than content level. This means that the couple should become accustomed to talking about the emotional process during their relationship rather than strictly focusing on the content, or who said/did what when. Bernal and Barker (1979) identify levels that help the couple to assess where they fall in the continuum of cognitive to affective. These levels are listed below:

1. *Objects Level*: The couple communicates in a factual, detached manner.
2. *Individual Level*: Communication is characterized by each partner discussing how other people are responsible for his or her actions.
3. *Transactional Level*: Partners in the couple have the ability to step back and look at their pattern of interaction.
4. *Relational Level*: The couple can make inferences about the reasons for their behavior and established patterns. The couple has developed awareness about why they make decisions to behave a certain way and are able to express this rationale to their partner.
5. *Contextual Level*: The couple can connect present behavior with past experiences and history. The couple is able to explore their family-of-origin patterns and connect it to their present behavior, thereby providing further insight into their individual behavior and the manner in which it affects the couple.

The phrase "practice makes perfect" is certainly true in building communication skills. Improving couple communication is more effective if the couple is able to practice these skills. The therapist should ask the couple to set aside time weekly for such conversation as well as opportunities to bond with one another. We recommend to our couples that they integrate three assumptions into their lives regarding communicating with one another:

1. They must view it as something to which they are committed.
2. They should assume that the other had good intentions and good will.
3. Their goal should be to understand.

Also in terms of communication and promoting intimacy, Gottman (1994) found that couples should try to maintain a 5:1 ratio of positive to negative exchanges, as couples who report their marriages are "working" maintain this ratio. Other strategies for working toward more effective communication include using "I" statements, validating one another, reflective listening, and learning to edit what you say (Weeks & Treat, 2001).

Working With Underlying Fears of Intimacy

Fears of intimacy and closeness, whether conscious or unconscious, are often exhibited through one's behavior. It is important to address this issue in the treatment of HSD, as some partners may fear intimacy to the point where their sexual desire for one another becomes compromised. Because the therapist assumes that the fear of intimacy may be an unconscious motivator in cases of HSD, this position should be shared with the couple. Then, the therapist helps the partners identify their fears through the use of a genogram that focuses on elements of one's upbringing that influence intimate behavior. The therapist educates the couple about the many reasons why individuals might fear intimacy so that they understand the concepts and will be willing to discuss the related issues as they apply to them. Several of the common factors related to fear of intimacy include a fear of abandonment or rejection, fear of losing control, fear of being dependent on the other partner, fear of anger or conflict, fear of feelings, and fear of exposure.

In HSD cases, a few of the factors related to fear of intimacy are more frequently seen. For example, the fear of losing control is sometimes manifested in relationships through a power imbalance that is so severe that one partner is perceived as a parent and the other a child. This issue has the potential to make sex feel almost incestuous. The fear of losing oneself is another common presentation. It relates to HSD in that desire is one aspect of the relationship that is in their control, and the fear that their partner wants to potentially control them is unconsciously reduced through reducing sexual desire for the partner. Also, when a partner fears anger and/or conflict, he or she may be viewing anger as solely negative or potentially destructive to the relationship. He or she will attempt to avoid experiencing this emotion by avoiding all emotional contact instead of learning that anger, if expressed, need not destroy the partner or the relationship. The therapist can address this by helping the couple to understand their attitudes toward anger and identifying what other emotions the anger might be protecting.

There are several guidelines for treating intimacy fears. First, it is important to identify the fear. Next, the therapist uses cognitive therapy to help neutralize the negative thoughts associated with the fear and replace them with appropriate and adaptive cognitions. The therapist and clients then work to disrupt the pattern of avoidance that results from the fear. It is important to validate the fearful partner's emotions without agreeing with them, as agreeing would lead to continued avoidance of the feared stimuli and, consequently, the behavior. When the therapist is confident that the couple can directly tackle the fear, the suggestion should be made that the fear is threatening to the present relationship and serves little or no purpose. It is essential that the therapist and couple explore the ways in which each person in the relationship contributes to the problem rather than placing the blame solely on the person with the fear.

Self-Monitor for Passive-Aggressive Behavior

Passive-aggressive behavior can also undermine treatment. Forgetting, procrastination, and reporting that a request was misunderstood are all indications of passive-aggressive behavior. The therapist can educate about the advantages of expressing anger directly rather than in ways that are hidden and destructive. Another example is self-righteousness in a partner. This form of communication places the other partner in an inherently weaker position. Also, self-monitoring for victimization is appropriate in circumstances where the low-desire partner accepts the role of the wounded party. In such cases, their partner is viewed as smarter, more assertive, and more verbal as support for their belief that they cannot defend themselves. Another aspect to self-monitor is the extent to which the partners rely on intellectualization and reasoning. Clients who use this as a shield for anger may not value emotions and instead depend on rationality to prevail.

Use of the Anger Genogram

DeMaria, Weeks, and Hof (1999) identified the use of the genogram for tracking anger patterns and expression and to increase the couple's awareness of how anger is experienced. The following questions can be used to identify and explore intergenerational sources of anger:

1. How did your parents deal with anger and conflict?
2. Did you see your parents work through anger/conflict?
3. When members of your family (name each one) got angry, how did other members respond?
4. What did you learn about anger from each of your parents?

5. When your parents became angry with you, how did you feel and what did you do?
6. How did members of your family respond when you got angry? For example, who listened to you? Who failed to listen to you?
7. Who was allowed/not allowed to be angry in your family?
8. What is your best/worst memory about anger in your family?
9. Was anyone ever hurt as a result of someone's anger? Who?

The therapist should educate the couple that appropriate expression of anger can benefit their relationship. In fact, the couple can learn that expressing anger respectfully might bring them closer to one another. Moreover, it can reaffirm their expectations of one another and clarify their boundaries in the relationship.

Bibliotherapy

The therapist can recommend several books to clients which may be helpful to addressing fear of anger and conflict in a relationship. Harriet Lerner's *The Dance of Anger* (1989) focuses on the benefits of expressing anger, particularly for women, but this book can also be helpful for men. Alberti and Emmons's *Your Perfect Right* (1995) is written from a behavioral perspective and centers on communication, anger, and assertiveness.

Guidelines for Arguing Constructively

In HSD clients, there may be a tendency to circumvent conflict through avoiding anger. This results in a cycle of frustration, failed attempts to solve the problem, and ineffective processing of the issue. Once the couple understands the benefits of appropriate expression of anger in their relationship, guidelines for arguing constructively can be provided. These guidelines emphasize the process of identifying the underlying feelings the anger is protecting (i.e., hurt, fear, etc.) through description of the problem as well as one's feelings about the problem. After the couple is able to identify their emotions related to a particular issue, the next guideline is to advise the couple on ways to make a clear complaint without blaming. Blameful statements will often produce anger and defensiveness in the other partner and perpetuate a cycle of blaming. Therefore, couples should be helped to use I statements in order to identify the reasons for their anger; thus, they are able to offer the complaint in a productive, nonaccusatory manner. Using I statements helps each partner express their feelings without putting the cause of those feelings onto the other person. In HSD cases, some clients are angry or resentful toward their partners and express anger through avoidance of sex and inhibited desire. The therapist can assess how these clients might be feeling in certain situations and encourage them to overtly address hidden feelings of anger.

Another guideline is to instruct the couple to employ time-out procedures when appropriate. Several specific rules apply when couples take a time-out. First, the time-out should last at least 20 minutes, per Gottman's (1994) research indicating that individuals' physiology takes at least that long to return to its baseline. Further, the spouse that initiates the time-out is responsible for beginning the discussion again. Once a time-out is called, the discussion should immediately end until it is revisited.

The final guideline is to encourage an atmosphere of compromise and negotiation as opposed to winning or losing the argument. Once the couple has adopted the attitude of compromise, adaptive behaviors can be interjected into their pattern. Old destructive patterns are consistently monitored and identified as blocks to stopping effective communication as new behaviors are integrated. Couples are also given a list of behaviors to avoid as they are correlated with relationship discord. These behaviors include complaining, mind reading, defensiveness, demonstrating contempt, stonewalling, and criticism.

Steps in Conflict Resolution

As the couple is helped to learn to argue constructively, the therapist reinforces the guideline that each individual is responsible for his or her actions and feelings. Then, principles of active listening are instituted. Active listening enables the partners to discuss problems without criticism, mind reading, blaming, defensiveness, or other toxic emotions. The partner with the issue is responsible for holding a discussion regarding the topic that needs attention. The other partner reflects back both the initial complaint and feelings, without responding defensively to the issue. Once the feelings and behaviors are understood, a response can be made. Then the initial speaker becomes the active listener. Next, the person with the issue should be responsible for posing a solution. The idea is for the couple to consider a wide range of possible solutions and choose one that appears the more workable. Discussion should then focus on establishing a plan of implementation as well as periods of time where they return to the situation and evaluate its effectiveness.

Sensate Focus Techniques

Because HSD is the couple's problem, the treatment requires that the partners be ready to work together effectively toward the common goal of pleasurable intimacy. When the therapist determines that the couple is sufficiently committed to treatment and to the relationship, sensate focus techniques are implemented. Sensate focus exercises consist of a series of graduated physical exercises to be performed at home. They are designed to reduce anxiety and promote relaxation during physical intimacy. The term sensate implies that the couple will learn to enjoy the sights, sounds, smells, and so on, related to physical touch. Moreover, the term sensual does not necessarily imply sexual. The physical prescriptions are nondemanding of intercourse and tailored to the needs of each couple. Thus, judicious timing and careful evaluation of each incremental step is essential.

There are several objectives in sensate focus exercises. These are included in the supplemental handout on page 90. Further, the environment should be conducive to supporting sensate focus techniques, including an environment of collaboration and readiness for the techniques. During the exercises, the couple creates an intimate environment by making their physical surroundings comfortable and pleasant. Any source of distraction is eliminated, such as phones, television, and so forth. An overview of sensate focus techniques may be found on page 90.

In HSD cases, the sensate focus exercises are instrumental in the assessment process as well as treatment. HSD partners are instructed to note negative or antisexual thoughts that occur and make a note of them later. They are asked to quickly notice these thoughts and then return to the exercise mentally by staying in the moment, focusing only on the pleasurable sensations of the moment and that they want to keep those sensations present. Later, the negative cognitions are addressed in session and the partners learn techniques of thought-stopping and thought-substitution. The sensate focus techniques described for those experiencing sexual dysfunction are also followed for HSD clients, with the caveat that transition to intercourse only occurs when the HSD partner begins to feel some sexual desire. Educate the couple that at times, it is natural to feel more desire than at other times. When they are ready to have intercourse, the couple is reminded to focus on the sensations, positive thoughts, and fantasies that were instrumental in reactivating the desire.

CONCLUSION

Treating HSD can be complicated, as it might involve a series of contradictions. First, this disorder is the couple's problem, not just the individual's problem. Next, although the couple often believes that the HSD partner lacks interest or feelings about sexual intimacy, HSD may be a way of indirectly expressing strong emotions related to the individual's values, beliefs, and fears. Additionally, the individual experiencing low desire may develop this problem in response to conflict within the couple's relationship. Often, partners with this problem want to feel desire for their partner, yet the more they try to force themselves to feel desire, the more difficult it becomes to do so.

The role of the therapist is to first perform an assessment of the couple's situation and to identify their fit for treatment. The intersystem model can guide the therapist to decode and address the many problem areas in couples presenting with this complex dilemma. The therapist works with the couple to identify and reduce risk factors arising from sexual ignorance, and faulty beliefs about sex and intimacy that existed prior to the present relationship. Each partner's individual risk factors are also addressed. Finally, the focal point becomes the couple's relationship. The therapist uses a variety of cognitive and behavioral techniques to help the couple to communicate effectively and enhance physical and emotional intimacy.

Hypoactive Sexual Desire (HSD)
Assessment Handout

There are several phases in the assessment of HSD: the telephone evaluation, the preliminary assessment, the preliminary Intersystem assessment, and a cognitive assessment. Each of these phases will be described below.

The Telephone Evaluation: During this conversation, the therapist should ask how the client was referred and answer questions on the phone. The therapist should use the phone call to:

- become familiar with the problem.
- identify ways to combine individual and couple therapy.
- develop a treatment plan.
- find a way to get both partners into session.

Preliminary Assessment: In the preliminary assessment phase, the therapist begins to gather data and generate a hypothesis to later be tested. This process is facilitated by:

- noting initial impressions and reactions of the couple.
- taking an adequate history of the problem.
- recording recent significant changes in the client's life.
- establishing goals by identifying the changes that each partner would like to occur in the relationship.

Preliminary Intersystem Assessment: As part of the assessment, the therapist employs rapid assessment techniques. These questions can be taken home by the couple:

1. How often do you have sex?
2. How often do you feel like having sex?
3. Do you believe your desire level is too low?
4. When did you first notice yourself losing desire for sex?
5. What was happening at that time?
6. Did you lose desire rapidly or slowly?
7. What was your level of sexual desire earlier in your relationship?
8. What medications are you taking now?
9. Any changes in your health?
10. On a scale of 1 to 10, how much desire do you feel in general? Prior to sex? During sex?

Cognitive Assessment: Assess each partner's negative emotions about the self, the partner, the relationship, from the family-of-origin, and so on. The cognitive assessment helps to determine which of the thoughts can be changed though cognitive therapy techniques, and to assess other problems in the relationship that need to change through couple therapy.

Favorable Conditions and Contraindications for Therapy for Hypoactive Sexual Desire (HSD) Clients

The Intersystem Model to treat HSD is favorable when

- partners have positive sex beliefs and *want to* experience desire again.
- both partners are relatively free from psychiatric problems that can impede treatment .
- response anxiety or the pressure to feel desire in the absence of sexual desire is present.
- couples are unable to break the cycle of negative sexual cognitions and obsessive thoughts that interfere with building sexual desire.
- HSD clients keep a secret from their partner such as sexual abuse, physical abuse, or emotional abuse.
- negative sexual attitudes based on religious beliefs, internalized negative sex messages from the family-of-origin, and the resulting sexual guilt are present.
- situational life stressors, such as divorce, severe work stress, or death of a loved one affect one partner.
- anxiety is present where there is a real or imagined loss of health, or when the individual or couple do not appreciate the normal physiological changes of aging and maintain the same expectations as they did when they were younger.
- difficulties in negotiating issues of power, control, inclusion, and autonomy are present.
- the couple's sexual script has not been successfully negotiated, or the partners may have different preferences or ease of arousal.
- there is treatable discord in other areas of the relationship, such as ineffective communication, unresolved anger, and expectations.
- HSD can be related to other sexual difficulties in either partner such as erectile dysfunction, inhibited female orgasm, or vaginismus.

The Intersystem treatment for HSD is *not* appropriate

- when the HSD partner does not wish for or care about sexual desire or has sexual aversion.
- if the problem is viewed as solely belonging to the partner who lacks desire and the other partner is unwilling to participate in the therapy.
- when there is a great deal of untreatable discord.
- when couples are unable to work together cooperatively.
- when one or both partners are not committed to the relationship.
- when significant psychopathology is present in either partner that makes couple/sex therapy problematic.
- when one or both parties have a lack of commitment to treatment or the relationship such as during an affair or active addiction.

Sensate Focus Objectives

1. Partners learn to be focused on themselves rather than wondering if they are pleasing their partner.
2. These activities provide an opportunity for both to communicate their likes and dislikes, wishes and desires, and so forth.
3. The goal is to experience sensual pleasure from each individual activity without the pressure of having to complete the sex act with vaginal intercourse.
4. Once couples begin to experience sexual intimacy in a positive manner, positive anticipation of future intimacy occurs and desire becomes enhanced.

Sensate Focus Techniques

1. Ask that the couple not engage in intercourse until asked to do so at a later point, because forcing the goal of intercourse might increase anxiety and reduce relaxation.
2. Discuss the rationale for sensate focus activities, explaining that it is a form of systematic desensitization.
3. Begin with an assignment that is carefully selected ahead of time by the therapist and the couple (e.g., foot rubs, massages, backrubs, and other forms of loving touch). Partners are encouraged to experience as much pleasure as they can and to communicate about what feels good.
4. Remind the couple not to exceed the prescription.
5. Advise the partners to communicate with each other if something does not feel right and to do something else.
6. Routinely check the completion of assignments. In other words, what worked? What did not work? This technique might involve many graduated steps until the couple is comfortable with sensual touch and ready to progress to genital stimulation.
7. Gradually move to the phase of touching breasts and genitals. Follow this phase again with questions and activities.
8. Gradually transition to intercourse.
9. Educate the couple that at times, it is natural to feel more desire than at other times.

CONTRIBUTORS

Katherine M. Hertlein, PhD, is an Assistant Professor in the Department of Marriage, Family, and Community Counseling at the University of Nevada, Las Vegas. She received her doctorate in marriage and family therapy from Virginia Tech. She has published in several journals including *Journal of Couple and Relationship Therapy*; *American Journal of Family Therapy*; *Contemporary Family Therapy*; *Journal of Feminist Family Therapy*; and *Journal of Clinical Activities, Assignments, and Handouts in Psychotherapy Practice*. In addition to other research awards regarding infidelity, she was the recipient of the 2002 American Association for Marriage and Family Therapy Graduate Student Research Award for her dissertation on Internet infidelity. She serves as reviewer for several journals, as a coeditor for two books on therapy interventions for couples and families, and as a coeditor on a book for the clinical treatment of infidelity. Her areas of interest include infidelity and sexuality, research methodology and measurement, and training in marriage and family therapy. Dr. Hertlein may be contacted at 4505 Maryland Parkway, Box 453045, Las Vegas, NV 89154-3045. E-mail: katherine.hertlein@unlv.edu

Gerald R. Weeks, PhD, ABPP, is Professor and Chair of the Department of Counseling at the University of Nevada, Las Vegas. He is an Approved Supervisor and Clinical Member of the American Association of Marriage and Family Therapy, and is board certified by the American Board of Professional Psychology and the American Board of Sexology. Dr. Weeks has published 17 professional textbooks in the fields of sex, marital, and family therapy. Among his publications are *Couples in Treatment*, *Paradoxical Psychotherapy* (available in six languages), *Erectile Dysfunction*, *Treating Hypoactive Sexual Desire*, *Treating Infidelity*, and *The Handbook of Family Therapy*. He has presented throughout the United States and Europe. Dr. Weeks can be reached at 4505 Maryland Parkway, Box 453045, Las Vegas, NV 89154-3045. E-mail: gweeks@ccmail.nevada.edu

Nancy Gambescia, PhD, maintains an active private practice specializing in relationship and sex therapy in Rosemont, Pennsylvania. In addition, she teaches and supervises psychotherapists in the assessment and treatment of sexual dysfunctions and couples therapy. Dr. Gambescia is an Approved Supervisor and Clinical Member of the American Association of Marriage and Family Therapy and a board certified sexologist and diplomate of the American Board of Sexology. Dr. Gambescia has coauthored three books: *Erectile Dysfunction*, *Hypoactive Sexual Desire*, and *Treating Infidelity* (Norton). Dr. Gambescia may be contacted at 1062 E. Lancaster Avenue, Suite 26, Rosemont, PA 19010. E-mail: Ngambescia@aol.com

RESOURCES

Alberti, R. E., & Emmons, M. L. (1995). *Your Perfect Right* (25th ed.). San Luis Obispo, CA: Impact.

American Psychiatric Association. (2000). *Diagnostic and Statistical Manual of Mental Disorders* (*DSM-IV-TR;* 4th ed. text rev.). Washington, DC: Author.

Basson, R. (2000). The female sexual response: A different model. *Journal of Sex and Marital Therapy, 26*, 51-65.

Basson, R. (2001). Are the complexities of women's sexual function reflected in the new consensus definitions of dysfunction? *Journal of Sex and Marital Therapy, 27*, 105-112.

Bernal, G., & Barker, J. (1979). Toward a metacommunication framework of couples intervention. *Family Process, 18*, 293-302.

DeMaria, R., Weeks, G., & Hof, L. (1999). *Focused Genograms: Intergenerational Assessment of Individuals, Couples, and Families*. Philadelphia: Brunner/Mazel.

Gottman, J. (1994). *What Predicts Divorce: The Relationship Between Marital Processes and Marital Outcomes*. Hillsdale, NJ: Lawrence Erlbaum.

Laumann, E. O., Palik, A., & Rosen, R. C. (1999). Sexual dysfunction in the United States: Prevalence and predictors. *Journal of the American Medical Association, 281*, 537-544.

Lerner, H. (1989). *The Dance of Anger*. New York: HarperCollins.

Morokoff, P., & Gilliland, R. (1993). Stress, sexual functioning, and marital satisfaction. *The Journal of Sex Research, 20*, 43-53.

Segraves, K., & Segraves, R. (1991). Hypoactive sexual desire disorder: Prevalence and comorbidity in 906 subjects. *Journal of Sex and Marital Therapy, 17*, 55-58.

Sternberg, R. (1986). A triangular theory of love. *Psychological Review, 93*, 119-135.

Strong, S., & Claiborn, C. (1982). *Change Through Interaction: Social Psychological Processes of Counseling and Psychotherapy*. New York: Wiley.

Trudel, G., Ravart, M., & Matte, B. (1993). The use of the multiaxial diagnostic system for sexual dysfunctions in the assessment of hypoactive sexual desire. *Journal of Sex and Marital Therapy, 19*, 123-130.

Weeks, G. (1994). The intersystem model: An integrative approach to treatment. In G. Weeks & L. Hof (Eds.), *The Marital-Relationship Casebook: Theory and Application of the Intersystem Model* (pp. 3-34). New York: Brunner/Mazel.

Weeks, G. (2004). The emergence of a new paradigm in sex therapy: Integration. *Sexual and Relationship Therapy, 20*(1), 89-103.

Weeks, G., & L'Abate, L. (1982). *Paradoxical Psychotherapy: Theory and Practice With Individuals, Couples, and Families*. New York: Brunner/Mazel.

Weeks, G., & Treat, S. (2001). *Couples in Treatment: Techniques and Approaches for Effective Practice* (rev. ed.). New York: Brunner/Mazel.

Female Sexual Arousal and Orgasm: Pleasures and Problems

Sally A. Kope

Women and their sexual responsiveness have had a complicated relationship with the medical and psychological professions since the rudimentary beginnings of these practices. In the Victorian era, for example, practitioners pondered whether a woman's brain and her ovaries could work simultaneously; therefore, sexual arousal or strenuous activity was commonly considered to be overtaxing to her health (Blumberg, 1997). What a conundrum for women: On one hand they were perfectly capable of pleasure and responsiveness, and on the other hand they were subtly or overtly discouraged from the exploration of this capacity by their treating clinicians, not to mention their social and religious communities.

This contribution discusses an evolving model of female sexual response. It will depict how sexual response for women has been understood and defined over the past 60 years. The anatomy and physiology of arousal and orgasm is presented. Clinicians and consumers face challenges to sexual functioning, and these are discussed along with interventions. The role of hormones in contemporary practice is presented. A case example is explored in depth.

CURRENT THINKING ABOUT FEMALE SEXUAL PROBLEMS

The advent of the birth control pill, not commonly available until the 1960s, provided a gateway to what became referred to as the "Sexual Revolution." Did this revolution result in widely greater sexual satisfaction for women (the crux of sexual arousal and orgasm)? That becomes difficult to quantify for the consumer as well as the clinician. First, we have little reliable data regarding how satisfied women were *before* the renowned revolution. Clinicians have more recently looked to the respected, although criticized, National Health and Social Life Survey to extrapolate how women feel about their sexual experiences. In brief, this survey stated that 43% of American women between the ages of 18 and 59 reported having a sexual dysfunction (Michael et al., 1994).

Prominent sex therapists have made a strong point in analyzing this survey: As reported, *dysfunction* does not automatically indicate *dissatisfaction* (Hicks et al., 2005). For example, a woman may report being frequently anorgasmic, but this report as an isolated statistical entity does little to inform the clinician of the woman's overall experience of her sexual encounters and how pleasurable – satisfactory – they are to her.

It is important to note, however, that describing female sexual dysfunction (FSD) only in terms of the presenting patient's dissatisfaction has serious limitations as well. The *Consensus-*

Based Classification of Female Sexual Dysfunction (CCFSD; Basson et al., 2000, cited in Sugrue & Whipple, 2001) is the outcome of an effort of a multidisciplinary team of sexologists and medical practitioners to look at sexual problems with a much broader view than just what is normal biologically. However, Sugrue and Whipple point out that, although a description of personal distress is essential in the diagnosis of sexual dissatisfaction, subjective distress alone as a diagnostic criterion presents its own problems (Sugrue & Whipple, 2001). Consider the case of a woman who claims no sexual interest, arousal, or orgasm and no distress about this. But she is partnered with an individual who finds this incredibly distressing. Does this mean that the woman has no sexual problem, but her partner has the problem? Or that the woman has a sexual problem but is in denial about it and her partner is just fine? Or does the couple have a problem? This presents a conundrum for the evaluating clinician as well as for the couple.

The caution to us as clinicians is to examine the context and breadth of sexual complaints, and not to approach symptoms of arousal and orgasm difficulties as if they were connected only to genitals and not to people, and frequently people in relationships (Hicks et al., 2005).

AN EVOLVING MODEL OF FEMALE SEXUAL RESPONSE

The field of sex therapy was initially established on the research findings of Dr. William Masters and his colleague Virginia Johnson in the late 1950s. They conducted studies using human subjects – men and women – in a controlled setting, charting and filming their responses. Perhaps for the first time, sex was explored through the literal lens of women's sexual responsiveness. They focused on what happens, and how and where it happens when a woman's clitoris is stimulated (Foley, Kope, & Sugrue, 2002). Although subsequent research proved their focus to be too narrow in scope to define female responsiveness, their human sexual response model became – and primarily remains – the gold standard for delineating sexual response and thus providing a model for diagnosing, evaluating, and treating sexual problems.

It is important to note that there were many foremothers and forefathers who contributed to the knowledge base and evolution of our ideas about sexuality well before Masters and Johnson. There were nurses and midwives and physicians and psychiatrists and zoologists and behavioral scientists. These luminaries marched us through an historic view of sex as bad and dangerous (as late as the end of the 19th century) to the detailed reports of Kinsey in the 1950s that disclosed what people really *do* sexually, thus normalizing much sexual behavior, to the 1980s when I sat at a lecture by William Masters in St. Louis, Missouri, where he said, "Sex is a quality of life issue." Now, in the early years of the 21st century, the evolution continues.

HISTORY REVIEW

Masters and Johnson Sexual Response Cycle

The Masters and Johnson model includes four discrete areas: excitement (the physical signs of arousal and narrowing of concentration), plateau (the sustained level of high arousal before orgasm), orgasm (the physical response of orgasm and release of sexual tension), and resolution (the return of the body to prearousal state) (Masters, Johnson, & Kolodny, 1982). The work of Masters and Johnson was revolutionary. Until that time, what was known about human sexual response was extrapolated from observing animal behavior. William Masters, a physician, and Virginia Johnson, a behavioral scientist, believed that it was imperative to study the physiological responses of people. They developed technology, such as the use of a tiny, intervaginal camera that could show what actually happens *inside* a woman's vagina during sexual stimulation.

Helen Singer Kaplan's Contributions to a Female Sexual Response Model

Helen Singer Kaplan, professor of psychiatry at Cornell University College of Medicine in New York, became a prominent figure in the realm of sex therapy in the 1970s (Kaplan, 1974). In addition to her defining and classifying sexual dysfunctions for the *Diagnostic and Statistical Manual of Mental Disorders* (*DSM-IV*; American Psychiatric Association [APA], 1994), she worked to eliminate pejorative terms such as frigidity from the practice of sexual medicine and sex therapy. One of Dr. Kaplan's significant contributions was the addition of sexual desire to the description of the sexual response cycle. Dr. Kaplan promoted the concept that sexual functioning does not really require emotional connection (e.g., masturbation is initiated and motivated on one's own). It was not her goal to treat people like sexual robots, functioning completely without emotional connection. Building on the work of Masters and Johnson and her own clinical experiences, she was well aware of "performance anxiety" and hoped to free women and men from the tyranny of this anxiety by assisting them to focus on and take responsibility for their own sensations and arousal.

The Erotic Stimulus Pathway Model

The Erotic Stimulus Pathway Model was developed by David Reed in 1989. His unpublished work was presented at the annual meeting of the American Association of Sexuality Educators, Counselors, and Therapists by his long-time colleague Bill Stayton in May 2005 (Stayton, Angelo, & Kaye, 2005). This model is a precursor to the sexual response models that focus on pleasure rather than the "cycle" model. The "cycle" model has been emphatically criticized for being too phallocentric (based on the anticipated and normal progression for males), implying that one phase leads to the next with the progression ultimately concluding in orgasm. Reed divides sexual response into four phases. The first phase is *seduction*. Seduction, in this definition, does not begin with a come-on between two partners. It begins with early experiences in life, perhaps long before genital activity with a partner begins. It means that we have learned to set the stage for later experiences by step-by-step, long-term preparation. Moving to the adult phase of seduction involves the invitation to engage in sexual activity.

The second phase is *sensation*. As Whipple and Brash McGreer state: "Reed described the senses as nature's aphrodisiacs. Touch, sight, hearing, smell and taste contribute to sexual arousal and pleasure" (Whipple & Brash McGreer, 1997, p. 514). The sensation phase has as its center the ability of the individual to tune out external stimuli and tune in to her own physical sensations.

Stayton and colleagues describe Reed's third phase as *surrender*. This phase may involve orgasm, but definitely implies that the individual has enough self-empowerment to turn herself over to the fullness of the sexual experience. Stayton and Reed note that power struggles between a couple are often played out in this phase (Stayton et al., 2005). *Reflection* is the final phase of this model, and is significant because it is this phase that sets the mind-set (positive or negative) for future sexual experiences. So a reflection of "that was great!" or "glad that's over" is the fertile soil for one's expectations for the next encounter.

Nonlinear Models of Female Sexual Response

In 1997, Whipple and Brash McGreer expanded Reed's Erotic Stimulus Pathway Model to include (a) the capacity to experience pleasure whether or not orgasm is present, (b) receptivity to sexual pleasure, (c) the physical capacity to respond to sexual stimulation, and (d) the capability (not the mandate) to experience orgasm (Whipple, 2002).

The Non-Linear Model of Female Sexual Response, developed by Rosemary Basson, B.C. Centre for Sexual Medicine, Vancouver, British Columbia, is a new model that emphasizes the significance of the context, the relationship in which the woman is experiencing sex. She draws a circular model with no hierarchy (Basson, 2005). Masters and Johnson approached their research on sexual response as if sexual desire or motivation was a foregone conclusion (otherwise why would a woman engage in a sexual experience?) and did not even include it in the response cycle. I want to emphasize that their findings were invaluable to medicine, and birthed sex therapy as a discipline. Helen Singer Kaplan noted that sexual desire was a significant component of responsiveness. This led to research and awareness of low or absent sexual desire, and sexual aversion, including trauma-based desire disorders.

Basson brings to the forefront the concept that women currently, traditionally, and historically have entered sexual activity with willingness to participate, based on a variety of motivations, including the desire for intimacy and closeness, with sexual desire not necessarily being an initial component of that willingness (Basson, 2005). As Whipple consistently asserts, women's sexuality and sexual responses are exceedingly complex and differ substantially from those of men. Assuming that men and women progress identically in sexual response runs the risk of pathologizing women's normal response (Whipple, 2002).

Basson continues to describe female sexual responsiveness as including subjective sexual arousal if sexual stimulation is gratifying, wanted, focused, and intense to her specifications. Physiological sexual arousal and desire arise from her willingness and from the sexual activity she is engaged in. Sexual satisfaction occurs with or without orgasm and arises from numerous sources including the gratification of a sense of intimacy, a personal sense of well-being, the joy of being in a pleasurable experience with her partner, and/or orgasm (Basson, 2005).

THE ANATOMY AND PHYSIOLOGY OF AROUSAL

Sexual arousal for women involves two distinct features. One is what is happening in the body that can be physically noted, and the second is how the person is responding to those changes. The subjective and objective experiences of arousal may be quite different; that is, signs of physical arousal may be present without the woman being "tuned in" so that she *feels* sexually aroused. In fact, in some cases the physical signs of sexual arousal, such as blood engorgement in the genital region or lubrication, can actually be physically uncomfortable or even cause aversion. Consider the case of a woman who had been sexually abused in her past and to her shame and horror noted that her body – designed to respond to sexual stimulation – did just that. That individual may need some therapeutic support to learn not just to tolerate, but to appreciate her body's ability to respond to sexual stimulation in circumstances of her own choosing. Rosemary Basson states:

> Sexual stimuli in context/environments that are appropriate for the woman are normally needed. Research confirms that her experience of sexual arousal is more influenced by her thoughts and emotions than by feedback from reflexive genital vasocongestion. Providing that the woman enjoys the subjective state of arousal and that the stimulation continues sufficiently long, sexual desire is triggered. A need for sex and sexual satisfaction now accompanies or may even override her original goals, eg, of feeling more emotionally close to her partner. (Basson, 2004, pp. 714-715)

The American Psychiatric Association's *DSM-IV-TR* (APA, 2000) does not include the absence of subjective sexual arousal in its definitions of arousal disorders. A "new definition" includes categories of *combined sexual arousal disorder* (diminished feelings of sexual excitement and pleasure as well as absence of objective signs of physical sexual arousal), *subjective arousal disorder* (physical symptoms of arousal may be present, but physical and emotional feelings are absent during stimulation), and *genital arousal disorder* (generally an acquired condition in which women report being emotionally excited but have absent or impaired genital arousal) (Basson, 2004).

Understanding that physiological signs of arousal may be present without a woman's actual participation in that arousal is an important distinction for the treating clinician. If the body and mind are working in concert, and there are no significant barriers (discussed later under "Challenges to Sexual Arousal and Orgasm"), there will be physical signs of arousal, and arousal will equal excitement, often escalating as sexual stimulation increases in intensity. An important (and too frequently absent) contributing factor to sexual excitement is the tuning in to the sensations of the experience, and tuning out of extraneous distractions (Foley et al., 2002).

Sexual arousal is a physical and emotional state that can last a few minutes or much longer. Blood pressure rises and the pulse rate increases. Vaginal and vulvar tissues swell through the process of blood engorgement called vasocongestion, which temporarily increases the volume of blood to the genitals. The hydraulics of sexual excitement keep the blood from flowing back out, similar to the process of penile erection. The process of vasocongestion to the genital region heightens sexual pleasure.

The clitoris swells with blood during sexual arousal. The visible portion of the clitoris is a small unit of tissue, but the clitoris is quite complex. The clitoris root and shaft separate into two parts, wishbone-like, anchored to the pelvic bone. This intricate organ contains about 8,000 nerve fibers (twice as many as the penis), making it extremely sensitive to touch and stimulation (Association of Reproductive Health Professionals, cited in Foley et al., 2002).

The presence of vaginal lubrication is a prime physical indicator of sexual arousal. A process called *transudation* occurs during sexual arousal. It begins with blood engorging the spongy tissue of the vaginal walls, resulting in a sweating of beads of a slick, clear, lubricating substance on the vaginal walls. Lubrication is different in composition from other vaginal secretions, it originates differently, and its presence has as its sole purpose to make the vagina and vaginal opening accessible to genital manipulation and possible penetration (Foley et al., 2002).

Internal changes occur during sexual arousal as well. Just how this manifests varies woman to woman and varies as well due to the focus of sexual stimulation. One internal locus of sexual arousal is the "G" spot, named for a German gynecologist, Ernst Grafenberg, who determined that there is an area internal to the vagina, on the anterior wall, that swells during sexual stimulation. This area became renowned in the 1970s and 1980s when Beverly Whipple and colleagues researched orgasm patterns in women focusing on the "G" spot (Ladas, Whipple, & Perry, 1983).

If the primary site of stimulation is the clitoris, the innermost part of the vagina, closest to the cervix, rounds and swells, creating a space. The uterus pulls forward as the upper third of the vagina expands, changing the position of the cervix (Foley et al., 2002). The area near the opening of the vagina swells, creating a gripping sensation.

THE ANATOMY AND PHYSIOLOGY OF ORGASM

First, I will repeat here what is commonly known: The brain is the primary site of orgasm for women. Consider that women can have orgasm dreams and that some women can orgasm through fantasy alone with no physical stimulation. There is more and more supporting evidence that areas of the brain play a key role in orgasm. Orgasm is felt in many body regions and can be stimulated from different sites, not just the genitals (Carnes, Wagoner, & Whipple, 2005). This is significant to the clinician who is evaluating a woman who has complaints about being anorgasmic or who has infrequent orgasms. Foremost: Orgasm is a *learned response* for women. The media (a primary source for sex education in our dominant culture) "teaches" women that orgasm is a spontaneously occurring event. In fact, orgasm for women is acquired, learned through self-awareness, focus, and experience. An orgasm is a personal responsibility, falling squarely on the woman to understand her own physiological responses and communicate her needs to her partner.

Pubertal development for boys and girls is different in one significant aspect: For boys there is a direct hormonal and maturational connection between pubertal development and ejaculation. For girls, there is no hormonal link between puberty and orgasm. Some girls learn to be orgasmic at a very young age through self-stimulation. Orgasm with a partner is another matter, and depends not just on stimulation, but on experimentation and communication.

Orgasm lasts a few seconds, but if we are to believe the popular media, we are failures as sexual partners if an orgasm does not happen, because the "hype" implies that orgasm is what a sexual encounter is all about. Orgasm is the rhythmic pulsing in the body as it releases sexual tension. The pelvic floor muscles are integral to the sensation, experience, and intensity of orgasm, although a "G" spot-generated orgasm involves fewer pelvic floor muscle contractions and is felt deeper in the body. The pelvic floor muscles (or *pubococcygeus* muscles) are the largest muscle group in the body. It is these muscles that contract during orgasm at 0.8-second intervals of varying intensity. Vaginal and uterine muscles also contract. Some women have the capacity to experience the famous "multiple orgasms" (Foley et al., 2002). This capacity exists for women because they do not have the same refractory period that a man has (the time lapse between the ability to ejaculate/orgasm). Multiple orgasms should not be considered to be the Olympic gold medal for sexual achievement. For some women, the high stimulation and sensitivity of an orgasm can mean further stimulation is irritating rather than pleasurable.

CHALLENGES TO SEXUAL AROUSAL AND ORGASM

Sexual Pharmacology

Some commonly prescribed and over-the-counter medications are associated with arousal and orgasm dissatisfaction. Of course medical conditions should not be neglected, but women should discuss medications frankly with their health care provider, including sexual side effects and possible alternatives.

Cocaine, Marijuana, and Other Agents

Cocaine has a reputation for being a drug associated with sexual turn-on. At initial use it does appear to intensify orgasms. However, this never lasts. Higher doses are sought to achieve a similar response, and higher doses have the opposite effect. "Chronic cocaine use will likely result in anhedonia and complete lack of sexual desire, arousal and orgasm" (L. Siegel & R. Siegel, 2005, p. 6). Marijuana appears to increase sexual desire and receptiveness but does not result in improved orgasm ability or increased lubrication.

GHB is the "date rape" drug. It has the reputation of increasing desire, sensitivity, and orgasm intensity, but it is an unstable, dangerous substance, often created by "bathtub chemistry." MDMA is the "love" drug Ecstasy. This is an amphetamine-type drug. Users report increased desire and satisfaction, but in spite of this perception, MDMA appears to impair sexual performance (L. Siegel & R. Siegel, 2005).

Illness, Disability, and Pain

It does not take more than a ferocious cold and a few days on the couch for all even "temporarilyabled/healthy" people to understand what havoc can be wreaked when a woman and her partner have to deal with a prolonged illness, chronic condition, or chronic pain. There are few such conditions that do not take a toll on arousal and orgasm (and, of course, interest). Not just the conditions, but their treatments (such as radiation for cancer) have an impact. Almost all conditions have a website, online chat rooms, and helpful material to assist women to compensate for their circumstances (e.g., The American Cancer Society, www.cancer.org). As sex therapists, we encourage women to be as informed as possible about any extenuating situation they may be dealing with, remembering that we are sexual throughout a lifetime, "in sickness and in health."

Menopause and Beyond

As women in the baby-boomer generation reached the millennium, they became the first generation in history to anticipate living as many (or more!) years postmenopausally than they did during adult reproductive years. As Foley et al. (2002) note in *Sex Matters for Women: A Complete Guide to Taking Care of Your Sexual Self*, menopause indeed brings challenges. Not since adolescence has a woman's body gone through such developmental changes. But women who have attained the age of menopause are not adolescents in their ability to cope with these changes. They have years of problem solving to draw from. They are free from the worries of pregnancy or contraception for the first time. They have vast sources of resources, including medical care providers who do not view older women as sexually retired (even though the media may strongly contribute to that view). Often women do not approach sex with the goal of having frequent sexual encounters or even of having orgasm. They are usually looking for and striving to achieve and maintain closeness with their partners (Alexander et al., 2003).

Persistent Sexual Arousal Syndrome (PSAS)

Whereas most sexual arousal dissatisfactions focus on inadequate sexual arousal, an uncommon complaint of hypersexual arousal has recently gained attention. Hypersexual arousal is an extremely distressing circumstance where the physiological characteristics of sexual arousal are abundantly present for extended periods of times, even days. This arousal pattern is independent of a sense of sexual excitement. It is experienced as unwanted. There are no commonalities that help decipher this perplexing problem: The women complaining can be young, old, in different hormonal states from normal to subnormal, and are generally normal by psychiatric standards. It is uncertain whether this is a new, or newly recognized, syndrome. No treatment protocols have been established because of the ambiguous etiology of this disorder (Lieblum & Nathan, 2002). It has been determined that PSAS is associated with subjective and objective decrease in sexual functioning and satisfaction (Brown et al., 2005).

HORMONES

Patients and practitioners alike were delighted some years ago when hormone replacement therapy (HRT; estrogen or estrogen with progestin) reduced the symptoms of women with surgical, medical, or menopausal loss of estrogen. Women reported less vaginal irritation and dryness, less dyspareunia, and increased sexual interest and responsiveness (Bachmann & Lieblum, 2004). Estrogen replacement in postmenopausal women restored their sensitivity to clitoral and vaginal vibration (Berman & Bassuk, 2002). However, the Women's Health Initiative

(WHI) Estrogen Plus Progestin Trial (HERS), an 8-year study of 16,800 healthy women aged 50 to 79 years old was discontinued 3 years early because of a discovered increased risk of invasive breast cancer (Women's Health Initiative, 2002). Other risks have been associated with HRT, including a small increase in stroke, coronary heart disease, and pulmonary emboli. Bachmann and Lieblum cite many beneficial aspects to HRT, and point out that the WHI did not include women with menopausal symptoms in their studies, so of course the benefits to sexual health and relief of symptoms were not factored in to the risks and benefits (Bachmann & Lieblum, 2004). Alexander postulates that if men were having penile dryness resulting in blood spotting of their undershorts, there would be warnings from the Surgeon General everywhere (Alexander, 2005)! She goes on to say that there are advocates for cardiac health, colorectal health, indeed all kinds of "health," but vaginal and vulvar health are ignored or undertreated.

Hormonal replacement options remain available to women. Vaginal creams contain low-dose estrogen, are used topically, and deliver healing results directly to the tissue. Once the tissues are thickened, absorption of the estrogen into the system decreases. It takes about 2 weeks for tissues to be restored. After that, if further treatment is needed, it can be given on an as-needed basis. Estrogen (or estrogen with progestin if a woman has her uterus) can be delivered through an estrogen ring that is inserted vaginally and provides relief from a variety of symptoms. Pills and patches are also available and can be delivered in a cyclical plan so that risk is reduced. It is imperative, when considering any hormone replacement option, that women discuss their options with their health care providers to make the most informed decision possible.

Androgen in the form of testosterone is the hormone most closely associated with sexual motivation in women. Testosterone also contributes to the pleasure and intensity of orgasm and arousal. Andropause is the steady and gradual decline in available testosterone. It begins in a woman's 40s and continues until her 70s. This differs from the sharp decline of estrogen experienced during menopause (Johnson, 2005). Testosterone is constantly being evaluated as to its role in sexual arousal and responsiveness. Testosterone is likely associated with clitoral swelling during arousal and loss of clitoral sensation when testosterone is low (Basson, 2002). When testosterone is low, women experience more fatigue and less sexual receptivity. Despite the clear evidence that testosterone contributes to sexual pleasure and orgasmic intensity, the studies regarding testosterone supplementation are inconclusive as to the actual effect on sexual function. This is further evidence that women's sexual responsiveness is very complex (Basson, 2004).

Currently there are no approved replacement testosterone treatment options available in the United States for women experiencing sexual dissatisfaction (Garcia-Banigan & Guay, 2005). Estratest is a conjugated estrogen with testosterone; it is approved for treating vasomotor symptoms during menopause, although it is used off label by many medical care providers for treatment of low sexual desire and diminished arousal or orgasm.

Intrinsa is a testosterone-for-women product developed by Procter and Gamble. The Intrinsa trials have been 4 years in development, including a double-blind study in 2004. FDA approval was denied in December 2004. The majority of the advisory panel agreed that the product showed a benefit to its users, but they voted against approval because they wanted to see more clinical data regarding long-term safety (Carnes et al., 2005).

ZESTRA AND EROS

Zestra is a product developed from a proprietary blend of botanical by-products. It is applied directly to the vulva. In one small, double-blind study it appears to have increased sexual arousal and pleasure and enhanced the ability to have orgasms. Several participants experienced vulvar or vaginal irritation (Ferguson et al., 2003).

Numerous plant-derived and herbal treatments for sexual dissatisfactions exist. Unfortunately, these treatments lack empirical research, so their efficacy and safety are difficult to determine. There may well be a role for these treatments – some of which have been in popular use throughout the world for eons – but further investigation is necessary (Rowland & Tai, 2003).

Eros Therapy is a clitoral vacuum device that is nonintrusive and uses a mild vacuum pressure to engorge the clitoris. It is an FDA-approved device (Billups, 2002). It may well be helpful for women who experience genital arousal disorder. Its use should be judicious; it could actually be irritating rather than gratifying to a woman who has subjective arousal disorder.

VIAGRA (SILDENAFIL) AND WOMEN

Viagra and its counterparts have had a significant impact on pharmaceuticals and women. Sexual products are big business, and the idea that a sexual problem for women could be controlled, cured, or overcome by a pill is too irresistible for drug companies to overlook. Quoting an online article "Sex on the Brain: Researchers Look at What Women Want" (Associated Press, 2005, p. 1):

The pharmaceutical industry has failed women miserably – there isn't a single sexual drug on the market that can help them. Pfizer Inc. last year abandoned an eight-year Viagra study involving 3,000 women, conceding that it's [sic] famous blue pill only works for men. "I hate to say it, but women are much more complex than men," said Beverly Whipple, researcher who co-wrote "The G Spot."

Sildenafil works by increasing blood flow to the clitoris, but it does not increase vaginal lubrication or satisfaction. In men, the primary neurotransmitter to the penis is nitric oxide, and Sildenafil affects the nitric oxide neurotransmitters. Nitric oxide may play a minor role in the pathways of female sexual arousal (Basson, 2002; Traish et al., 2002). The neuropathways to the vagina are mediated by the neurotransmitter Vasoactive Intestinal Peptide, and this is not impacted by Sildenafil (Basson, 2002).

The medicalization of female sexuality raises serious concerns expressed by some clinicians, while others, such as Raymond Rosen, believe that the development of drugs for female sexual dissatisfaction has untapped potential (Smith, 2003).

"Many physicians are approaching this as a largely biological phenomenon," says psychologist Dennis Sugrue, PhD, a past-president of the American Association of Sex Educators, Counselors and Therapists. "They're doing a disservice to the fact that a woman's sexual experience is an incredibly complex phenomenon that is shaped by cultural scripting, family-of-origin experience, relationship dynamics as well as biological factors. (p. 1)

Leonore Tiefer, a sex therapist, has been an unabashed advocate for women, consistently expressing concern about women's sexuality being pathologized by standards that may be largely formed from a male script. She expresses concern that women may look to a pill or cream to "fix" a sexual difficulty that might have much more complex roots than simple biology (Smith, 2003).

INTERVENTION

Case Example*

Isabel and Mark were from different cultures and were a decade apart in age (Mark is older), but they were deeply in love. Isabel was from Panama and Mark was from the United States. They sought couple counseling after months of dealing with what they considered to be a real problem: Isabel couldn't have orgasms, under any circumstances. What was particularly interesting about this couple was that during their first 2 weeks of marriage Isabel was wildly excited about sexual activity with Mark (she was a virgin when they were married). She was easily orgasmic and surprised at this response, which delighted them both. Unfortunately, shortly after their honeymoon, the couple endured a forced separation for 3 months. Mark was involved in military training, and Isabel was adapting to an entirely new environment, with no family near. When Mark returned, they were both utterly dismayed that Isabel's sexual response seemed cool by comparison to their earlier experiences, and she came nowhere near to having orgasms. Her religious convictions prohibited her from "rehearsing" through masturbation while Mark was away. Their efforts became entirely focused on the big "O." Mark, the more assertive of the two, purchased books and vibrators. The couple focused on stimulating Isabel's clitoris endlessly, until she developed a physical and emotional numbness toward this approach, and the couple drifted further and further from a sense of sexual and emotional gratification.

Discussion

Oh, the complexities in Isabel and Mark's case. First of all, we make a nod to the neurobiology that allowed those first, unhampered weeks of sexual and intimacy bliss. Helen Fisher, an anthropologist, has focused her work on romantic love. When love is new, romantic love is the most powerful drive on earth. It is associated with norepinephrine and dopamine flooding the brain, overcoming inhibitions and fear (Isabel's sexual inexperience and relocation from her home in Panama). This physiological and psychological context (Fisher cautions that this never lasts) provided a completely unimpeded pathway for Isabel and Mark to fully and completely experience sexual pleasure (Fisher, 2004). Although Isabel and Mark's experience of experiencing full sexual pleasure despite inexperience is not typical, it was their experience – one that turned out to be for better or for worse.

The "worse" came when the couple reconnected. By this time the lofty brain chemicals had subsided. Isabel had some resentment about being married and "abandoned" in a strange community (although, of course, she had signed up for this arrangement) just weeks after the marriage. Mark was primed to "go" sexually and simply could not understand why the couple was not picking up right where they left off months before. Mark's – and ultimately Isabel's – explanation was that Isabel needed more stimulation somehow to get them back on track. My first intervention was to ask them to abandon the books and sexual aids and simply reconnect as a couple. I described the difference between sensuality and sexual arousal and suggested that because things had gotten off track for them, they simply focus on touch and connection and pleasure and completely forget about orgasm – for now. Isabel was greatly relieved at this suggestion, and Mark appeared to go along with it. However, at our next session, Mark admitted that he had purchased yet another book on orgasm. "I just thought it would help," he said, a bit chagrined.

My education with this couple was reassuring but firm. I offered a plausible explanation about why things had initially gone well and then went badly. Isabel asked, without my prompting, "You aren't going to talk about masturbation, are you?" I acknowledged that this

---

* Names and identifying characteristics have been changed to protect confidentiality.

would be an important component of her learning about her own sexual responses, but allowed her the freedom at that time to put the discussion off, at least for the present. Again, Isabel was relieved, but Mark was perplexed. He simply wanted to approach the "problem" as if Isabel had a physical trigger, and if they learned to stimulate this trigger, things would be fine.

Subsequent sessions broadened the scope of therapy far beyond the few centimeters of Isabel's clitoris and its response to Mark's stimulation. Both partners came to acknowledge that it was an enormous developmental event for Isabel to leave her entire environment including her family, friends, job, restaurants she knew and cherished, and most everything that identified Isabel as Isabel, and join Mark's environment. His 3-month absence shortly after their honeymoon was an unfortunate contributor to the problems they subsequently experienced. Isabel not only felt, she *was* abandoned by Mark, even though he had no control over the circumstances. The literal circumstances of their life (Isabel being new in the environment, and feeling and being abandoned) became the working metaphor: Their sexual life actually mirrored their "real" life. This metaphor gave me leverage to work on the normal developmental and adjustment aspects of their situation. To Isabel, this treatment approach fit like a glove. Mark would have preferred to focus on Isabel's clitoris or vagina and get on with the business of getting his beautiful wife back! But Mark was not a Neanderthal. When he watched Isabel cry in distress over the losses she felt she had endured, his nurturing parts came through and he was able to support his wife and abandon his quest to resume their idyllic sexual life.

Clinical Considerations in Treating Sexual Arousal and Orgasm Dissatisfactions

For intervening in both arousal and orgasm difficulties, the following issues are important.

Medical Evaluation

I never forget the fact that in the 1980s, when I was listening to William Masters lecture in St. Louis, he said that 70% of erectile difficulties for men were physiological and 30% were psychological. (He offered no such statistics for female sexual dissatisfaction.) Twenty years later, the numbers were reversed: 30% of erection difficulties were physiological and 70% psychological. The difference was not due to a suddenly psychologically more robust population of males. The difference was that we had MRI and other technology that could track small venous leaks in the penis. I cannot offer a correlating female problem where the numbers have reversed and a female sexual dissatisfaction, originally thought to be entirely psychological, turned out to be primarily organic. This is an important issue. Underlying disease processes, hormonal disruptions, or other medical issues need to be fully explored. It works best to work with the medical care practitioner if there is a sexual dissatisfaction that requires medical evaluation and/or treatment.

Sensual Stroking of Skin

A prescription to a woman who is in a partnership who wants to increase her sexual arousal and/or orgasmic response is the sensual stroking of skin, the largest organ of the body that can be sexually or sensually stimulated. This broad stroking can result in sexual receptivity and increased arousal and sexual response (Basson, 2002).

Who Initiates Penetration (if penetration is an issue)

Many women depend upon the arousal of their partner, and how much they are desired versus desiring to decide when penetration should occur and coitus to commence. Women need to learn to take responsibility for their own sexual receptivity and readiness and learn how to unapologetically communicate this readiness.

Exercise Is an Enormous Antidote to Female Sexual Dissatisfaction, *whatever the organic or psychological cause*

Women Should Masturbate

Although this is a personal issue and no woman should enter an activity she is not prepared to do, a woman's best source of information about her own physical responses is to try for herself and then learn how to overtly and subtly convey this self-taught information to her partner.

How Was Sex Experienced Before the Current Symptoms?

As in most circumstances, the best information for how things are going to go lies in the past. If there has been a sudden onset of symptoms, it is important to decipher the biological aspects (what changed?), relational aspects (what changed?), or other developmental or environmental factors. If sex has always been problematic, it is important to assess the woman's motivation for change. Far too often, the motivation may be found in the partner's pressure (often legitimate) for things to change. Of course the partner's motivation never automatically transcends to the presenting client's motivation to change. When it comes to sexual issues, I often stop right at motivation until that aspect is clear.

Intervene in the Dogged Achievement of Orgasm

If a woman is going at her clitoris with every implement possible without success, I am not going to suggest another technique or vibrator. I will do the opposite. I recommend that she focus entirely on the pleasurable (or nonpleasurable) sensations she is receiving during sexual stimulation. I suggest that she focus on these sensations without the idea of a specific outcome (orgasm). I educate her, and perhaps her partner, about what is normally expected for a woman and orgasm (perhaps more women rather than fewer do not have regular orgasms with sexual intercourse, for example). If she feels "I'm right there and can't make it" and is experiencing a high level of sexual excitement without discharge, I recommend that she stop for a few minutes before she resumes stimulation. One clinical study focused on genital sensation with vibratory stimulation. The study concluded, "during the sexual cycle there is a decrease in genital sensitivity to vibratory stimuli in normal healthy females" (Lowenstein et al., 2005). So pursuing orgasm by increasing or prolonging stimulation may actually be counterproductive. I encourage a woman to learn to recognize the signs of orgasm to which she may not be paying attention, such as the sensations in the pelvic floor muscles.

Take Stock of the Context of the Sexual Experience

Interestingly, because of the desirable versus desiring aspect, many women engage in sexual activity they do not really want. It probably takes a stronger sense of self to say "no" than it does to say "yes." The context question involves relationship questions.

Education of the Woman and Her Partner

Whatever the sexual dissatisfaction, education is and remains an important component. Using the terminology of sex without embarrassment to model for the couple and informing the client or couple about sexuality concerns, is and remains an invaluable tool in intervention with sexual problems.

Evaluate Whether the Symptom Being Expressed Represents an Underlying Psychological Cause

In many cases this is self-explanatory. If a couple coping with infertility expresses difficulty getting sexually aroused, it does not take much intervention to describe to them that their reproductive (thus genital) systems are being approached from a pathological rather than health perspective, and that sex on demand is far more functional than fun. Other cases may be more difficult to decipher. If a woman says she feels clitorally "dead" and she proves to have a normal hormonal range, she may have "divorced" her genitals in an attempt to distance herself from, say, a previously traumatic or unwanted sexual experience.

CONCLUSION

Sexual arousal and orgasm are quality of life issues, important to women throughout a lifetime. These concerns are profoundly influenced by personal and relational circumstances. We know, for example, that many women will live their later years without a partner. This becomes a challenge far beyond the purview of the treating clinician. Even though women are tenacious and adaptable, this is a circumstance that does not present an immediate compensation. Both arousal and orgasm are intricate biopsychosocial events for women. They can be mitigated by biology, and biology can be mitigated by women's not settling for diluted sexual experiences, but through education, humor, and practice, and perhaps medical intervention. Sexual arousal has not always been embraced by society where women are concerned, but women are learning to embrace their own innate and marvelous abilities to be and remain sexually responsive in circumstances of their choosing and desire.

CONTRIBUTOR

Sally A. Kope, ACSW, is an AASECT certified sex therapist, educator, and supervisor, and is the chairperson of the Sex Therapy Certification committee of the organization. She is the retired program director of Sexual Health Counseling Services, University of Michigan Health Systems. Ms. Kope is the coauthor of *Sex Matters for Women: A Complete Guide to Taking Care of Your Sexual Self.* She is in private practice in Ypsilanti, Michigan. Ms. Kope may be contacted at 2918 Stommel Road, Ypsilanti, MI 48198. E-mail: sakope@provide.net

RESOURCES

Alexander, J. L. (2005, May). *The Systemic Nature of Sexual Functioning in the Postmenopausal Woman.* Plenary presentation at the annual meeting of American Association of Sexuality Educators, Counselors, and Therapists, Portland, OR.

Alexander, J. L., Kotz, K., Dennerstein, L., & Davis, S. R. (2003). The systemic nature of sexual functioning in the postmenopausal woman: Crossroads of psychiatry and gynecology. *Primary Psychiatry, 10*(12), 53-67.

American Psychiatric Association. (1994). *Diagnostic and Statistical Manual of Mental Disorders (DSM-IV;* 4th ed.). Washington, DC: Author.

American Psychiatric Association. (2000). *Diagnostic and Statistical Manual of Mental Disorders (DSM-IV-TR;* 4th ed. text rev.). Washington, DC: Author.

Associated Press. (2005, September). Sex on the brain: Researchers look at what women want. *WTAE TV,* p. 1. Retrieved September 7, 2005, from http://www.the pittsburghchannel.com/health 4939037/detail.html

Bachmann, G., & Lieblum, S. (2004). The impact of hormones on menopausal sexuality: A literature review. *Menopause: The Journal of the North American Menopause Society, 11,* 120-130.

Basson, R. (2002). The complexities of female arousal disorder: Potential role of pharmacology. *World Journal of Urology, 20,* 119-126.

Basson, R. (2004). Recent advances in women's sexual function and dysfunction. *Menopause: The Journal of the North American Menopause Society, 11*(6), 714-725.

Basson, R. (2005). Women's sexual dysfunction: Revised and expanded definitions. *Canadian Medical Association Journal, 172*(10), 1327-1333.

Berman, J., & Bassuk, J. (2002). Physiology and pathophysiology of female sexual function and dysfunction. *World Journal of Urology, 20,* 111-118.

Billups, K. (2002). The role of mechanical devices in treating female sexual dysfunction and enhancing the female sexual response. *World Journal of Urology, 20,* 137-141.

Blumberg, J. (1997). *The Body Project: An Intimate History of American Girls.* New York: Random House.

Brown, C. S., Lieblum, S. L., Wan, J., & Rawlinson, L. (2005, November). *Comparison of Sexual Function in Women With Persistent Sexual Arousal Syndrome, Female Sexual Arousal Disorder, and Healthy Controls Using the Female Sexual Function Index.* Presentation at the International Society for the Study Of Women's Sexual Health, Las Vegas, NV.

Carnes, P., Wagoner, J., & Whipple, B. (2005, May). *What's New and What Works: Pioneering Solutions for Today's Sexual Issues.* Opening plenary at the annual meeting of the American Association of Sexuality Educators, Counselors, and Therapists, Portland, OR.

Ferguson, D., Steidle, C., Singh, G., Alexander, S., & Weihmiller, M. (2003). Randomized, placebo-controlled, double blind, crossover design trial of the efficacy and safety of Zestra for women in women with and without female sexual arousal disorder. *Journal of Sex and Marital Therapy, 29*(s), 33-44.

Fisher, H. (2004). *Why We Love: The Nature and Chemistry of Romantic Love.* New York: Henry Holt & Co.

Foley, S., Kope, S. A., & Sugrue, D. P. (2002). *Sex Matters for Women: A Complete Guide to Taking Care of Your Sexual Self.* New York: Guilford.

Garcia-Banigan, D., & Guay, A. (2005). Testosterone treatment in women. *Contemporary Sexuality, 39*, insert.

Hicks, K., Kleinplatz, P., Davidson, J., & Cole, E. (2005, May). *The New View Approach to Treatment of Women's Sexual Problems.* Presentation at the annual meeting of the American Association of Sexuality Educators, Counselors, and Therapists, Portland, OR.

Johnson, C. J. (2005, December). *Female Sexual Dysfunction: Diagnosis and Clinical Management.* Plenary at the 14th annual Primary Health Care of Women Conference, University of Michigan Medical School, Ann Arbor, MI.

Kaplan, H. S. (1974). *The New Sex Therapy: Active Treatment of Sexual Dysfunctions.* New York: Brunner/Mazel.

Ladas, A. K., Whipple, B., & Perry, J. D. (1983). *The G Spot: And Other Discoveries About Human Sexuality.* New York: Bantam Doubleday Dell.

Lieblum, S., & Nathan, S. (2002). Persistent sexual arousal syndrome in women. *The Female Patient, 27*, 40-43.

Lowenstein, L., Gruenwald, I., Gertamn, I., Yarnitzky, D., & Vardi, Y. (2005, November). *Female Genital Sensation Before, During and After Sexual Stimulation.* Presentation at the International Society for the Study of Women's Sexual Health, Las Vegas, NV.

Masters, W., Johnson, V. E., & Kolodny, R. C. (1982). *On Sex and Human Loving.* Boston: Little, Brown and Company.

Michael, R. T., Gagnon, J. H., Laumann, E. O., & Kolata, G. (1994). *Sex in America: A Definitive Survey.* New York: Little, Brown and Company.

Rowland, D. L., & Tai, W. (2003). A review of plant-derived and herbal approaches to the treatment of sexual dysfunctions. *Journal of Sex and Marital Therapy, 29*(3), 185-205.

Siegel, L., & Siegel, R. (2005). *Sexual Pharmacology: An Introduction and Overview of Drugs, Medication, and Sexual Functioning.* Boynton Beach, FL: Sage Institute for Family Development.

Smith, D. (2003, April). Women and sex: What is 'dysfunctional'? *APA Online.* p. 1. Retrieved August 31, 2005, from http://www.apa.org/monitor/apr03/women.html

Stayton, W., Angelo, M., & Kaye, S. (2005, May). *Erotic Stimulus Pathways: The New Sexual Response Cycle.* Presentation at the annual meeting of the American Association of Sexuality Educators, Counselors, and Therapists, Portland, OR.

Sugrue, D. P., & Whipple, B. (2001). The consensus-based classification of female sexual dysfunction: Barriers to universal acceptance. *Journal of Sex and Marital Therapy, 27*, 221-226.

Traish, A. M., Kim, N. N., Munarriz, R., Moreland, R., & Goldstein, I. (2002). Biochemical and physiological mechanisms of female genital sexual arousal. *Archives of Sexual Behavior, 31*(5), 393-400.

Whipple, B. (2002). Women's sexual pleasure and satisfaction: A new view of female sexual function. *The Female Patient, 27*, 39-44.

Whipple, B., & Brash McGreer, K. (1997). Management of female sexual dysfunction. In M. L. Sipski & C. J. Alexander (Eds.), *Sexual Function in People With Disabilities and Chronic Illness* (pp. 511-536). Gaithersburg, MD: Aspen.

Women's Health Initiative. Writing Group for the WHI Investigators. (2002). Principal results from the Women's Health Initiative randomized controlled trial. *Journal of the American Medical Association, 288*, 321-333.

Female Genital Pain: Vaginismus and Dyspareunia

Jill W. Bley

Genital pain is possibly the most disturbing to the patient of all sexual problems. It is also one of the most complex and difficult issues for the health care provider to treat. It is even difficult, at times, to make the differential diagnosis of vaginismus versus dyspareunia, as I discuss below. It is so difficult, in fact, that some practitioners, such as Bergeron et al. (2003), believe that there may not be any real need to differentiate the two because there is so much overlap of the symptoms and because they are both pain syndromes that happen to occur in the genitals (Reissing, Binik, & Khalife, 1999).

In 1834, Huguier described vaginismus in the scientific literature. Later, Sims called the symptom that had been described by Huguier "vaginismus" (Leiblum, 2000). Since that time vaginismus has been defined in the *Diagnostic and Statistical Manual of Mental Disorders* as recurrent or persistent involuntary spasm of the musculature of the outer third of the vagina that interferes with sexual intercourse (*DSM-IV*; American Psychiatric Association, 1994). According to the medical literature, there are two types of vaginismus: primary, which means that the woman has always had it, and secondary, which means that the woman was able at one time to experience penetration but lost the ability (Katz & Tabisel, 2002).

Dyspareunia is described in the *DSM-IV* as recurrent or persistent genital pain associated with sexual intercourse in either a male or a female. Binik, Bergeron, and Khalife (2000) pointed out some of the difficulties in this diagnosis. They reported that patients may describe their pain as dull/aching pain, burning/cutting pain, or sore/sharp pain. The pain may be at the vaginal opening or it may be experienced at different depths of the vagina or only with thrusting. Katz and Tabisel (2002) defined dyspareunia in their book *Private Pain: It's About Life, Not Just Sex . . . Understanding Vaginismus and Dyspareunia* by dividing the presenting symptoms into onset, frequency, and location. They also described typical variations which may include primary, situational, deep (thrusting always hurts in missionary position, other positions are okay); secondary, situational, insertional (with current partner at beginning of penetration, goes away as soon as penis is halfway in, and never happened with prior partners); primary, complete, superficial, and deep (always had the pain with all partners, in all positions, throughout the sexual act); and secondary, complete, superficial (initial penetration has been painful since gynecologic surgery regardless of lubrication or position).

A study that did not attempt to differentiate between vaginismus and dyspareunia conducted by Lauman et al. (1994) for the National Health and Sexual Life survey reported that between 10% and 15% of women experienced sexual pain during the 6 months before the survey. Leiblum (2000) cited some studies on the prevalence of vaginismus that have indicated rates of from 12% to 17% with higher rates reported in Canada and Ireland. Katz and Tabisel (2002) concluded that we will never know the prevalence of these disorders because they are "private pains."

HISTORICAL APPROACHES TO TREATMENT OF SEXUAL PAIN

In their pioneering work *Human Sexual Response* (1966), Masters and Johnson mentioned dyspareunia only in the context of the aging female in a chapter of that title. They did not mention vaginismus at all. Eight years later Kaplan wrote *The New Sex Therapy* (1974) in which she did not mention dyspareunia but she did devote an entire chapter to vaginismus. She stressed the importance of treating the "phobic" element of the disorder and "in vivo deconditioning of the involuntary spasm of the muscles which guard the vaginal entry" (p. 418). She cited a "common method" recommended by Masters and Johnson, the gentle insertion into the vagina of graduated catheters. Kaplan stated that vaginismus is the most common cause of unconsummated marriage.

In 1983, Kaplan wrote *The Evaluation of Sexual Disorders: Psychological and Medical Aspects*. She included a chapter written by Kaufman, "The Gynecologic Evaluation of Female Dyspareunia and Unconsummated Marriage." Kaufman gave only one paragraph to the discussion of vaginismus. The rest of the chapter was devoted to dyspareunia. He categorized vaginal pain into pain on entry (vaginismus was included here), midvaginal pain, pain on deep thrusting, and pain on orgasm.

The first generation of sex therapists did not give much attention to these troubling problems, probably because the origin of the muscle spasms and pain is difficult to understand. There is often no obvious disruption of the sexual response cycle for, as Leiblum (2000) noted, some women with vaginismus can become sexually aroused, lubricate, and even have multiple orgasms with manual or oral stimulation. The spasms and/or pain also are almost never due to performance anxiety, per se. Therefore, the symptoms do not usually respond to sensate focus exercises or to traditional "talk" therapies.

TREATMENT OF VAGINISMUS

As mentioned previously, Masters and Johnson (1970) advised that vaginismus should be treated using the gentle insertion of graduated sizes of catherters. The use of catheters soon evolved into the use of graduated dilators developed for the specific purpose of helping a woman gradually desensitize to her fear of vaginal dilation and penetration. These dilators made it possible for clinicians to instruct a patient about how to use them, enabling her to practice relaxation techniques while using the dilators at home. This approach is called "in vivo desensitization." Focus International (Schoen & Nathanson, 1984) developed a 30-minute videotape, *Treating Vaginismus* with sex therapist LoPiccolo, that portrays therapy sessions during which LoPiccolo instructs the couple in the use of dilators. The film graphically shows the woman doing relaxation exercises and using the dilators. The dilators were sold and marketed to physicians. Hence, they were expensive, and many women could not afford the treatment.

Fuchs et al. (1978) described a method for treating vaginismus using hypnodesensitization therapy. This intervention is systematic desensitization during the hypnotic state either *in vitro* (where the patient imagines the stimuli) or *in vivo* (where the patient confronts the real stimuli).

In her 1975 book *For Yourself: The Fulfillment of Female Sexuality*, Barbach first suggested to women that they could use phallic-shaped objects (as dildos) that will not splinter, cut, or harm vaginal tissue that may be found in their home for learning how to have orgasms. She paved the way for practitioners to begin to think "outside the box" for ways that the average woman with limited income could be treated for vaginismus. Many sex therapists began to suggest that women use implements and/or vegetables they might have in their home. They could start with very thin implements and graduate to larger things such as carrots and cucumbers that they could easily and cheaply obtain on their own. They could follow the self-help directions for learning to relax the muscles of the vagina as they insert objects that gradually increased in size. Because the medical dilators could only be ordered through a physician at a high cost, Barbach's ideas were (and continue to be) extremely useful to therapists who wanted to help those who could not afford the more costly dilators.

Another important part of the treatment of vaginismus is teaching the woman to learn to relax the musculature of the vaginal area. The therapist must instruct the woman in learning how to do these relaxation exercises. The exercises are described in the Focus International video (Schoen & Nathanson, 1984), *Women Discover Orgasm: A Therapist's Guide to a New Treatment Approach* (Barbach, 1980), and *Becoming Orgasmic: A Sexual and Personal Growth Program for Women* (Heiman & LoPiccolo, 1988). Heiman and LoPiccolo believed that some women with this problem seem to become more tense when they try to do muscle relaxation exercises. They recommended that women do exercises they called "body awareness." After the client learns to relax her body, the therapist asks her to focus her attention to her vaginal muscles (primarily the pubococcygeal muscles) and to learn to isolate those muscles. She then learns to tense and relax them. Those exercises are called Kegel Exercises and were developed by Kegel (1948). They are described in the Heiman and LoPiccolo book and both Barbach books; a brief set of instructions is included in the handout, "Kegal Exercises (Pelvic Floor Exercises)," on page 321 of this contribution.

Once the woman has mastered the use of the dilators, she is encouraged to use her fingers. The next step is to allow her partner to be present as she uses her fingers and shows him how she gently inserts her finger. Then she allows her partner to insert his finger as she guides him. Finally, when she feels that she is ready, she allows insertion of the penis with her controlling the insertion. The key to the treatment is to make sure that the woman feels that she is in control of the whole process. Therefore, it is important to solicit the cooperation of her sexual partner.

As many researchers have noted, treatment of vaginismus does not always produce positive results using the in vivo or in vitro desensitization techniques. There are times when the clinician has to learn more about what is causing the problem. Sometimes the origin can be traced to sex-negative messages that the young girl received from her parents, her church, or her friends. When these are the etiological factors, the clinician needs to help the woman relearn positive information about sexuality. The therapist may need to "normalize" behaviors such as masturbation, premarital sex, consensual sexual explorations, and so on.

Sometimes, sexual abuse is the cause. Other times, genital trauma, such as intrusive and/or insensitive medical procedures, are the cause. More recently, clinicians are learning that it may be a reaction to vulvodynia (see the later section on dyspareunia), which is a very painful condition (Leiblum, 2000). When trauma is found to be the cause, approaches known to ameliorate the effects of trauma need to be used. As van der Kolk (2002) has pointed out, Eye Movement Desensitization and Reprocessing (EMDR) can be a very effective integrative psychotherapy tool.

Perhaps one of the most important reasons that some cases of vaginismus are difficult to treat is that the spasm-based definition of vaginismus may not be an adequate diagnostic marker. In 1999, Reissing et al. suggested that vaginismus should be considered a type of genital pain and that it should be described in terms of its quality, intensity, location, and time course. Later, Reissing et al. (2004) found that clinicians were unable to differentiate between vaginismus and dyspareunia resulting from vulvar vestibulitis syndrome. They suggested that the diagnosis needs to be changed to include a multidemensional reconceptualization of vaginismus so that the clinician must consider whether or not the woman presents with pain and fear of pain, pelvic floor dysfunction, and behavioral avoidance.

TREATMENT EXAMPLE OF VAGINISMUS*

A 25-year-old woman who was planning to be married in 2 months was referred for sex therapy by her gynecologist. Her gynecologist had attempted to do an exam but was unable to insert anything, even a swab, into the young woman's vagina. She was very distressed and fearful that she would not be able to have intercourse with her husband on her wedding night. She stated that she had "saved herself for the man she marries." She believed that sex was sinful outside of marriage. Her sexual history indicated that she was raised in an orthodox Christian faith and attended a Christian Academy. Her parents had severely punished any sexual behaviors of her or her siblings. When she was 16 years old, her mother saw her kiss a boyfriend and insisted that she never see the boy again, stating that the boy only wanted "one thing" from her and that he was not a "gentleman."

She had never had a gynecological exam because her mother did not think it was necessary, and she was told by her mother never to use tampons because she would no longer be a virgin if she did. When she went to college she resisted her parents' desire for her to attend a private school. That was her first "rebellious" act. After graduating from college she started medical school where she met her fiancé. She realized that she needed to have a gynecological exam but put it off until her fiancé put pressure on her to do so. Her sexual experience was limited to kissing and petting, but the petting did not include touching the inside of her vulva. She said that her fiancé would be very cooperative and helpful. He had assured her that he wanted to marry her whether or not she was able to have intercourse on the wedding night. He expressed confidence that she could overcome this problem.

The therapist decided that it would be important to the success of the treatment to explore with her what her own religious beliefs about sexuality were. She said that she was definitely more liberal than her parents, but that she shared their belief that sex should only be shared with the person to whom you are married. She felt that her parents' punishments of sexual behavior were inappropriate, but she was raised to be fearful of incurring her parents' wrath, so she complied with their dictates about sex.

During the therapy session she was instructed in progressive muscle relaxation which she was able to do very well. She was given a handout that had information about how to do Kegel exercises (see p. 321). Her assignment was to practice the muscle relaxation and Kegel exercises every day during the next week.

She reported success in learning how to relax and in isolating her vaginal muscles. The homework for the next week was to do the relaxation exercises, then tense and relax the vaginal muscles. When she felt very relaxed she was to use a handheld mirror to look at her vulva. At the next therapy session she said that she was ashamed to admit but it had been very difficult for her to look at her vulva. She was very surprised at herself, because as a medical student she had looked at many vulvas of other women. She realized that she felt very "disconnected" from her own body and could view other people's bodies in a detached "clinical" manner, thereby not needing to feel her real emotions about vulvas and vaginas.

She was asked to continue the relaxation exercises, but this time after she felt relaxed and started focusing on Kegel exercises she should try to insert a swab into the vagina as she released the tension in the vaginal muscles. At the next session, she was upset because she began to cry every time she tried to insert the swab. The therapist used EMDR and asked her to close her eyes and recall the experience of trying to insert the swab. She began to cry and explained that her thoughts had immediately gone to an experience during childhood when her mother had found her playing "doctor" with a friend and had held her hand under hot running water for a long time while yelling at her and telling her how dirty her mind and hands were.

---

* Names and identifying characteristics in all case examples have been changed to protect confidentiality.

After this very intense session she was able to do the assignment. She progressed to larger objects until she was able to insert a tampon. She was elated at this achievement. When it was time to move on to larger objects, her progress slowed a bit; however, she kept trying and eventually was able to insert a cucumber with a circumference slightly bigger than her (now) husband's penis. Although she was not able to allow penetration on her wedding night, she was able to enjoy her first intercourse 5 weeks after the wedding. One week before her first intercourse she was able to have her first gynecological exam.

Discussion of Case

This case had a very successful outcome because of the confluence of five key factors: (a) The client was very motivated to overcome her problem; (b) she was receptive to changing her cognitions about sexuality; (c) she was able to resolve childhood memories of abuse related to sexuality; (d) her fiancé/husband was respectful of her needs and cooperative with treatment; and (e) the symptom was not complicated, that is, there was no other pain syndrome.

As Leiblum (2000) pointed out, not all cases of vaginismus are successful. Many women who achieve their goal of being able to tolerate penetration continue to avoid intercourse. When this is the case the therapist may continue to probe to learn more information about the etiology of the avoidance symptoms. If the partner has not been a part of the therapy, he should be included at this point. The therapy may need to be redirected toward an emphasis on desire issues. With some couples the partner is willing to have intercourse only when the woman is willing. However, a partner with that much patience and understanding is not the usual case. Therefore, working toward an outcome that both partners can accept will mean that the therapist must be able to provide an "integrated" approach (as mentioned in the first contribution of this book; see section entitled "The Third Generation" on pp. 10-11). (For more information on an integrated approach to treatment, see "Additional Resources" on p. 117.) However, success is often difficult to achieve even when multiple dimensions of the problem are treated.

TREATMENT OF DYSPAREUNIA

As those of us who have treated women presenting with genital pain know, sometimes vaginismus is a secondary manifestation of the primary cause which was the experience of pain with penetration. The pain may be felt as soon as there is the slightest penetration, or it may be felt as penetration reaches part way into the vagina, or it may occur with deep penetration and/or thrusting. There are some medical conditions that can cause pain in midvagina which are easily diagnosed by a physician, such as trigonitis (inflammation which is confined to the mucous membrane of the openings of the ureters and the urethra of the bladder), cystitis (inflammation of the bladder, usually associated with urinary tract infections), and urethritis (inflammation of the urethra) (Kaufman, 1983). Likewise, there are many medical conditions that can cause pain with deep penetration and/or thrusting, such as endometriosis and pathology of the ovaries (Kaufman, 1983). Kaufman stated that pain on entry may be caused by dermatological conditions of the vulva, pathology of the glands near the vaginal opening (the Skene or Bartholin glands), or vaginismus.

Actually, as noted earlier in this contribution, there is so much overlap between the two diagnoses of dyspareunia and vaginismus that it is often difficult and perhaps impossible to make the distinction. Bergeron et al. (2003) proposed that the two diagnoses be dropped, not only because the differential diagnosis of the two is difficult, but because they feel it is not clear why painful genital sexual activity is even considered a sexual dysfunction. They point out that other pain syndromes may interfere with sexual activity, such as lower back pain. They also point to the fact that lower back pain is never referred to as work-related pain, even though it frequently is the cause of being unable to perform one's work. They assert that the International Association for the Study of Pain (IASP) has included vaginismus and dyspareunia in their classification of chronic pain.

These authors believe that most dyspareunia is caused by vulvar vestibulitis syndrome (VVS), which is a subtype of vulvodynia (painful vulva). VVS is characterized as a sharp pain located within and limited to the vulvar vestibule (vaginal entry) and elicited upon pressing or touching the vestibule of the vagina or attempted vaginal entry (Bergeron et al., 2002). They stressed the need for a multimodal approach to the therapy, a "biopsychosocial model" that includes organic, cognitive, affective, behavioral, and relationship factors. They believed that even though the source of the pain is a medical issue, the pain gives rise to many psychological and social problems as well.

Team Treatment Approach

Recently, some clinicians and research teams (Bergeron et al., 2003; Katz & Tabisel, 2002; Reissing et al., 1999, 2004) have advocated an approach to the treatment of vaginismus and dyspareunia that requires a team approach. An example of this method is outlined in the book *Private Pain: It's About Life, Not Just Sex . . . Understanding Vaginismus and Dyspareunia* by Katz and Tabisel (2002). They call their treatment the "DiRoss Treatment Approach." They describe it as a "hands-on, hands-in, hand-in-hand" approach. They believe that vaginismus is too complex to be treated at home. They believe that the insertion of dilators does not prepare the woman for "The Five Penetrations of Life": inserting a finger, an applicator, a tampon, having intercourse, and having a pelvic exam. Further, they maintain that relaxation exercises do not help because the symptom of vaginismus is a "fight-or-flight" reaction rather than just a response to stress. They also think that teaching a woman to strengthen the pelvic floor muscles is not helpful because "vaginismus is not about voluntary muscle control or about strengthening weak muscles, but rather about the involuntary muscle component of the pelvic floor, which is strong and tight because of its ongoing fight-or-flight activity" (p. 194). The treatment team includes a physician or physical therapist and a psychotherapist working together at the same time with the woman.

They believe that since vaginismus is a body-mind phenomenon, it has to be treated through both the mind and the body. This approach includes medical and psychological management and a strong emphasis on education of the woman about her body, myths and misconceptions about sexuality, and identifying and eradicating the negative coping mechanisms she has been using. The pelvic floor musculature and how it works is an important part of the education process.

Most of the clinicians who advocate this team approach acknowledge that it is impossible to have that kind of team available to all therapists. Therefore, they strongly urge mental health providers to work closely with a physician and/or physical therapist throughout the treatment process. The call for a multidisciplinary approach provides a breakthrough in the treatment of these very distressful pain conditions. However, most mental health professionals do not have ready access to other professionals or the facilities needed to accomplish this ideal approach to treatment. Therefore, every mental health practitioner who attempts to treat dyspareunia or vaginismus should be well informed regarding the medical management and the physical therapy techniques used to control the pain. They must also be willing and able to interface with those professionals and to make the effort to coordinate the treatment so that, when necessary, they are providing simultaneous treatments.

The assertion that most dyspareunia is caused by VVS may or may not be true. Perhaps the setting in which the woman presents for treatment may bias the perception of the etiology of this symptom. Speculatively, one might surmise from the literature that the cases presenting in the medical facilities where a multidisciplinary treatment team exists may have certain characteristics in common: patients may be very well educated; they may have access to the

Internet, which can direct them to those facilities; and they probably have insurance plans that can pay for the multiple providers necessary to access those treatment teams.

Private practice practitioners generally do not report their case outcomes for publication. Further, their failed cases may often become the cases that are eventually treated in the academic/hospital settings. The reported statistics from those treatment centers do not take into account the cases that are successfully treated by the individual practitioner. Clearly, there is a need for more research on the epidemiology of genital pain. There is also a need for more research on the successes and failures of the treatment of genital pain by private practitioners

Treatment Examples of Dyspareunia

Case Example #1

A tall, rather thin woman, age 35, was referred for psychological treatment of dyspareunia by her gynecologist. The gynecologist had diagnosed the problem about 3 months prior and had been seeing the patient two times per month. The treatment consisted of (a) very explicit education about the physiology and anatomy of the female genitals and sexual response; (b) pelvic floor exercises; and (c) gradual insertion of dilators. When the physician attempted to insert her fingers into the patient's vagina, the patient recoiled in pain and became tearful. Because penetration and dilation with the dilators had been successful, the physician was convinced that there must be some psychological issues related to penetration with a finger.

Although the patient was very motivated to eliminate the pain she experienced, she was unable to complete a detailed sex history form (see sample on pp. 308-315) that the therapist requested of her. She brought the form back to her second session and explained to the therapist that she had great difficulty as she tried to answer the questions. One reason was because she did not have very many memories about her childhood and early adolescent years; therefore, she could not answer some of the questions about those years. She also became very anxious, almost to the point of a panic attack, when she had tried to answer those questions about which she did have memory. She could not explain her reactions and felt very inadequate to have to admit that she could not do such a "simple" task.

The patient was asked to try to answer the questions while wearing an EMDR audio-scan (a device developed by Neurotek). As they went through the questions together over the next three sessions, the patient began to recall events from her past that she had not been able to remember before. The memories of events were generated by the patient without being "led" by the therapist. The memories were usually just informational, but a few were very painful. On a number of occasions she had watched her mother, who had an eating disorder, put her finger down her throat and vomit. This memory elicited much emotion. As she began to talk about this memory, she realized that her mother had done this to her.

When she was about 12 years old her mother began to "badger" her about her weight. Her mother believed that she was too chubby and that boys would never like her if she didn't start paying more attention to her appearance. Whenever she was "caught" eating something that her mother thought was fattening, her mother would take her in the bathroom and insert her finger down her throat to make her vomit. This continued with her mother inducing vomiting or her mother making her do it until she was able to leave home to go to college at age 17. She did not continue this behavior after she left home.

She said that she was a very compliant child until she went to college. Once away from her mother's control, she became rebellious. She ate whatever she wanted and soon found that she could eat without gaining weight. She became sexually involved with most of the men she dated. She did not have any problems having sexual intercourse until she became engaged to "the man of my dreams." They met 3 years ago and had a very enjoyable sex life until he proposed to her. She stated that it happened "overnight." One day she was able to have intercourse and thoroughly enjoy it, the next day he proposed and the next day she experienced horrible pain when they tried to make love. She sought help from her gynecologist when her fiancé told her that he did not want to get married until the problem was solved.

Regaining the memories of the abuse from her mother enabled the patient to deal with her anxiety related to penetration. She was able to verbalize the connection between the forced penetration of her throat with her fear that if she allowed anyone to have "control" of her in a committed relationship, that person could also force penetration of her body. She worked with the therapist to desensitize her fears and was able to allow her gynecologist to insert a finger and then to have a complete gynocological exam.

Her partner joined in the treatment. They were given homework exercises that enabled in vivo desensitization to being penetrated. She faithfully practiced the pelvic floor exercises and the breathing techniques that she learned in sessions with both her gynecologist and her therapist. Soon she was able to insert her own finger into her vagina with her partner present. Then she was able to guide her partner's finger into her vagina. When she was comfortable with digital penetration, she was able to insert a dildo that was about the size of her partner's penis. Then she guided her partner while he inserted the dildo. When she was comfortable with the dildo being inserted, she was able to allow vaginal containment of her husband's penis as she guided the penetration. Finally, she was able to let her partner guide the penetration.

During the last few sessions of the psychological treatment the focus was on helping the couple learn to enjoy their sex life again and dealing with fears that they both expressed that the symptom may return. They were given advice about how to deal with a situation if pain should recur; that is, taking a break, focusing on the pelvic floor muscles, breathing with the tensing and releasing of the muscles, and allowing her to control the speed and timing of penetration.

Case Discussion. This was a successful case because this patient was motivated and trusting enough to allow her gynecologist to work with her on the medical/physical issues. She was also trusting of the therapist and willing to try EMDR even though she was very frightened of what she might feel if she tried to answer the questions on the sex history form. This case illustrates how abuse other than sexual abuse can be the etiological factor for a sexual dysfunction. It also demonstrates the major goals of therapeutic interventions as stated by Binik et al. (2000): (a) reducing or controlling the pain; (b) dealing with the negative consequences of having experienced the pain; and (c) reestablishing a pleasurable sex life.

This case was not difficult to treat because the referring gynecologist had already begun the treatment and elicited the trust and hope from the patient that helped to motivate her to work hard. There are times, however, when a patient comes to the office of a mental health practitioner only to appease her partner and never having sought treatment from any other caregiver. The reluctant patient is always a challenge. She is a particular challenge when the issue is something as personal and embarrassing as sexuality.

Case Example #2

This client was a 38-year-old, sullen and reluctant woman who presented for therapy with her husband. He called to make the appointment and informed the therapist that he may have to come alone because he was not sure that his wife would come with him. She came but announced almost immediately that she was there only because she felt that her husband would be angry if she did not come. He stated that they had been married for 5 years. This was her first marriage and his second. He had left his first marriage because his wife of 3 years had an affair. They had no children but he desperately wanted a child. They were unable to have intercourse very often because she had what she described as excruciating pain whenever he tried to penetrate her.

She was very outspoken about being angry with him for forcing her to be humiliated by talking to someone about this problem. She considered it to be a problem mostly for him because she was happy with the sex that they could have. She was able to enjoy some forms of stimulation sometimes. However, there were certain times when she felt pain even at the slightest touch to her genital area. She believed that her husband was inconsiderate because he did not accept the fact that her pain was "natural."

When questioned about her belief that her pain was "natural," she said that her mother told her that all women have pain when they have intercourse and that you learn to "grin and bear it." Her mother's prediction of pain with intercourse was confirmed by two of her high school girlfriends, who told her that they had bled when they had intercourse and that it hurt. The couple was asked to fill out a sex history questionnaire and return the following week to individual sessions where the therapist would review the questionnaire with them. The woman returned with her questionnaire minimally filled out with "yes" and "no" responses to all questions, even to those that obviously required more. She said that she thought that this whole process was ridiculous and did not see what anyone could do to change the "way things are."

Her history revealed that she had had intercourse with only one other partner prior to her husband. The first intercourse had been painful, as she knew it would be. She was in love with her partner and felt that the pain was worth it until she learned that she had genital warts. Her physician informed her that this was a sexually transmitted disease (STD), and, since she had never had sex with anyone other than that partner, she knew that he had had sex with someone else while they were dating. She ended the relationship and vowed never to have sex again until she was married.

The therapist asked her to do a test at home by taking a cotton swab and touch the vulvar area with it. She reported that the touch with the cotton swab had felt painful. She was asked then to go to see a gynecologist who was known to have expertise in working with patients with sexual problems. The gynecological exam indicated that the patient probably had vulvadynia, perhaps VVS. When the patient heard this diagnosis she felt justified about her pain and angrier with her husband for seeming not to understand her pain.

She was encouraged to pay attention to the timing of the pain throughout an entire menstrual cycle. She learned that the pain was most severe during the time that she was ovulating. This presented a major obstacle to conception and increased her husband's despair about ever having a child. At this point the couple and the therapist determined that they needed to work out a comprehensive treatment approach that would necessitate each of them being totally honest about what they wanted in the relationship. They learned that they both wanted a child, but she was afraid of the potential pain involved in conceiving and in giving birth. They both wanted to have a fulfilling sex life, but she could not imagine sex not being painful. After two sessions during which the therapist educated both partners about the physiology and anatomy of sexuality, the myths and facts about pain with first intercourse, and emphasizing the pleasures of sexuality, the woman was able to express hope that she could cope with and minimize her expectations of pain.

They decided to work to learn to control the pain. She eventually was able to have intercourse occasionally without pain. They decided to consult their physician about using artificial insemination if they could not have intercourse during ovulation. After making that decision, she found that she was able to have intercourse and endure the pain during one of the days when she would be fertile in her cycle. At termination of the treatment they were not pregnant yet but they were happy with their sexual relationship.

Case Discussion. This case was very interesting in that it was never clear whether or not the woman had VVS. Because she had been infected with an STD, one could hypothesize that her knowledge that sexual intercourse caused the STD created the pain, and, therefore, that the pain was psychosomatic. It is also possible that the STD was the physical etiology of the VVS. It was clear that she developed many fears about sexual penetration as a young woman and those fears were confirmed for her. The therapy helped this couple to learn what their priorities were and how to achieve them together. It helped them to master the pain together instead of struggling against it and each other.

CONCLUSION

Genital pain is perhaps the most disconcerting type of sexual problem that mental health professionals must confront. Accurate assessment and evaluation are critical to successful treatment. However, both are very challenging even for seasoned clinicians and even after good assessment it is difficult to predict. Most patients come to the therapist with a history of failed previous treatments that leave them feeling hopeless and inadequate. Etiology includes negative sexual messages as a child and young adolescent, to sexual abuse, emotional abuse, medical traumas, relationship dysfunction, personal psychopathology, anger with the spouse, and so forth. It can lead to other sexual problems such as loss of desire, loss of ability to have orgasm, loss of ability to lubricate, and sexual avoidance, all of which further complicate the treatment.

It is the successes that sex therapists have with these cases that keep them hopeful and motivate them to keep studying and learning new theories and treatment techniques. Perhaps because there are so many causes of genital pain, there are many treatment approaches that bring at least some relief to many patients. Hopefully, sexologists will continue to do the research that will provide the answers needed for women who are desperately looking for resolution to their complaints of genital pain.

CONTRIBUTOR

Jill W. Bley, PhD, is a clinical psychologist. She is certified by the American Association of Sexuality Educators, Counselors, and Therapists as both a sex therapist and a supervisor. She taught sex therapy to graduate students in clinical psychology at the University of Cincinnati. During that time she trained and supervised many students. Dr. Bley wrote a syndicated column, "Speaking of Sex," which appeared in some downtown newspapers. Her columns addressed the diverse issues related to human sexuality. She is a founder of Women Helping Women/Rape Crisis Center and a Sex Therapy Clinic, both in Cincinnati. She has lectured extensively on topics of sexuality. Dr. Bley is a Volunteer Associate Professor in the Department of Psychiatry University of Cincinnati Medical Center. Dr. Bley may be contacted at 750 Red Bud Avenue, Cincinnati, OH 45229. E-mail: drjillbley@cinci.rr.com

RESOURCES

Cited Resources

American Psychiatric Association. (1994). *Diagnostic and Statistical Manual of Mental Disorders* (4th ed.). Washington, DC: Author.

Barbach, L. G. (1975). *For Yourself: The Fulfillment of Female Sexuality*. New York: Doubleday.

Barbach, L. G. (1980). *Women Discover Orgasm: A Therapist's Guide to a New Treatment Approach*. New York: Free Press.

Bergeron, S., Brown, C., Lord, M., Oala, M., Binik, Y., & Khalife, S. (2002). Physical therapy for vulvar vestibulitis syndrome: A retrospective study. *Journal of Sex and Marital Therapy, 28*(3), 183-192.

Bergeron, S., Meana, M., Binik, Y., & Khalife, S. (2003). Painful genital sexual activity. In S. B. Levine, C. R. Risen, & S. E. Althof (Eds.), *Handbook of Clinical Sexuality for Mental Health Professionals* (pp. 131-152). New York: Brunner-Routledge.

Binik, Y. M., Bergeron, S., & Khalife, S. (2000). Dyspareunia. In S. R. Leiblum & R. C. Rosen (Eds.), *Principles and Practice of Sex Therapy* (3rd ed., pp. 154-180). New York: Guilford.

Fuchs, D., Hoch, Z., Paldi, E., Abramovici, H., Brandes, J. M., Timor-Tritsch, I., & Kleinhaus, M. (1978). Hypnodesensitization therapy of vaginismus: In vitro and in vivo methods. In J. LoPiccolo & L. LoPiccolo (Eds.), *Handbook of Sex Therapy* (pp. 261-270). New York: Plenum Press.

Heiman, J., & LoPiccolo, J. (1988). *Becoming Orgasmic: A Sexual and Personal Growth Program for Women*. New York: Prentice Hill.

Kaplan, H. S. (1974). *The New Sex Therapy*. New York: Brunner/Mazel.

Kaplan, H. S. (1983). *The Evaluation of Sexual Disorders: Psychological and Medical Aspects*. New York: Brunner/Mazel.

Katz, D., & Tabisel, R. L. (2002). *Private Pain: It's About Life, Not Just Sex . . . Understanding Vaginismus and Dyspareunia*. Winnipeg: Kromar Printing Ltd.

Kaufman, S. (1983). The gynecological evaluation of female dyspareunia & unconsummated marriage. In H. S. Kaplan (Ed.), *The Evaluation of Sexual Disorders: Psychological and Medical Aspects* (pp. 128-138). New York: Brunner/Mazel.

Kegel, A. (1948). Progressive exercise in the functional restoration of the perineal muscles. *American Journal of Obstetrics and Gynecology, 56*, 238-248.

Lauman, E., Gagnon, J., Michael, R., & Michaels, S. (1994). *The Social Organization of Sexuality: Sexuality Practices in the United States*. Chicago: University of Chicago Press.

Leiblum, S. R. (2000). Vaginismus: A Most Perplexing Problem. In S. R. Leiblum & R. C. Rosen (Eds.), *Principles and Practices of Sex Therapy* (3rd ed., pp. 181-202). New York: Guilford.

Masters, W. H., & Johnson, V. E. (1966). *Human Sexual Response*. Boston: Little, Brown.

Masters, W. H., & Johnson, V. E. (1970). *Human Sexual Inadequacy*. Boston: Little, Brown.

Reissing, E., Binik, Y., & Khalife, S. (1999). Does vaginismus exist?: A critical review of the literature. *Journal of Nervous and Mental Disease, 187*, 261-274.

Reissing, E., Binik, Y., Khalife, S., Cohen, D., & Amsel, R. (2004). Vaginal spasm, pain, and behavior: An empirical investigation of the diagnosis of vaginismus. *Archives of Sexual Behavior, 33*(1), 5-17.

Schoen, M. (Producer), & Nathanson, B. (Director). (1984). *Treating Vaginismus* [Video]. New York: Focus International.

van der Kolk, B. A. (2002). Beyond the talking cure: Somatic experience and subcortical imprints in the treatment of trauma. In F. Shapiro (Ed.), *EMDR as an Integrative Psychotherapy Approach: Experts of Diverse Orientations Explore the Paradigm Prism* (pp. 57-85). Washington, DC: American Psychological Association.

Additional Resources

Love, P., & Robinson, J. (1990). *The Emotional Incest Syndrome: What to Do When a Parent's Love Rules Your Life*. New York: Bantam Books.

Pridal, C., & LoPiccolo, J. (2000). Multi-element treatment of desire disorders: Integration of cognitive, behavioral and systemic therapy. In S. Leiblum & R. Rosen (Eds.), *Principles and Practice of Sex Therapy* (3rd ed., pp. 57-81). New York: Guilford.

Schnarch, D. M. (1991). *Constructing the Sexual Crucible: An Integration of Sexual and Marital Therapy*. New York: W. W. Norton.

Weeks, G. R. (2005). The emergence of a new paradigm in sex therapy: Integration. *Sexual and Relationship Therapy, 20*(1) 89-103.

Assessment and Treatment Of Erection Dysfunction

Frederick L. Peterson, Jr. and Donald E. Fuerst

Perhaps no other area of sex health has changed so rapidly and dramatically as has the treatment of erection dysfunction (ED) over the last decade. At a 1993 Consensus Conference on Impotence at the National Institutes of Health (NIH), the term "impotence" was declared obsolete in favor of the more neutral as well as precise term "erection dysfunction." ED is defined as the inability to achieve or maintain an erection of sufficient rigidity and duration to permit satisfactory sexual performance (NIH Consensus Development Panel on Impotence, 1993). According to the *Diagnostic and Statistical Manual of Mental Disorders* (*DSM-IV-TR*; American Psychiatric Association, [APA], 2000), it must have been a continuing problem for at least 6 months and caused distress to the individual man or his partner. There are many men who do not have erections, do not have sexual intercourse, and do not have ED because they and their partners do not define it as a problem.

The goal of this contribution is to help mental health professionals develop a better understanding of how to respond to clients who complain of ED from the context of the multidisciplinary field of sex health. To meet this objective, erection function as well as dysfunction, a best practice assessment approach, and empirically based treatment options will be reviewed. Because there are few published research studies on homosexual men with ED, this contribution discusses the assessment and treatment of heterosexual men with ED, although many, if not most, of the interventions would likely be effective with men of any sexual orientation. Three clinical vignettes are included to illustrate key principles and practices.

This contribution is intended to provide an intermediate level of understanding for the assessment and treatment of ED, because providing all information needed for proficiency in treating ED is well beyond the scope of this contribution. Mental health professionals who wish to pursue advanced skills in sex therapy are encouraged to join the membership of the American Association of Sexuality Educators, Counselors, and Therapists (ASSECT), which is an accrediting body offering four levels of certification of practice. The advantages of pursuing AASECT certification and the process of developing a sexual health component to one's mental health practice was recently described by Peterson and Bley (2005).

INTRODUCTION TO ERECTION FUNCTION AND DYSFUNCTION

To better understand how the various physical and psychological factors affect erections, it is important to be aware of the many processes that take place before, during, and after sexual tumescence begins. Under the right circumstances a desire for sexual activity precedes physical arousal. Desire is influenced by both physical and psychological factors. The physical factors include adequate testosterone levels, medications, and the absence of other disease states or impairments. Assuming these factors are in balance, the message has to get from the brain to the penis by way of the nervous system.

When the neural message arrives, the arteries start to dilate and more blood flows into erectile tissue in the penis (primarily the corpora cavernosa). Erection is accomplished by the release of nitric oxide that, in turn, causes the production of a chemical (cGMP). cGMP relaxes the smooth muscle in the corpora cavernosa so that the penis becomes tumescent and rigid. As the penis fills with blood, the venous system becomes compressed; this allows increased pressure to take place, giving the penis the rigidity needed for penetration. Normally, there is an enzyme (PDE5 inhibitor) that breaks down the cGMP, allowing the smooth muscle to contract and decrease the blood flow into the penis (which ends the erection). Once orgasm has occurred, the arteries constrict, the veins open up, and the erection subsides. This description represents the current understanding of the multiple factors involved in erectile function.

One of the best recent prevalence studies on ED was conducted in 1992 by the National Health and Social Life Survey (NHSLS) and consisted of a national probability sample of 1,410 men aged 18 to 59. The NHSLS estimated a point prevalence of approximately 5% and a lifetime prevalence of approximately 10% (Laumann, Paik, & Rosen, 1999).

The Massachusetts Male Aging Study (MMAS), a large longitudinal study following men aged 40 to 70, reported findings consistent with the NHSLS. The MMAS found 10% of that sample having "complete impotence" and approximately 35% reporting "moderate to complete erectile dysfunction" (Feldman et al., 1994). If considering any level of erectile functioning (even mild and temporary), then the prevalence increases to 52% (Feldman et al., 1994). These studies and others demonstrate a consistent association between aging and erectile dysfunction for men. In general, the incidence and severity of ED increase as men age and are also affected by men's health status (Laumann et al., 1999; Masters, Johnson, & Kolodny, 1995).

Traditional approaches to understanding ED emphasized a division between two types of ED based on causality: physical (often called "organic") or psychological. Physical causes include pharmacological (such as use of antihypertensives), endocrinologic (diabetes), or neurologic (spinal cord injury) factors; lifestyle choices (e.g., smoking); or penile disease or trauma. Psychological risk factors for ED include sexual trauma history, depression, anxiety, guilt, or having significant conflict with one's sexual partner.

An integrated systems perspective has evolved which views the division of causal factors into "physical or psychological" as artificial and not reflecting the true nature of the client's experience. Although identification of the contributing factors to ED is paramount, most cases of ED have a multicausal etiology ("mixed etiology"), and causal factors often have reciprocal influences upon one another. For example, a significant percentage of men who develop diabetes mellitus will experience some level of erectile dysfunction. A man who has a predisposition for developing diabetes and who also has clinical depression may engage in behaviors that facilitate the development of diabetes, such as not exercising, failing to follow a healthy diet, abusing alcohol to self-medicate, and becoming obese. Once the diabetes becomes severe enough to cause ED, he may become more depressed, develop marital discord, and experience heightened anxiety when his partner leaves him. In such cases, patient satisfaction and outcome may be improved with counseling even when the ED is secondary to a medical condition or mixed etiology (American Association of Clinical Endocrinologists [AACE], 1998; NIH, 1993).

Clinical Vignette: Young Married Man With Erection Dysfunction*

This clinical vignette involves a heterosexual couple in their 30s, Jill and Dave (pseudonyms). They were a handsome pair of DINKS (Double-Income professionals with No Children). They sought sex therapy for Dave's erection dysfunction (ED), which was secondary

---

* Names and identifying characteristics in all case examples have been changed to protect privacy.

to injuries sustained in a motor vehicle accident. They had previously worked with a sex therapist to address communication issues as a young married couple, build sexual literacy, and get assistance dealing with the ED. They described the therapy as beneficial but short-lived, as the couple relocated from California to a mid-sized city in the Midwest.

Dave reported a history of normal erectile function before his injury at age 26. Immediately after his accident, he was fortunate enough to receive care at an excellent medical center that included sexual health as part of his rehabilitation. The professionals initially worked with him on understanding the specific injuries he suffered as a result of pelvic bone splintering into his vascular system and the subsequent scar tissue that developed from surgical removal of the bone. The physician started Dave on a first-line treatment of a vacuum constriction device (VCD, also known as the penile pump), which he found satisfactory in terms of helping him get and maintain erections suitable for intercourse. Dave was referred for outpatient follow-up to a psychologist who had specialized competence in sex therapy. As mentioned, the couple worked with their first therapist regarding sexual health literacy in general and specifically about the issues and myths about erection dysfunction. Dave wanted to try other treatment options as the couple found the VCD somewhat cumbersome and an interference with the natural flow of their foreplay.

Dave was started on a 50 mg dose of sildenafil citrate (Viagra) but without effect. He reported some improvement when using 100 mg, the maximum dosage for a 24-hour period. He denied any significant side effects that were not tolerable. He recalled moving from a satisfaction rating of about "40" for getting and keeping erections to about "60 to 70" with the pharmacological aid of Viagra. The couple was able to have sexual intercourse on a more regular basis, but Dave still was not satisfied with the level of firmness or rigidity of his erections.

When the couple started with their second sex therapist (the first author), Jill's response to Dave's improved sexual function became a focus of therapy, especially her ambivalent affective response to having sexual relations with Dave. It was obvious that Jill dearly loved her husband and that she was willing to do about anything sexually to please him. At the same time, she was experiencing mild to moderate feelings of discomfort and, on occasion, disgust when engaged sexually with him.

Jill denied any sexual trauma history or any lapse in her memory of childhood. Jill slowly started to identify aspects of her socialization as a female, especially messages from her parents about sex, which contributed to her adverse visceral response to sex. She always thought that "sex and I are not a good match" and that her negative feelings about sex were part of her biology; that she simply did not like sex like other people did. Some individual counseling to supplement the couple's sex therapy helped her come to an understanding that it was her socialization that was contributing to her negative visceral response. She literally described an "epiphany experience" that this realization facilitated, and almost immediately she reported feeling empowered in minimizing and eventually eliminating her negative visceral response to her own sexuality as well as sexual intercourse with Dave.

Dave wanted to explore enhancing his sexual relations with Jill. The personal growth Jill experienced in terms of fulfilling more of her own sexual health potential opened up the possibilities for further developing their sexual life together. Jill reported less frequent negative feelings, and she started initiating sexual relations. Dave felt his sexual initiatives were more often welcomed by Jill, and he was more comfortable exploring other treatment options for his ED. After reviewing patient health education videos regarding second-line treatment options, Dave consulted with his urologist regarding injection therapy. Using the product Caverject, Dave found a double benefit over his use of Viagra. First, he reported an increase in the rigidity of his erections. Secondly, Dave reported increased consistency (reliability) of getting and keeping erections (from "60-70" to "80+") as well as some increase in the lasting duration of erections.

THE ASSESSMENT PROCESS FOR ERECTION FUNCTION

The comprehensive assessment of ED is a complex process which requires multidisciplinary input and review. This integrated, multidisciplinary approach is reflected in what Fagan (2003) refers to as "the perspectives," evaluating client data from disease, dimension, behavior, and life story points of view. This section informs mental health professionals of their role in this process and what to consider from the perspective of other disciplines. Comprehensive assessment includes a review of presenting complaints and the couple's expectations (including desired outcomes), psychosexual history, substance uses, standardized measurement of the severity of ED, psychological assessment of personality factors if indicated (depression), and medical examination/measurement if there is indication of medical conditions/factors contributing to the presenting complaint. Determining if the patient is clinically depressed, has a sexual trauma history, experiences anxiety and/or guilt regarding sex, or reports partner conflict are also key factors in the assessment of ED.

Assessment of ED, unless it is solely of psychogenic etiology, usually requires multiple sessions. Single-session assessment of ED by mental health professionals usually is not effective unless it is an extended-time single session (2-4 hours) and/or a low-complexity case, such as performance anxiety as the sole causal factor. Moderate- to high-complexity cases usually require multiple sessions to allow detailed developmental histories to be taken from both individuals and conferring with other healthcare providers for medical evaluations.

It is recommended that the assessment process comprise two to three assessment sessions followed by a results-sharing conference. If multiple-session assessment is to occur, this structure is best communicated to a client prior to the first face-to-face meeting. Multiple-session assessment allows more time for an in-depth evaluation of the client's medical, social, and psychosexual history. Because there is an emphasis on the relationship as well as the dysfunction in sex therapy, both the identified client and his partner should be involved in the assessment, including individual assessment without the other present. A sexual development history should be completed with both the male client and his partner. With heterosexual couples, this individual time allows for his, her, and their view of the problem to be explored.

The psychosexual history and interview are important to include with every client (NIH, 1993). A family-of-origin review, how the client learned about sex, family rules about communicating about sex, masturbatory history, first sexual contacts (same and opposite sex as well as animal contacts), sexual functioning with principle sexual partners, extramarital affairs, frequency of naturally occurring erections, and previous experiences with ED and what has been tried to resolve it should be included in the psychosocial history. Although standardized self-report instruments (discussed later) also measure severity of the ED, comparing both partners' subjective estimates on specific behavioral elements of ED (i.e., percentage of time attempts at intercourse are unsuccessful, time before erection is lost) is recommended. The content and frequency of current sexual fantasies should be explored to determine the degree of confluence between fantasy life and behavioral sexual expression.

It is important to note that most complaints of not achieving or maintaining erections suitable for intercourse lend themselves to the diagnosis of ED, and it is a matter of assessing the level of severity. Clients do anxiously present with situational erectile difficulties that are transient in nature, such as not achieving an erection after heavy use of alcohol, a day of strenuous exercise resulting in fatigue, or being with a new sexual partner. At times, these clients do not meet the duration criteria for a diagnosis of ED, and spontaneous remission often occurs.

Standardized self-report measures have an important role in assessing the complaints of ED and moving from presenting complaints to a diagnosis. Highly recommended is the

International Index of Erectile Functioning (IIEF), a 15-item, self-administered scale useful as one evaluation strategy in a comprehensive assessment of ED (see sample on pp. 288-289). The scale has been normed cross-culturally (10 languages), is psychometrically sound with high reliability and validity, and demonstrates sensitivity and specificity for detecting changes in erectile functioning (Rosen et al., 1997).

Assessment of Psychological Etiological Factors in Erection Dysfunction

The objective of this section is to describe the process of evaluating five psychological factors associated with ED. A patient may be in need of sex therapy when there is coexisting concern that the patient is clinically depressed, has a sexual trauma history, experiences anxiety and/or guilt regarding sex, or reports conflict with his partner. Findings from further evaluation of these risk factors may lead to an array of psychosexual interventions designed to achieve symptom relief and allow the patient to enjoy his optimal level of sexual health.

There are six questions useful to mental health professionals related to screening patients for psychological risk factors for ED. The first two questions indicate further in-depth evaluation if answered in the affirmative. These questions are (a) Do you have naturally occurring erections in the morning, and can you get an erection by yourself (via masturbation)? and (b) Have you ever been sexually molested or sexually assaulted, either as a child or as an adult?

The last four questions are answered on the following 4-point scale: 0 = no, not at all; 1 = yes, seldom; 2 = yes, quite a bit; 3 = yes, frequently. An answer of "2" or "3" on any of these four questions indicates further evaluation and possible treatment. These four questions are (a) Do you feel depressed? (b) Do you feel nervous or anxious regarding sex? (c) Do you feel guilty regarding sex? and (d) Do you have significant conflict with your partner regarding sex?

A client's report of regularly waking up in the mornings with an erection is usually, but not always, a sign that the patient has normal neurologic and vascular function. This information is often used to indicate that complaints of ED have a psychogenic basis. Be aware that self-reports are not always reliable; nocturnal penile tumescence and rigidity (NPTR) testing is still recommended by some authorities (Montague, 1998). Additionally, those who oppose NPTR testing argue that sleep erections may be different in their causal mechanisms from erections occurring in response to sexual stimulation (Montague, 1998). If the patient reports morning erections and reports that he is able to masturbate to satisfaction (able to get and maintain erection, and experience orgasm and ejaculation), then it is highly likely there is a psychogenic basis to his complaints of ED when he is with his partner.

If the patient has a sexual abuse history, a careful evaluation of the trauma nature and severity is in order. Sexual dysfunction may be a long-term sequela of sexual trauma. Male victims of adult-child sexual contact are three times more likely to experience erectile dysfunction as men, especially if the patient had a female perpetrator and/or the patient is engaging in sexual activity similar in nature to the original sexual abuse.

If it is found that sexual trauma is related to the complaints of ED, then intensive psychotherapy focusing upon trauma resolution is indicated. The process of trauma resolution may be short- or long-term, depending upon the complexity of the case. Factors that increase case complexity include younger age at onset of the abuse, longer duration of the abuse, greater number of perpetrators, and degree of force and violence used. Male survivors who experienced mild to moderate levels of severity of the latter three factors are likely to find ways to feel safe and overcome the ED, provided that they have an understanding partner willing to participate in the therapy process. Severe degrees of these factors indicate a poor prognosis for overcoming ED. However, it is to be understood that sexual trauma by itself may not be related to the presenting complaint of ED and may not require psychotherapy focused on resolution of trauma issues.

Because a patient's complaint of ED may be related to depression, a standardized screening for depression is recommended, such as the Beck Depression Inventory (BDI; Beck, Steer, & Brown, 1996). BDI scores of 1 to 10 indicate a normal range of affect, but a score of 22+ indicates a severe level of depression, which likely needs treatment to resolve. Care should be taken not to exacerbate complaints of ED by prescribing antidepressants, which may further suppress erectile response (Beck et al., 1996).

Commonly, anxiety or guilt may serve as psychogenic obstacles to erectile response. The patient's anxiety may be more specifically related to sex and is frequently referred to as "performance anxiety," concerning whether he will be able to get and maintain an erection when with his partner. Guilt related to sex is most often associated with strict religious training that typically has a specific view of sexuality as something a man does only for procreation and within the confines of marriage. Men who have been widowed sometimes have transient experience with ED when they start dating again. The same is true for some men who have extramarital affairs or during and after a divorce.

Anger and resentment between the couple may be expressed sexually by avoidance of sexual relations, sometimes perceived as punishment by one individual. These perceptions often manifest in the history, especially when interviewing each person individually. If significant relationship conflict does exist, it needs to be resolved at least to a point where the couple mutually desires and is ready for physical intimacy.

Assessment of Substance Use Etiological Factors in Erection Dysfunction

Sometimes referred to as a "lifestyle factor," substance use should always be a part of the assessment of ED. Patients should usually be referred for specialty treatment when they have an addiction to alcohol, tobacco, or illegal drugs, which have adverse effects on erectile functioning. Addictions to substances, whether legal (alcohol and tobacco) or illegal (amphetamines, cocaine, heroin, marijuana, morphine, or steroids) represent risk factors for ED. These six illicit drugs are listed because they have been found to have adverse effects on erectile response (Kolodny, 1985; Process of Care Panel of the University of Medicine and Dentistry, New Jersey, 1998; Wilson, 1988).

As tobacco use is a significant risk factor for ED (Shabsigh et al., 1991), all patients should be assessed for their use of tobacco products (not just cigarettes). All patients who are smoking should be referred to an intensive smoking cessation program if cessation efforts fail in the primary care or private practice setting (AACE, 1998; Agency for Health Care Policy and Research [AHCPR], 1996). Addressing clients' smoking status and assisting them to be tobacco free is within the professional role of psychologists (Wetter et al., 1998) and psychiatrists (APA, 1996). This is true for all clients, not just those complaining of ED, as smoking is widely considered the number one preventable cause of premature disability and death in the United States (AHCPR, 1996).

Patients with addictions to alcohol and/or drugs should be referred for further assessment and treatment to a polysubstance abuse program (Masters et al., 1995; NIH, 1993). There are four questions useful to mental health professionals for screening patients for addictions as risk factors associated with ED. These questions are referred to as the "CAGE" assessment and are often used to differentiate between social drinking and alcoholism (Fagan, 2003; Peterson, 2000). The four CAGE questions are as follows:

1. C – Have you thought you should CUT down on your drug use?
2. A – Have you been ANNOYED recently about being criticized for your drug use?
3. G – Have you felt GUILTY about your drug use?
4. E – Do you need an EYE OPENER in the morning by using your drug to get going?

Assessment of Medical Etiological Factors in Erection Dysfunction

When assessing ED, it is important for mental health professionals to have at least some basic understanding of medical and laboratory aspects of the patient's condition. That way, they can work better with the medical provider in assessing and treating the patient. There are basically five etiologic categories to be evaluated in assessing a patient with ED: (a) hormonal, (b) vascular, (c) neurological, (d) anatomical, and (e) psychological. In almost all cases, there is more than one etiological category involved. For example, diabetes can affect the hormonal balance, vascular supply, and nerve supply to the penis. In addition, there is usually an overlying psychological component, most often depression.

Clients often ask mental health providers about the relationship between testosterone and libido. It is important to note that a history of decreased libido does not predict low testosterone (Govier, McClure, & Kramer-Levien, 1996) and that low testosterone is found to be a contributing factor for ED in as few as 3% to 6% of cases (Buvat & Lemaire, 1997; Heaton, 1998). Unfortunately, there is not a standardized laboratory panel that is widely accepted to evaluate ED. NIH recommends a moderate work-up with measurement of testosterone in all patients, and serum prolactin, complete blood count, urinalysis, creatinine, fasting lipid profile, fasting blood sugar, and thyroid function testing in many patients (Department of Veterans Affairs [DVA], 1999; NIH, 1993).

Specialized medical testing is sometimes used in the diagnosis of ED. Mental health professionals should be aware that these diagnostic measures exist and are sometimes recommended by medical providers: nocturnal penile tumescence (NPT) testing, nocturnal penile tumescence and rigidity (NPTR) testing, test injections of vasodilators, cavernosometry, cavernosography, and duplex ultrasonography (especially color duplex Doppler ultrasound [CDDU]). For detailed information, readers are referred to Broderick (1998) and Montague (1998). NPTR and other specialized testing are being used less often with the shift to primary care management of ED (Peterson, 2000; Rosen, 2003). Mental health professionals do not need to understand these procedures in detail but should be aware of them in order to engage in discussions of the results with medical specialists.

Ending the Assessment With a Results-Sharing Conference

Once all assessment information is collected, a results-sharing conference should conclude the assessment process. A results-sharing conference includes at least three elements. First, the therapist should share the results of standardized measures and summarize what he or she has learned about the client from all sources (interviews, psychological testing, medical and lab reports, and reports from previous therapists). Second, the therapist should share the conclusions drawn from this information. Here the client should be told the diagnosis, the type of ED (mixed, organic, psychogenic), any other disorders found (such as depression), and severity of the ED. Finally, recommendations should be shared which are likely to lead to resolution of ED. The results, conclusions, and recommendations may be shared with the couple in written form as a draft treatment plan (see "Sharing the Treatment Plan for Sex Therapy" on pp. 301-306). The draft treatment plan outlines key elements of the assessment, desired treatment outcomes, specific treatment goals, recommended treatment strategies to assist the couple in achieving their goals (inclusive of appropriate patient education on sexual health), evaluative criteria (by which clients will know progress is being made and a treatment end point is defined), and their client rights and responsibilities, which include all obligatory information to be shared with clients via professional ethics.

TREATMENT STRATEGIES FOR ERECTION DYSFUNCTION

Treatment of ED should always be based upon a foundation of a comprehensive assessment and adequate patient education. Whether this patient education is integrated into the assessment process (sometimes as part of the results sharing) or as part of the treatment process (more commonly) varies according to healthcare setting and provider. Recommended components of patient education for couples seeking professional help for ED include the following: typical communication and relationship strains that couples experience when dealing with ED, anatomy and physiology of male and female sexual response, causes and types of ED, and all treatment options for ED whether or not that particular healthcare setting provides all treatment options.

There are several considerations that guide the selection of treatment for ED. The first question the provider should ask is if there is sufficient severity and duration of the problem to require treatment. Most times the answer will be in the affirmative. Occasionally, couples will seek out your assistance about their concerns, yet they are within a normal range of functioning or may have a mild level of severity. Appropriate interventions may include helping the clients normalize their situation or perhaps engage in some therapy designed at enhancing their present level of sexual satisfaction as opposed to treating them for a sexual disorder.

Second, before any treatment is initiated, the clinician should ask if there are any reversible causes of ED that could account for the presenting complaints. If so, working with appropriate professional colleagues to make changes in those factors would be in order. Third, noninvasive (lower risk) treatment options are considered before more invasive (higher risk) options. Considering risk, the treatment options for ED are prioritized into first-, second-, and third-line therapies. Reversibility, cost, and ease of administration are also considerations. Selection of treatments should be made considering a combination of client preference, appropriateness of treatment for the etiologic base of ED, medical conditions that may rule out some options, and patient reimbursement factors such as out-of-pocket costs (Process of Care Panel, 1998).

Interventions With Reversible Causes

Specifically, consider four factors: prescription medication use, nonprescription drug use (including legal addictive drugs of alcohol and tobacco), hormonal replacement, and penile anatomical abnormalities. Very commonly, prescription medications have unintended adverse effects on erectile functioning (as well as sexual desire, ejaculation, and orgasm). In particular, antihypertensives, antidepressants, antiarrythmics, antiandrogens, and H2 blockers most often are suspect. The patient will need to work with the prescribing healthcare provider to explore if adjusting a dosage or substituting another medication may relieve the ED.

Before the physiological mechanisms for erections were well understood, testosterone, sometimes used indiscriminately, was one of the most widely prescribed drugs for ED. Today it is understood that testosterone does not have a direct effect on erectile response, although it does influence libido, which in turn may alter erection function. Although low testosterone level as a causal factor for ED has a low hit rate (3%-6%), it is reasonable to use supplemental testosterone if low libido is part of the presenting complaints (DVA, 1999; Heaton, 1998).

Anatomical abnormalities of the penis may adversely affect erectile ability and may be reversible, especially in younger men (under age 45) who have suffered penile trauma. Microsurgical revascularization of the penis is usually what is most helpful, particularly if the ED stems primarily from an arterial occlusion without veno-occlusive dysfunction (Process of Care Panel, 1998). Peyronie's disease, which causes devastating penile deformity and affects up to 2% of men, should not be considered a reversible cause of ED. Men with Peyronie's disease, which usually affects those between the ages of 40 and 60, should always be referred to a urologist (Levine, 1998).

For any clients who are smoking, referrals should be made to specialized smoking cessation programs employing the AHCPR guidelines, which incorporate behavioral, educational, and nicotine replacement therapies and oral medications as treatment options. Clients using alcohol and/or drugs should be asked to abstain from use to evaluate whether the drug has an acute effect on their sexual performance. Those unable or unwilling to abstain should be referred for further assessment and treatment to a polysubstance abuse program (NIH, 1993; Peterson, 2000).

Addictions to substances represent risk factors for ED whether they are illegal addictions or legal addictions such as to alcohol and tobacco. Questions sometimes arise with providers and patients as to the "staging of treatment" or which addiction should be treated first (and if treatment of ED should proceed if addictive behaviors continue). Generally, treatment for addiction to illegal drugs is prioritized over treatment for legal addictions. As is often the case, if a patient is addicted to alcohol and illicit drugs, treatment for these addictions should be prioritized over smoking cessation.

Clinical Vignette: Middle-Aged Male With Reversible Causes for ED

A 45-year-old, obese male veteran came into the primary care clinic and completed a screening tool which indicated an elevation of symptoms for depression. Being referred from the nurse, the man was confused about why he was scheduled for an appointment with a "shrink." The depression score was explained to him and he accepted the evaluation because he felt "stressed out." The patient went on to report that he had been laid off from his employer and had been out of work for 6 months. He was feeling overwhelmed by financial obligations and experiencing marital discord because of his unemployment as well as having problems "in the bedroom." He went on to explain that he had recently been diagnosed with moderately high blood pressure and started on a hypertensive medication, which interfered with erection function.

The patient was not interested in counseling for his depressed mood or marital issues to improve his relationship with his wife. But, while being evaluated for depression, he acknowledged that he smoked about two packs per day; he also reported that his wife smoked one pack per day. He was counseled regarding his cardiovascular risk for heart attack and invited to join the smoking cessation program. He talked it over with his wife and they decided to join the program together to improve their health as well as save a significant amount of money per month that they spent on cigarettes.

During nutrition counseling, which is part of the smoking cessation program, they learned to improve their diet, cutting out high-fat and high-cholesterol foods as well as increasing their physical activity to minimize weight gain. This couple decided to start "mall walking" and at first could not walk more than 20 minutes before getting fatigued. Slowly they built up to walking 90 minutes three to four times per week.

As a result of improved diet and increased exercise over a 6-month period, this patient lost 35 pounds! From the combination of losing this amount of weight and not smoking (nicotine is a vasoconstrictive agent), the patient's blood pressure fell to normal limits without medication and he was able to discontinue its use. His erection function resumed and the marital sex relationship improved. Exercise is one of the best antidotes for depression and, additionally, the couple reported increased marital satisfaction through shared support and goal attainment. In addition to all these benefits, the couple saved hundreds of dollars per month while reducing their risk for heart attack!

First-Line Therapies: Sex Therapy, Vacuum Constriction Devices, and Oral Medications

Sex therapy, vacuum constriction devices (VCDs), and oral medications are all considered first-line therapies because of the relatively low risk for adverse events (considering medical contraindications). Sex therapy is indicated as the best treatment for most psychogenic-based cases of ED and is considered an important adjunct therapy with most organic and mixed etiology-based cases of ED (AACE, 1998; Masters et al., 1995; NIH, 1993). Sex therapy and VCD use do not involve any invasive procedures, while oral medications (such as sildenafil citrate [Viagra]) introduce substances into the body that may have adverse side effects in a minority of men (Padma-Nathan, 1998).

Undeniably, oral medications have become extremely popular, partly due to people preferring a "quick fix" external solution to ED over an "internally learned" behavioral strategy that takes more time and money, even though the latter goes beyond ED into benefiting other areas of sexual health and an overall relationship. Clearly this indicates a major shift in the treatment of ED, from the domain of urologists and mental health specialists to that of primary care clinicians (Padma-Nathan, 1998; Rosen, 2003). The implication is far-reaching, as family medicine and general internal medicine physicians are being asked to practice sexual healthcare, an area in which most physicians have not received comprehensive training. Hence, there are expanding opportunities for mental health professionals who have proficiency, if not a specialty, in sexual health and sex therapy (Althof, 1998).

Sex Therapy

Sex therapy is the treatment of choice for most psychogenic-based cases of ED and can be an important adjunct therapy with most other cases of ED. Sex therapy focuses upon the five most common psychological factors associated with ED: sexual trauma, depression, anxiety, guilt, and marital discord. If sexual trauma is related to the complaints of ED, then intensive psychotherapy focusing upon trauma resolution is needed to break the bond between past trauma and present sexual functioning. The process of trauma resolution may be short- or long-term, depending upon the history of the trauma and complexity of the case. Paramount is the process of the patient finding ways to feel psychologically safe. Unfortunately, many male survivors experiencing severe ED never form long-term relationships nor come into treatment. When they do, partner education and participation in the therapy process is critical to treatment outcome. However, it is important to again note that sexual trauma by itself may not be related to the presenting complaint of ED and may not require psychotherapy focused on resolution of trauma issues.

When sexual trauma is pertinent to complaints of ED, it may be an underlying cause of depressive symptoms. When abuse history is not present and the patient's complaint of ED is related to depression, brief psychotherapy should be the first strategy to bring relief. If psychotherapy does not reduce the depressive symptoms in the short term, psychotherapy and psychotropic medication may be combined for more intensive treatment. Again, care should be taken not to exacerbate complaints of ED by prescribing antidepressants, which may further suppress erectile response (AACE, 1998). When anxiety or guilt serve as psychogenic obstacles to erectile response, they can be effectively treated through relaxation training, cognitive therapy, and behavioral prescriptions, as described below (Kaplan, 1986; Masters et al., 1995).

Sex therapy represents the combination of psychotherapy and prescribed behavioral exercises which focus on relaxation and skill acquisition related to sensual touch. Between talk therapy sessions, sexually related behavioral assignments are completed within the couple's own value system in the privacy of their home. The most common of these behavioral prescriptions are referred to as "sensate focus" exercises; their effectiveness has been extensively studied (Masters et al., 1995).

Sensate focus is defined as graduated touching exercises assigned to couples in therapy to reduce anxiety and teach nonverbal communication skills (Masters et al., 1995). Sensate focus exercises create a "nondemand" touching encounter, force a couple to attend to sensual aspects of their bodies other than erogenous zones, and allow the patient to relax and "let Mother Nature take over" so he can once again enjoy erections with his partner. The series of touching exercises becomes increasingly sophisticated, progressively including the entire body, and may involve vaginal containment of the male.

Vacuum Constriction Devices

Invented in 1962, vacuum constriction devices (VCDs) have been a popular treatment choice for men with ED since the mid-1980s, when they received FDA approval and were legitimized as medical treatments by some prominent urologists. Historically, VCDs were one of the first "alternative" therapies developed (other than implants, which are surgical alternatives offered by urologists, and sex therapy offered by mental health specialists). A VCD consists of a plastic cylinder that is placed over the flaccid penis, a pump that is used to create an erection through negative pressure (vacuum) in the cylinder, and a tension ring used to constrict venous blood flow out of the penis. Additionally, a patient education videotape is usually included with the device for proper instruction. Even better, the client is instructed in use by in vivo demonstration before leaving the clinic. There are no restrictions on how many times the client may use the VCD per day or per week.

There are relatively few contraindications to using a VCD. The most important one to consider is whether the patient and/or his partner have the mental and physical capability to safely use it. They must be able to physically load the band for trapping the blood in the penis onto the device. They also must be able to remove the band when finished. They need to understand that there is a 30-minute time limit for the band to remain on the penis. Another consideration is the patient on anticoagulation therapy. He might experience more bruising or even bleeding into the tissues of the penis due to the trauma of the vacuum device and its band.

Treatment outcome is good but contingent on appropriate patient education and motivation. Because they are nonpharmacological, VCDs have no drug interactions, and side effects are minimal. Side effects include occasional penile numbing, pivoting at the penile base, mild bruising from the tension ring, pain with orgasm, and decreased penile tumescence and ejaculation. The most frequent complaint from men using VCDs is the unnatural interruption of the act of making love to achieve an erection via use of the device (Trapp, 1998). VCDs are referred to by many names, including vacuum tumescence device, external vacuum therapy, or, informally, "the pump." Manufacturers report high levels of patient satisfaction, but this may reflect initial patient response, not long-term satisfaction. Once only available by prescription, VCDs are now being sold over the counter in drug stores.

Oral Medications

One of the most significant advances in the treatment of ED has been the development of oral medication to help with erections. Currently, there are three FDA-approved oral medications for erectile dysfunction. All of them have basically the same mechanism of action but differ in their side effect profiles and duration of activity in the body. These medications are not aphrodisiacs, nor are they approved for use in females.

As mentioned previously, the FDA approval and marketing of these orally administered agents for the management of ED has not only provided a new aid to sexual health, but also has greatly changed the clinical practice of sexual health, particularly sexual medicine. A good example of this is the Department of Veterans Affairs (DVA), one of the largest healthcare systems in the world and one that primarily serves older men. Although ED has been a condition plaguing veterans long before establishment of the VA some 130 years ago, ED could be argued to be the most underdiagnosed medical condition in the VA, if not everywhere medicine is practiced. Not until the release of these medications and the subsequent consumer demand was there a sustained national focus within the VA on the topic of ED. The lead author served as the contributing psychologist to the National VA Technical Advisory Group that developed practice guidelines for primary care management of erection dysfunction (DVA, 1999).

These drugs are classed as PDE5 inhibitors. Remember, erections are accomplished by the release of nitric oxide that, in turn, causes the production of a chemical (cGMP). This relaxes the smooth muscle in the corpora cavernosa so the penis becomes tumescent and rigid. Normally, there is an enzyme (PDE5) that breaks down the cGMP allowing the smooth muscle to contract and decrease the blood flow into the penis, thereby ending the erection. The new medications inhibit the PDE5 so that blood flow remains increased and the erection is improved. Eventually, the body metabolizes these drugs and the whole system returns to a resting state.

The three FDA-approved medications are Viagra (Sildenafil), Levitra (Vardenafil), and Cialis (Tadalafil). The onset of action of each of them ranges from 20 to 60 minutes. Absorption of Levitra and Viagra may be decreased if taken with a fatty meal, rendering them less effective. The second author has had several patients sent to him with a history of failure using Viagra only to find that they were taking it with a meal. Once they stopped eating fatty meals prior to taking the medication, the Viagra worked. Cialis does not appear to have this problem. Another difference is in the length of action in the body. Viagra lasts 4 to 6 hours, Levitra 5 to 12 hours, and Cialis up to 36 hours. This does not mean the erection lasts that long. All it means is that the length of time to initiate sexual activity varies with the medication. The medication does not give a man an erection; it gives him the ability to have an erection when he is sexually stimulated.

As with all medications, there are risks and possible side effects that the practitioner needs to be aware of. All of these medications can cause headaches, facial flushing, nasal stuffiness, and occasional indigestion. Viagra, in addition, may cause visual disturbances, specifically changes in blue/green colors. Recently, there has been concern raised about more serious visual problems and possible strokes associated with this medication. The exact mechanism of these reactions is not clear, and it is also controversial whether there is an actual cause-and-effect relationship. It is known that certain medications will react with these drugs in a potentially fatal way. The most common problems occur with nitrates and alpha blockers. Nitrates are used to dilate heart arteries and relieve angina. There have been several reported fatalities when these drugs were taken during the same 24 hours. This was especially true for Viagra. The time span will be different for Levitra and Cialis. Alpha blockers are drugs used to lower blood pressure and also to relax the prostate to allow men to void better, reducing the need for surgery. There have been many reported adverse reactions to this combination, including some mortalities.

Second-Line Therapies: Intracavernosal Injections and Intraurethral Suppository

Intracavernosal Injections

In 1982, surgeon Ronald Virag was performing a routine procedure when he noticed that the injection of a vasodilating drug (papaverine) into a pelvic artery produced an erection in the anesthetized patient. One year later, Dr. Giles Brindley dropped his pants and injected himself in front of an audience at the American Urological Association to demonstrate the immediate effectiveness of erectogenic drugs, producing an erection without aid of psychological or tactile stimulation. Soon after, vasoactive injections revolutionized the urologic diagnosis and treatment of ED by providing the first direct test of penile health and the first specific drug therapy for ED (Broderick, 1998).

Patients often refer to self-injection therapy as "the shot." For those who chose to withstand the "wince factor," an effective therapy was created that proved successful for 70% to 80% of men. As dozens of men have told this writer, the exchange of 5 minutes of discomfort for a sustained erection of 60 to 90 minutes is a good trade, especially for those men who have not had an erection – let alone intercourse – in several years. The two medications used for injections are prostaglandin E1-alprostadil sterile powder and alprostadil alfadex (AACE, 1998). Appropriate dosing usually occurs in the physician's office to ensure proper patient instruction and erectile response. In 10 to 20 minutes, a sustained erection is produced which usually does not subside with orgasm or ejaculation. Full and natural tumescence is enjoyed independent of sexual desire (Montague et al., 1996).

Besides the "wince factor," the disadvantages include being limited to three injections per week, developing scar tissue at injection sites, needing to have good dexterity, ability to learn the multiple steps involved in self-injection, and risk of overdose producing priapism in less than 1% (Process of Care Panel, 1998). When the patient injects too high a dose or has an atypical reaction, priapism can result, with the patient having to report to the nearest emergency room if the erection lasts longer than 4 hours. Intracorporal injection therapy may be unsuitable in patients with inadequate hand dexterity (due to arthritis), visual impairment (due to diabetic neuropathy), or difficulty gaining sufficient access to the penis, such as with obesity (DVA, 1999).

Intraurethral Suppository

Intraurethral suppository therapy uses the same drug used in self-injection (alprostadil) but employs a different route of administration. A small plastic dispensing applicator is lubricated and inserted into the urethral meatus (the urinary opening at the tip of the penis). This method of administration is generally more acceptable than injection (AACE, 1998). These dispensing devices come individually and sterilely wrapped with a premeasured dosage ranging from 250 to 1,000 micrograms. Once fully inserted (approximately 2 inches), a small suppository of the medication in semisolid pellet form is deposited into the penis for absorption. The dispenser is extracted from the urethra and thrown away. As with the injected vasodilator, a sustained erection will develop which may last approximately an hour (AACE, 1998).

Absorption into the spongy tissue of the penis is 80% complete within 10 minutes. Soon after, an erection occurs (10-20 minutes). Approximately 65% of men using this therapy in the physician's office achieved erections suitable for intercourse, while efficacy dropped to 50% of men being able to complete intercourse when using the therapy at home (Process of Care Panel, 1998). Although transient penile discomfort may occur with most men, 5% to 10% of patients will have substantial pain that will preclude any further use of this form of medication administration. Priapism may also occur with urethral suppository use of vasodilators, although this is rare. Some clinicians give patients medications (adrenergic agents such as ephedrine) in case the erection lasts more than 2 hours. If the erection is sustained more than 4 hours, aggressive and immediate treatment is necessary (AACE, 1998).

Third-Line Therapy: Surgery

Surgical revascularization of the penis or venous ligation for venous leakage is sometimes performed on younger males. But after a review of the high rate of failure for these procedures, NIH issued a statement suggesting these procedures be done only as part of research protocols (NIH, 1993). Of course, special cases involving destruction of or severe injury to the penile artery in men under 45 years of age after trauma or radiation therapy may indicate specific consideration of revascularization surgery as the treatment of choice (AACE, 1998) provided there is no other evidence of vascular disease.

Penile implants were introduced in 1972 with semirigid prostheses being inserted into the physical space where corpora tissue naturally lies. Implants are always the "last resort" intervention because they are the most invasive of all treatments and because the man will permanently lose any ability to have unassisted erections (as a result of scarring of the corpus cavernosum). This is why many urologists will not consider patients for penile prostheses if they have had any naturally occurring erections in the last 6 months.

Over the last 2 decades, the semirigid rod has been the more common model implanted. Treatment failures attributable to infection, erosion, or mechanical failure (especially in patients with diabetes) previously was as high as 36% (AACE, 1998). The technology over the last 25 years has greatly advanced. There are now several subtypes of the two general categories of implants: semirigid and hydraulic prostheses. Semirigid prostheses come in two subtypes: more popular malleable rods or the mechanical type with articulating segments made out of high molecular weight polyethylene. Hydraulic prostheses come in one- to three-piece models (Mulcahy, 1998). However, they all consist of cylinders for the erection, a reservoir, and a pump.

As hydraulic implant designs improved, they have come to be seen as the "Cadillac model" with higher patient satisfaction ratings. A disadvantage of the multiple component hydraulic prostheses is that there are more parts to malfunction. The overall satisfaction rate is high, with 80% to 90% of men and their partners reporting that they are happy with the results of the implants. Complaints of implant recipients include some reports of diminished penile sensitivity and the implant resulting in an erection that is shorter than the natural erection (Mulcahy, 1998).

Clinician Vignette: Older Male With Repeated Rejections of Penile Implant

The second author has had extensive experience with penile prostheses and taking care of their complications. He has had several patients who had multiple procedures to correct their implants due to infection, and erosion that required the implant to be removed. Although it is technically challenging, new prostheses can be inserted in many of these patients. The following case is an example of one such patient who was able to return to a higher level of sexual function and sexual health.

A 64-year-old male patient came for a consultation in the urology department because of impotence. His history was remarkable in that he had undergone several penile implants that were removed because of infection. He was not a diabetic patient. His current urologist had told him that all he could do for him was to reinsert a malleable prosthesis due to the build-up of scar tissue in the penis.

On examination, some scarring was found, but it was the second author's belief that a channel could be made for a malleable implant. An inflatable prosthesis could just as well be inserted, and that was what the patient really wanted. He was educated about the risks of the procedure (as described earlier) and acknowledged that he understood the risks and benefits of the prosthesis. Additionally, he understood that the second author might not be able to insert any implant. Having confidence the patient was fully informed, it was decided to proceed.

The second author was able to insert an inflatable device, and this time the patient healed without infection. When the patient was last seen (at approximately 3 months follow-up), he was getting married to his long-time partner who had been with him through all of his previous trials and tribulations. She now had an ear-to-ear grin and gave the second author a hug while sharing her thanks for restoring her husband-to-be's self-esteem.

ERECTION DYSFUNCTION IN THE FUTURE

The future treatment of ED may pose intriguing possibilities. The three new oral medications described in this contribution are only the start of a parade of sexual medicines that will be discovered and placed on the market over the next few decades. The entire media buzz that Viagra started will likely seem minor in anticipation of sexual medicines that increase sexual desire. In the near future, molecular biology may be used to study ED in penile smooth muscle cells and make needle biopsy a routine procedure in the differential diagnosis of ED, determining whether etiology is organic, psychological, or mixed (Christ, 1998). With the potential of the human genome project identifying tens of thousands of genes which play a role in penile tumescence and rigidity (which could be transferred), the future of genetic therapy for ED may be promising (Christ, 1998). There is a serious dearth of research comparing the efficacy of different treatments in large-sample, randomized studies. In the new century, the clinical management of ED will hopefully benefit from empirical investigation of the most effective treatment regime, combining several clinical interventions from across disciplines. Finally, it is conceivable that erection dysfunction will eventually become 100% correctable, if not eventually eradicated, in America.

CONTRIBUTORS

Frederick L. Peterson, Jr., PsyD, is a health psychologist at the Veterans Healthcare System of Ohio, Dayton Campus, where he coordinates a Sexual Health Clinic and the Smoking Cessation Programs. Dr. Peterson is the Co-Director of the Psychology Internship Program. He completed postdoctorate training as a Clinical Fellow at the Masters and Johnson Institute. Research interests include sex therapy, tobacco use treatment, and the effects of masculinity-related personality factors on health. He holds three academic appointments at Wright State University, including the School of Medicine (Department of Psychiatry), the School of Professional Psychology, and the College of Education and Human Services. Dr. Peterson can be reached at the Sexual Health Clinic, VA Medical Center, Dayton, OH 45428. E-mail: Docpete100@aol.com

Donald E. Fuerst, MD, is currently Chief of Urology at the Dayton VA Medical Center, Dayton, Ohio. Prior to this he was the medical director for the Center for Sexual Function in Akron, Ohio and was assistant professor with Northeast Ohio University College of Medicine. Dr. Fuerst has published several articles on male sexual function. He received his training in Urology at the University of Texas Health Science Center, Houston, Texas, and is board-certified in Urology. Dr. Fuerst can be contacted at the Dayton VA Medical Center, 4100 West Third Street, Dayton, OH 45428. E-mail: Donald.Fuerst2@va.gov

RESOURCES

Agency for Health Care Policy and Research (AHCPR). (1996). *Clinical Practice Guidelines on Smoking Cessation* (Centers for Disease Control and Prevention Publication No. 18). Washington, DC: U.S. Government Printing Office.

Althof, S. (1998). New roles for mental health professionals in the treatment of erectile dysfunction. *Journal of Sex Education and Therapy, 23*(3), 229-231.

American Association of Clinical Endocrinologists (AACE). (1998). AACE clinical practice guidelines for the evaluation and treatment of male sexual dysfunction. *Endocrine Practice, 4*(4), 220-235.

American Psychiatric Association (APA). (1996). *Clinical Practice Guidelines for Smoking Cessation* [Special supplement edition]. Washington, DC: Author.

American Psychiatric Association (APA). (2000). *Diagnostic and Statistical Manual of Mental Disorders* (*DSM-IV-TR*; 4th ed. text rev.). Washington, DC: Author.

Beck, A., Steer, R., & Brown, G. (1996). *Beck Depression Inventory Manual.* San Antonio, TX: The Psychological Corporation.

Broderick, G. (1998). Impotence and penile vascular testing: Who are these men and how do we evaluate the etiology and severity of their complaints? *Journal of Sex Education and Therapy, 23*(3), 197-206.

Buvat, J., & Lemaire, A. (1997). Endocrine screening in 10,022 men with erectile dysfunction: Clinical significance and cost effective strategy. *Journal of Urology, 158*, 1764-1767.

Christ, G. (1998). The control of corporal smooth muscle tone, the coordination of penile erection, and the etiology of erectile dysfunction: The devil is in the details. *Journal of Sex Education and Therapy, 23*(3), 187-193.

Department of Veterans Affairs (DVA). (1999). *The Primary Care Management of Erectile Dysfunction* (Published by the Pharmacy Benefits Management Strategic Healthcare Group and the Medical Advisory Panel, Publication No. 99-0014). Washington, DC: U.S. Government Printing Office.

Fagan, F. (2003). Psychogenic impotence in relatively young men. In S. Levine, C. Risen, & S. Althof (Eds.), *Handbook of Clinical Sexuality for Mental Health Professionals* (pp. 217-235). New York: Brunner-Rutledge.

Feldman, H. A., Goldstein, I., Hatzichristou, D. G., Krane, R. J., & McKinlay, J. B. (1994). Impotence and its medical and psychological correlates: Results of the Massachusetts Male Aging Study. *Journal of Urology, 151*, 54-61.

Govier, F. E., McClure, D. R., & Kramer-Levien, D. (1996). Endocrine screening for sexual dysfunction using free testosterone determination. *Journal of Urology, 156*, 405-409.

Heaton, J. (1998). Androgens, andropause and erectile function. *Journal of Sex Education and Therapy, 23*(3), 232-235.

Kaplan, H. (1986). Psychosexual dysfunctions. In A. M. Cooper, A. J. Frances, & M. H. Sacks (Eds.), *Personality Disorders and Neurosis* (pp. 467-479). Philadelphia: Lippincott.

Kolodny, R. (1985). The clinical management of sexual problems in substance abusers. In T. Bratter & G. Forrest (Eds.), *Current Management of Alcoholism and Substance Abuse* (pp. 594-622). New York: Free Press.

Laumann, E., Paik, A., & Rosen, R. (1999). Sexual dysfunction in the United States: Prevalence and predictors. *Journal of the American Medical Association, 281*(6), 537-544.

Levine, L. (1998). Peyronie's disease: A brief review of a difficult sexual dysfunction problem. *Journal of Sex Education and Therapy, 23*(3), 226-228.

Masters, W., Johnson, V., & Kolodny, R. (1995). *Human Sexuality*. New York: Harper-Collins.

Montague, D. (1998). Erectile dysfunction: The rational utilization of diagnostic testing. *Journal of Sex Education and Therapy, 23*(3), 194-196.

Montague, D., Barada, J., Belker, A., Levine, L., Nadig, P., Roehrborn, C., Sharlip, I., & Bennett, A. (1996). Clinical guidelines panel on erection dysfunction: Summary report on the treatment of organic erectile dysfunction. *Journal of Urology, 56*, 2007-2011.

Mulcahy, J. (1998). Review of penile implants. *Journal of Sex Education and Therapy, 23*(3), 220-225.

NIH Consensus Development Panel on Impotence. (1993). NIH Consensus Conference on Impotence. *Journal of the American Medical Association, 270*(1), 83-90.

Padma-Nathan, H. (1998). The pharmacologic management of erection dysfunction: Sildenafil citrate (Viagra). *Journal of Sex Education and Therapy, 23*(3), 209-218.

Peterson, F. L., Jr. (2000). The assessment and treatment of erection dysfunction. In L. VandeCreek & T. L. Jackson (Eds.), *Innovations in Clinical Practice: A Source Book* (Vol. 18, pp. 57-71). Sarasota, FL: Professional Resource Press.

Peterson, F. L., Jr., & Bley, J. W. (2005). The development of a sexual health component in your practice. In L. VandeCreek & J. B. Allen (Eds.), *Innovations in Clinical Practice: Focus on Health and Wellness* (pp. 159-168). Sarasota, FL: Professional Resource Press.

Process of Care Panel of the University of Medicine and Dentistry, New Jersey. (1998). *The Process of Care Model for the Evaluation and Treatment of Erectile Dysfunction*. Unpublished manuscript used for continuing education, UMDNJ-Center for Continuing Education, Princeton, NJ.

Rosen, R. (2003). Erectile dysfunction in middle-aged and older men. In S. Levine, C. Risen, & S. Althof (Eds.), *Handbook of Clinical Sexuality for Mental Health Professionals* (pp. 237-256). New York: Brunner-Rutledge.

Rosen, R., Riley, A., Wagner, G., Osterloh, I., Kirkpatrick, J., & Mishra, A. (1997). The international index of erectile function (IIEF): A multidimensional scale for assessment and erectile dysfunction. *Urology, 49*(6), 822-830.

Shabsigh, R., Fishman, I., Schum, C., & Dunn, J. (1991). Cigarette smoking and other vascular risk factors in vasculogenic impotence. *Urology, 38*(3), 227-231.

Trapp, J. (1998). External vacuum therapy: A historical review. *Journal of Sex Education and Therapy, 23*(3), 217-220.

Wetter, D., Fiore, M., Gritz, E., Lando, H., Stitzer, M., Hasselblad, V., & Baker, T. (1998). The Agency for Health Care Policy and Research smoking cessation clinical practice guideline: Findings and implications for psychologists. *American Psychologist, 53*(6), 657-669.

Wilson, J. (1988). Androgen abuse by athletes. *Endocrine Reviews, 9*, 181-199.

Ejaculatory Problems

Michael E. Metz and Barry W. McCarthy

Male ejaculatory dysfunction ranges in severity from very mild to extreme and spans a continuum from ejaculation before intercourse can begin to complete inability to ejaculate. Other problems include penile pain on ejaculation, "dry" ejaculation (no fluids emitted), and ejaculation without orgasm. The most common ejaculation dysfunctions for men and the focus of this contribution are premature ejaculation (PE; rapid ejaculation) and ejaculatory inhibition (EI; retarded ejaculation).

The ejaculatory dysfunctions may co-exist with another sexual dysfunction. For example, orgasm pleasure may be diminished when the man attempts to suppress ejaculation, or PE may occur when the man who worries about erectile dysfunction overcompensates with overanxious excessive sexual arousal.

This contribution will focus on (a) the potential causes and effects of PE and EI, (b) specific assessment and treatment strategies and techniques, and (c) several case illustrations.

DESCRIPTIONS OF PE AND EI

Description of PE

There is no universally accepted definition for PE (Rowland & Slob, 1997). We describe PE as when the man does not have voluntary, conscious control, or the ability to choose in most encounters when to ejaculate, and this experience creates distress in the intimate relationship. PE has been defined equivocally (see Metz et al., 1997) in terms such as the length of time or duration of intercourse (e.g., less than 2 minutes); the number of intravaginal thrusts (e.g., 8 or 15 thrusts); or the capacity for voluntary control. Voluntary control is the most common criterion used for defining PE. Multiple criteria have been suggested such as a combination or continuum of time and voluntary control. Other approaches (e.g., Grenier & Byers, 2004) add the perspective of the man's partner as well as the types and level of severity (Metz & Pryor, 2000).

According to the *Diagnostic and Statistical Manual of Mental Disorders* of the American Psychiatric Association (*DSM-IV-TR*; APA, 2000), PE is a dysfunction of the ejaculation/orgasm phase of the sexual response cycle characterized by (a) the persistent or recurrent onset of orgasm and ejaculation with minimal sexual stimulation before, upon, or shortly after penetration and before the person wishes it, (b) marked distress or interpersonal difficulty, and (c) not resulting exclusively from the direct effects of a substance such as opiate withdrawal. The

DSM-IV-TR also advises the diagnostician to consider mediating factors such as age, novelty of situation or partner, and frequency of sexual activity. The description of sexual problems – including PE – is aided by considering the diagnostic parameters: (a) onset or duration: whether lifelong ("primary") or acquired ("secondary" or episodic); and (b) context or range: generalized (all situations) or situational.

Prevalence of PE

As would be expected, authors of surveys among different populations using different definitions reach variable conclusions about the prevalence of PE. The most respected epidemiologic study suggests that PE (defined as a problem for more than 1 month in the past 12 months) is the most common male sexual dysfunction, affecting approximately 29% of all men (Laumann, Paik, & Rosen, 1999).

A common myth among men, couples, and professionals is that PE will naturally improve with age. This does occur for many adult men as they gain sexual experience. For some men, there is a sexual "mellowing" with age (e.g., between 40 and 60 years of age), but aging does not resolve lifelong PE for the majority of men.

Description of EI

Ejaculatory inhibition is the "secret male sexual dysfunction." EI affects more than 1 in 12 (8.3%) men (Laumann et al., 1999) but is rarely recognized or addressed publicly or professionally. Yet EI can be a source of infertility (unlike PE), seriously block the reward of sexual pleasure, and significantly disrupt relationship intimacy. Often men with EI avoid or stop sexual activity altogether.

The now discarded traditional labels "retarded ejaculation" and "ejaculatory incompetence" were quite negative and added to the sense of stigma. In assessing EI, it is particularly important to carefully examine both objective (e.g., intensity of stimulation, time to ejaculation, masturbation pattern) and subjective (e.g., level of distress, focus of attention, arousal continuum) arousal. It is equally important to approach EI as a couples issue, employing the biopsychosocial model of assessment, treatment, and relapse prevention.

Primary EI refers to the man who has never or rarely ejaculated during intercourse. Most of these men are able to ejaculate with manual, oral, or their own self-stimulation, although some men are totally unable to ejaculate during partner sex. The estimate is that 1% to 2% of young men experience primary EI. The great majority of men are able to ejaculate during masturbation, but for those who cannot, a careful medical evaluation is necessary.

The much more common form of EI is the secondary, intermittent pattern which increases with age. The estimated frequency varies from 7% to 15% of men over 50 (Perelman, 2004). This is often misdiagnosed as an erection problem because the man eventually does lose his erection. However, the chief problem with EI is that he loses his erection because he "runs out of sexual energy." He is objectively aroused, but his subjective arousal is impaired. He is unable to establish an erotic flow that culminates in orgasm. For example, an older man might have developed a sexual response pattern where he was used to being the "giving" partner, stimulating the woman so she was ready for intercourse. Traditionally, intercourse thrusting alone might have been enough for him to become orgasmic. In truth, as men age, there are more similarities than differences between male and female sexual response, including the need for partner stimulation to enhance erotic flow and orgasmic response. Men who are unaware of these normal changes (see Metz & Miner, 1998) or who become self-conscious about sexual response are vulnerable to EI. In other words, men (like women) need additional erotic stimulation during intercourse in order to increase arousal and become orgasmic.

CAUSES AND EFFECTS OF EJACULATORY PROBLEMS

The causes, effects, and complications of ejaculation problems cluster into 10 "types." Assessing these types serves as the basis for an individualized, comprehensive treatment plan. To overlook a contributing or maintaining cause, or a detrimental effect, will sabotage treatment effectiveness and frustrate both the couple and the clinician.

The five physiologic types include (a) *physical system* conditions (e.g., congenital sexual physiologic problems), which is rare; (b) *physical illness* (e.g., respiratory illness, prostate infection), which occasionally occurs and is more common with aging; (c) *physical injury* (e.g., abdominal surgery), which is infrequent; (d) *drug side-effects* (e.g., some medications or recreational drugs), which is common; and (e) *lifestyle issues* (e.g., smoking, poor physical conditioning, obesity), which is common. Knowledge about the neurophysiology of ejaculation can help you understand physiologic causes of ejaculatory problems (see handout on p. 148).

The four psychological types include (a) *psychological system* problems (e.g., Obsessive-Compulsive Disorder, Generalized Anxiety Disorder), which occur infrequently; (b) *psychological distress* (e.g., reactive depression or anxiety, grieving), which is common; (c) *relationship distress* (e.g., empathy deficits, unresolved conflicts), which is common; and (d) *psychosexual skills* deficits (e.g., unrealistic expectations, "performance anxiety," lack of knowledge about pacing one's arousal), which is very common.

A 10th type is *"mixed,"* which occurs with another sexual dysfunction (e.g., erectile dysfunction and low desire, or PE and the partner's dyspareunia), which occurs perhaps a third of the time (Loudon, 1998).

Ejaculatory Problems Are Multidimensional

It is not just the causes that are complicated; so are the multiple effects. These effects play a role in the vicious cycle, making the PE or EI chronic and severe. In addition, ejaculation problems are also multidimensional. The subtle intermingling of each partner's thoughts, feelings, and behaviors adds to the complexity. There is an inevitable interaction between the physical, psychological, relational, and psychosexual skills dimensions. For example, the couple with PE who erroneously expects perfect ejaculatory control every time (psychosexual cognition) typically creates unnecessary emotional (psychological distress) and interpersonal (relationship distress) anguish because of such impossible expectations. For another couple, PE that results from a prostate infection (acute physical illness) may interact with the partner's distress (psychological distress), negatively affect communication (relationship distress), and influence feelings about other aspects of life such as one's career (psychological distress). The integrative approach helps organize and guide treatment of each dimension.

The Impact of PE or EI on the Intimate Relationship

There are often hidden negative cognitions – "meanings" – about the sexual dysfunction that increases the distress. Men with PE or EI commonly think they are inadequate or a failure, and feel ashamed, anxious, and/or frustrated. The partner may think there is nothing she can do and feel frustration, loneliness, and abandonment. Emotions are mediated by the cognitions that determine the meaning of the sex issue for each partner. For example, with PE, if the man (or woman) thinks, "This is okay; let's enjoy the touch, find an alternate way for lovemaking that bonds us," the negative emotional effect would be minimal. On the other hand, if the man believes, "She is angry with me for ejaculating rapidly. I must stop this, or she'll go to a different man!" or if she believes, "He is utterly selfish and doesn't really love me," the impact of PE will be major. These negative attributions are unrealistic, erroneous, and "catastrophize" the problem, and the subsequent negative feelings block partner cooperation. Helping the couple to identify and correct these attributions is important for couple cooperation.

One way to conceptualize the distress of the sex problem is to view it as a negative behavior (B-) (e.g., premature ejaculation) that is enmeshed with negative thoughts (C-) (e.g., " I am a failure, an inadequate lover"), and negative feelings (E-) (e.g., shame, frustration) of either or both partners. The more negative these dimensions, the more severe the distress from the sexual dysfunction and the more detailed clinical attention will be required. Therapy seeks to alter the harmful meaning and create sexual and relationship satisfaction. This involves facilitating functional sexual behaviors but also realistic, constructive cognitions as well as positive and intimate emotions.

ASSESSMENT OF EJACULATION PROBLEMS

The two essential features in assessment are determining (a) the causes and effects ("types") and (b) the severity. Identifying the types clarifies, organizes, and focuses the resources required for comprehensive treatment, while the severity determines the level of detail that your therapeutic effort will require.

The role of each suspected cause and effect of PE must be addressed or therapy may be insufficient and ineffective. For example, the case may simultaneously involve (a) a physiologic PE associated with a prostate infection that needs medical treatment (antibiotic); while (b) exacerbated or maintained by relationship conflict and warranting couples therapy addressing relationship dynamics; as well as (c) psychotherapy for depression; and (d) attention to the details of the man's sexual response because psychosexual skills help the couple recover from PE caused by other factors. PE is often an "interactive dance" of multiple causes with multiple effects affecting multiple dimensions of the individuals and couple, and each must be addressed to ensure healthy function and satisfying intimacy.

Use the "Sexual Dysfunction Diagnostic Decision Tree: Assessing the Types (Causes and Effects)" (pp. 149-150) to guide your consideration of all the possible features of the case.

Determining Arousal Style

Assessing the man's predominant style of sexual arousal is crucial. Mosher's (1980) concept of three types includes (a) *self-entrancement* (focusing on his own body's physical sensations), (b) *partner interaction* (focusing on his partner's body or their sexual interaction), and (c) *role enactment* (fantasy role play). Those men with psychosexual skills PE almost invariably use partner interaction arousal strategies and also use "spectatoring" (detached observation of his performance), which diverts sensual body focus. In addition, he typically initiates and anxiously pursues sex with highly arousing activity (what we call "sexual drag racing"). He starts with oral-genital sex or immediate intercourse rather than with relaxed kissing and light massage and gradually increasing pleasurable stimulation, and he ultimately fails to connect with or even dissociates from his physical sensations during sexual activity. Men with EI often have difficulty "blending" the three arousal styles in a progression that builds arousal that can culminate in orgasm. Men with psychosexual skills PE and EI find it difficult to describe sensual and sexual details of an arousal sequence with graduated excitement.

Determining the Severity of PE

Severity of PE can be assessed with the "Premature Ejaculation Severity Index (PESI)" (pp. 151-152), a 10-item self-report questionnaire that is based on important features such as the onset, percentage of sexual events that are PE, the man and partner's emotional distress, chronicity, and presence of another sexual dysfunction. Scores on the PESI above 60 (high or extreme) almost always require referral to a sex therapist.

Determining the Severity of EI

The severity of EI is assessed with the "Ejaculation Inhibition Severity Index (EISI)" (pp. 153-154). Also included in the EISI is a crucial assessment question to determine under what circumstances the man is easily orgasmic. For example, the man who is orgasmic with his own idiosyncratic masturbation pattern, but never with his partner, poses a very different therapeutic challenge from the man who is readily orgasmic with partner manual and/or oral stimulation but not during intercourse.

Another important assessment dimension is whether he uses erotic fantasies during self- and partner stimulation, and whether these serve as a bridge to arousal or whether the fantasy is totally controlling of his erotic response and interferes with couple sex. It is also crucial to assess whether he feels subjectively aroused or whether he is struggling to be orgasmic at low levels of subjective arousal. In terms of situational factors, assess what types of stimulation, fantasy, situation, and partner activities facilitate high arousal and orgasm, and what types of factors inhibit arousal and orgasm.

TREATMENT FOR PE

The Psychosexual Skills for Managing PE

Comprehensive treatment of PE requires progressing through four basic phases to learn 11 steps of psychosexual skills. The psychosexual skills are based on a number of traditional and newer cognitive and behavioral sex therapy techniques (Metz & McCarthy, 2003; Zilbergeld, 1999). Contrary to the wish for simple cures, no one psychosexual skill by itself is enough to overcome PE. Rather, a number of distinct skills need to be integrated within the context of couple sexuality. Among the blend of skills are:

1. Developing couple openness and comfort so they can work together as an "intimate team."
2. Pursuing the principles of "pleasure before performance" and couple cooperation.
3. Learning physical relaxation during lovemaking.
4. Identifying and respecting the point of ejaculatory inevitability.
5. Learning self-entrancement arousal and later blending this with partner interaction arousal.
6. Learning to use the pelvic muscle as a "monitor" of the degree of relaxation and as an arousal/ejaculation management technique.
7. Moderating arousal using cognitive pacing techniques.
8. Managing arousal using behavioral pacing techniques.
9. Learning the penile "acclimation" procedure during intercourse.
10. Developing an individualized relapse prevention program.

Overview of the Steps to Treat PE

Coping With Premature Ejaculation (Metz & McCarthy, 2003) describes in detail 11 sequenced steps for couples for effective treatment of severe PE. For milder cases, judicious selection of fewer steps can be effective. Each exercise in the steps requires 30 to 60 minutes, completed at home between therapy sessions.

In Phase 1, Comfort and Relaxation, the series of exercises promotes positive valuing of sex and individual and couple comfort with sexuality, and teaches individual cognitive and behavioral skills for relaxation. In Step 1, Increasing Couple Sexual Comfort, the couple is safely guided to talk of their sexual feelings in a positive way and develop openness. Step 2, Training Your Mind and Body for Relaxation, establishes the foundation for ejaculatory control and pleasure in physiological relaxation. Relaxation is facilitated by learning Pelvic Muscle (PM) Control (Step 3).

Cognitive strategies involve identifying and learning to consciously manage sexual arousal. In Step 4, Cognitive Pacing With the Sexual Arousal Continuum, the man develops awareness of his unique arousal continuum ("map"). This involves mapping out different activities or images according to the excitement level on a continuum of 0 to 100. This allows him to begin lovemaking with relaxed arousal, the point of Step 5, Relaxed Self-Entrancement Arousal. Rather than focusing attention on his partner's body, their interaction, and highly erotic features, he focuses exclusively on his own physical sensations. This exercise teaches him how to find his "calm erection" (especially helpful for the man whose PE may be overcompensation for fears of erectile dysfunction).

In Phase 2, Pleasure Toleration, the couple functions as an "intimate team" to maintain physiological relaxation with increasingly more erotic stimulation. He learns to welcome more – not less – pleasure, the focus of Step 6: Relaxed Couple Pleasuring. Step 7, Partner Genital Exploration, increases the challenge for the couple to establish and enjoy calm, relaxed touch in an otherwise erotic situation.

In Steps 8 and 9, Stop-Start Pacing, the couple develops comfort and confidence in arousal and ejaculation management. Here the man is integrating self-entrancement arousal with partner-interaction arousal while progressively pacing his arousal, pausing and resting when close to ejaculation, then slowing down, then blending partner-interaction arousal into sensual self-entrancement arousal. This blending of cognitive and behavioral "pacing" is a powerful strategy.

In Phase 3, Pleasure Saturation, the couple learns how to have extended intercourse. The essential skill is to integrate the cognitive and behavioral skills and to cooperate as an "intimate team" during intercourse. In Steps 10 and 11, Intimate Intercourse, the couple learns how to initiate and adapt to prolonged intercourse and to "personalize" the experience. In the exercise Initiating and Acclimating to Intercourse, he relaxes the PM while his partner inserts him; then, with as little movement as possible to maintain his erection, they wait for his penis to "acclimate" to her vagina. Acclimation may take as long as 5 to 25 minutes, but once reached (and keeping the PM relaxed), they can enjoy more vigorous movement without ejaculation. When they are ready for ejaculation, he tenses the PM and increases movement. In Progressive Intercourse, the couple cooperates to integrate these skills, open to spontaneity, and focus on enhancing pleasure for the woman.

Phase 4, Long-Term Satisfaction, melds the cognitive-behavioral psychosexual skills into the couple's sexual style. The essential skill is to integrate the couple's gains, and ensure long-term satisfaction with an individualized relapse prevention plan. Without this, couples will likely relapse and regress.

In the following case example,* we label cognitions as (C), behaviors as (B), and emotions as (E) to help identify the C-B-E dimensions.

Case Illustration of Persistent PE: Sherry and Alex

Part 1: The Situation

Alex's chronic PE led Sherry to perceive (C) him as selfish, dismissive, and rejecting of her desires, and she felt hurt (E). Alex did not intend (C) to be selfish. Rather, he was deeply

---

* Names and identifying characteristics in all case examples have been changed to protect confidentiality.

perplexed and believed he was a "failure" (C) at his performance (B) and feared disappointing Sherry (E). Yet his disengaging (B) after ejaculating appeared (C) selfish to Sherry.

With fast ejaculation (B), Alex appeared to Sherry (C) to be sexually satisfied by his orgasm (B), but he typically stopped pleasuring (B) Sherry ("he rolls over and goes to sleep"). Alex focused on his failure (C), often "apologized" (B) to Sherry, and stopped lovemaking, became quiet or withdrawn, or even left their bed (B), as he privately felt ashamed and frustrated with himself (E).

For several years, Sherry had experienced Alex's PE and observed him (C) failing to seek professional help (B). All of these actions (B) seemed to Sherry to be insensitive (C) to her wants and feelings, hurt her deeply (E), felt like an abandonment (E), and seemed hard to interpret as anything other than disregard for her and incredible selfishness (C). Her hurt (E) manifested as complaints, criticisms, and other expressions of anger (B), even rage at times. With this, Alex thought he was betrayed (C), and he misunderstood (C) Sherry's lack of support (B) when he failed (C) to control his ejaculation (B), but was confused (C) about what to do (B). Everything that he tried (B) (e.g., distracting himself, masturbating before lovemaking) failed (C). He felt completely hopeless (E) and labeled himself inadequate (C), and avoided Sherry (B). She believed she was abandoned (C), ignored by Alex (B), and felt hurt and angry (E).

Alex and Sherry's story shows how interacting detrimental cognitions, behaviors, and emotions serve to cause, maintain, or exacerbate PE, or become the psychological effects of PE. When they sought sex therapy, the therapist helped them stop these patterns and establish reasonable cognitions, cooperative behaviors, and positive feelings.

Part 2: The Process of Satisfaction

Assessment indicated that the PE had several possible causes and effects: Physical system (neurologic), psychosexual skills deficits, psychological distress, and relationship distress. The PESI score was 54, indicating moderate severity.

The multiple misunderstandings (negative attributions such as Sherry perceiving Alex as sexually "selfish" and "dismissive" of her feelings, or Alex believing he was a "failure" and "betrayed") were addressed through therapy discussions and homework exercises such as "Talking of Sexual Feelings."

The skills (for details, see Metz & McCarthy, 2003) that were most helpful were the calm, physiologic "Relaxation Training," "PM Training," the cognitive pacing "Arousal Continuum," "Self-Entrancement Arousal," "Stop-Start," and "Intercourse Acclimation" with relaxed PM management skills. They learned to enjoy varied lengths and intensity of intercourse most of the time, while pleasure and cooperative intimacy became more their focus than just sexual performance. They created a relapse prevention plan that included doing the Couple Pleasuring exercise once a month. This was particularly valuable for Alex to help him maintain a variable, flexible approach to couple sexuality.

TREATMENT FOR EI

As with treating PE, comprehensive treatment for EI includes biomedical, pharmacologic, psychological, relational, and psychosexual skills components. An individualized treatment plan is necessary. For example, EI with a partner may result from an excessive masturbatory pattern (e.g., a 45-year-old man masturbating daily to Internet pornography and then being unable to ejaculate intravaginally with his partner) (Perelman, 2004). This also causes psychological distress and/or relationship tension, and these effects must be addressed.

Motivation for Change

Assessing both the man and his partner regarding motivation for change is a crucial factor. The most common motivation for young men with primary EI during intercourse is the desire to become pregnant (whether the woman's desire for pregnancy or his own). Sometimes, although not for the majority, the symptom has the function of preventing pregnancy. A more common pattern is that the man does not understand the EI but over the years has adapted to it and does not view it as a major problem. As a young, single man he had a reputation as a "stud," especially among male peers. He viewed intercourse as primarily serving the woman, with him being orgasmic either with her stimulation or his own afterward. Often, his partner is more motivated to address the EI than he.

Because most sexual problems, including EI and PE, are best conceptualized and treated as a couple problem, it is crucial to assess the woman's motivation. In the best case scenario, she is motivated to be his intimate sexual friend and to enhance mutual pleasure. In the worst case scenario, she views the EI as a personal rejection of her sexual desirability and his ejaculation as a pass-fail test of the relationship. Some women use the EI as a form of blackmail, threatening to tell others and humiliate him. Often the EI is part of a complex relationship power struggle.

It is important to assess whether the EI represents a hidden sexual agenda (a variant arousal pattern, a sexual orientation conflict, a preference for masturbation more than couple sex, or a self-punitive reaction to a traumatic sexual secret). Even more important than understanding the cause(s) of EI is to assess his (and his partner's) motivation for change. Is the emphasis on sharing pleasure and intimacy, or is the focus on sexual performance (i.e., working to ejaculate)? The performance approach of forcing ejaculation to prove something to himself or his partner is likely to fail and ultimately to cause male inhibited sexual desire and avoidance. A healthy motivation is to positively anticipate couple sex; to feel that he deserves sexual pleasure, enjoys receiving erotic stimulation, gets into an erotic flow, uses orgasm triggers, and allows high arousal to naturally flow to orgasm. The woman is viewed as his intimate and erotic sexual friend, and her arousal enhances his.

Tailoring the Psychosexual Skills for Treating EI

In a way, EI is the inverse problem to PE. Rather than helping the man and couple "pace arousal" in order to delay ejaculation, you help the man and couple "pace arousal" in order to promote arousal and ejaculation. This does not mean the skills in a "drag racing" style, but rather learning skills to develop a relaxed, cooperative style that respects the man's physiological and psychological conditions for arousal and orgasm.

The cognitive-behavioral skills that facilitate orgasm include:

1. Physiological relaxation to create the nondemand foundation for sexual receptivity and responsivity.
2. Using his cognitive arousal continuum to promote graduated arousal. This includes reserving thoughts and behaviors that are more arousing until the couple is "turned on" and moving toward orgasm.
3. Relaxing the PM in order to reserve them until shortly before he wants to ejaculate. Then he tightens, relaxes, and tightens to activate ejaculation.
4. Avoiding prolonged intercourse. Intercourse is reserved for high levels of arousal in order to prevent "acclimation."
5. Using the mutual excitement of the relationship to heighten arousal and erotic flow.

Case Illustration of Lifelong EI: Brian and Alisha

Brian was a 28-year-old man who had never ejaculated inside the vagina and had been married to 29-year-old Alisha for 8 months. Alisha has a 4-year-old daughter from a prior marriage, and she and Brian were eager to have a child of their own. Alisha's first husband admitted to being gay during her pregnancy, and his mother blamed Alisha for "turning my son gay." Alisha felt doubly stigmatized by being a single mother and having a gay ex-spouse. When she met Brian she felt reassured by his sexual interest, hard erections, commitment to being an active stepfather, and desire for a baby. She assumed the EI would be cured by the commitment of marriage.

Brian had viewed the EI as a sign of masculinity ever since adolescence. He had no difficulty ejaculating by himself once or twice a day. The women he'd been with were usually impressed by his sexual prowess, and friends were envious of the number of partners. Brian thought of himself as a good, unselfish lover, viewing both foreplay and intercourse as for the woman's arousal and orgasm. When women would manually or orally stimulate him, Brian would enjoy it but not find it particularly erotic.

Early in the relationship, Brian found Alisha's desire and sexual responsiveness very satisfying. The problem arose over the pregnancy issue and quickly turned into a major marital crisis. A "friend" wondered what was wrong with Alisha, first marrying a gay man and then a man who couldn't get her pregnant. Brian was on the defensive. He did research on the Internet and said it would be very easy to become pregnant by using his sperm through a basting tube to impregnate her. Alisha was repulsed by the coldness of the technique; she wanted to become pregnant "naturally." They consulted a fertility specialist who fell into the trap of supporting Brian in the power struggle. They then consulted a minister who also fell into the power struggle trap, this time supporting Alisha's position.

By the time Brian and Alisha consulted a psychologist with a subspecialty in couple sex therapy, they felt alienated and had had no sexual contact for over 3 months. In the first session, the clinician assessed the state of the marriage and marital sex, each of their goals, their fears and concerns, whether they were still consulting the fertility specialist, minister, or anyone else, and whether they were ready to give up the power struggle and work as an intimate team to develop a couple sexual style and become pregnant. The individual sexual histories were scheduled to understand each person's emotional and sexual development and explore sensitive or secret sexual issues. The most important thing to explore was what inhibited (blocked) Brian's arousal/orgasm during couple sex and to establish positive motivation to change the EI. The most important thing to explore with Alisha was her willingness and ability to be Brian's intimate friend in resolving the EI, not just her desire to become pregnant. Her desire, arousal, and orgasmic response could be positive for Brian in enhancing his appreciation for couple sexuality.

It was both crucial and motivating in the couple feedback session for Brian and Alisha to develop a new narrative (understanding) about their sexuality. Brian had to realize how the EI interfered with his own and their enjoyment of sex. Brian's rationalizing that EI was not a big deal had to be confronted in an empathetic and constructive manner.

Couple sex therapy involves not just the office sessions; just as important are the psychosexual skills exercises which they did at home. The key for Brian was to be aware of his subjective arousal, share that with Alisha, and together enhance pleasurable feelings and get into an erotic flow. During the pleasuring exercises, Brian discovered he felt more aroused when he touched Alisha rather than being totally passive when in the receiving role. For Brian, partner interaction arousal was much more pleasurable than self-entrancement arousal. Brian needed to be an active sexual participant, both emotionally and physically. Alisha was very receptive to this scenario, and she valued Brian "really being there." The second focus was on Brian becoming aware of orgasm triggers and using them during couple sex. Brian learned to get into an erotic flow and, rather than trying to force orgasm, to use his orgasm triggers to naturally extend his arousal, let go and be orgasmic. He did this first with Alisha's manual stimulation by using his triggers of a highly erotic fantasy, moving his pelvis rhythmically, and verbalizing how "turned on" he felt. In transferring this to intercourse, the key was not to transition to intercourse until his arousal was a "7" or "8" (10 being orgasm), to engage in multiple stimulation during intercourse, and utilize his orgasm triggers. Brian became aware that Alisha's arousal could enhance his rather than the previous pattern of distancing himself by "servicing" her. He learned to "piggyback" his arousal with hers. For both Brian and Alisha this was much more satisfying couple sexuality.

Intermittent EI

Intermittent EI is more common and increases with aging. The man has a positive history of regular ejaculation, but then finds his subjective arousal waning, and it becomes increasingly difficult to reach orgasm. His confusion about what is happening sexually is compounded by the fact that because he does not ejaculate he eventually loses his erection. He is afraid he is developing erectile dysfunction. Sexual problems seldom remain static; unless successfully addressed they become more severe and chronic.

The sooner the man and couple address intermittent EI the better. Although, as with any couple sexual dysfunction, it is crucial to do a careful individual and couple assessment. There are two common causes: The first is that the man approaches sex in a habitual manner and no longer receives sufficient pleasure and arousal to develop an erotic flow which would naturally culminate in orgasm. The second is that he has become increasingly isolated from his partner and obsessed with orgasmic performance. The major therapeutic interventions are to increase intimate, interactive sexuality, specifically so that he becomes open and responsive to making sexual requests, and to transition to intercourse at higher levels of arousal and engage in multiple stimulation during intercourse.

Case Illustration of Intermittent EI: Grady and Susan

Grady began experiencing intermittent EI 4 years ago when he was 53. He discussed the problem with his physician who prescribed Viagra, as it has unsuitably become the all-purpose intervention for any male sexual problem. Grady found that Viagra somewhat improved his erectile confidence, but it had a negligible impact on EI.

Susan was confused by Grady's inability to ejaculate and worried that he no longer found her sexually appealing. In an effort to reduce pressure on him, Susan purposely cut back her own sexual interest and responsiveness. Although well-intentioned, this compounded the sexual problem so that both were experiencing inhibited desire, arousal, orgasm, and satisfaction.

Because EI is not discussed in the media or in most medical or therapy articles, it was enormously helpful when the couple consulted a couple sex therapist who correctly assessed and labeled the EI and its negative impact. In the feedback session the therapist recommended a comprehensive couple approach to address the problem. He told Grady and Susan that if they could build a new couple sexual style now it would inoculate them against sexual problems in their 60s and 70s.

Rather than Grady seeing EI as his problem alone, Susan was glad to step up in a positive role to enhance the sexual experience. Susan's sexual interest and responsiveness was an aphrodisiac for Grady. He could "piggyback" his arousal on hers – a new sexual scenario for them. In addition, Grady requested stimulation from Susan, enjoying both partner interaction arousal and role enactment arousal. Introducing playing out new sexual scenarios such as erotic dancing (striptease) and explicit sexual talk increased Grady's subjective arousal. Just as important in terms of erotic flow was the use of multiple stimulation, which included Grady doing manual clitoral stimulation, rubbing his penis between Susan's breasts, and she stimulating the head of his penis and testicles. Grady allowed himself to use erotic fantasies that served as a bridge to higher arousal – scenarios where he receives oral sex as he thrusts rhythmically and caresses Susan's breasts.

Because Grady was responsive to multiple stimulation during nonintercourse sex, it was natural that he responded to multiple stimulation during intercourse. Grady had to confront the inhibition that a "real man" only needs intercourse thrusting. As men age, they need more partner stimulation, and Susan (whose orgasmic response was consistent with manual and oral stimulation) said she enjoyed intercourse more when she knew that Grady needed her stimulation. This included kissing during intercourse, his doing breast stimulation and her doing buttock stimulation, his continuing to use erotic fantasies and she verbalizing how sexy she felt, and switching intercourse positions. Rather than expecting sex to be perfect each time, Grady and Susan transitioned to the "good-enough" (see below) criterion of 85% of the time Grady was orgasmic. When he was not, they could enjoy the encounter which might include Susan being orgasmic. Most importantly, each felt closer, more of an "intimate team."

SPECIAL CONSIDERATIONS

Relapse Prevention

To expect that the man will never have another experience where he ejaculates rapidly or does not reach orgasm is unrealistic and sets the couple up for failure, a return to sexual avoidance, and the blame and counterblame cycle. The key to relapse prevention is to establish positive, realistic expectations, including that arousal, intercourse, and orgasm are inherently variable. Whether once every 10 times, once a month, or once a year, PE or EI will reoccur. The reality of the Good-Enough Couple Sex model (Metz & McCarthy, 2004) is that problems with desire, arousal, and orgasm are an occasional part of most couple's sexual experience. The key is to cooperate as an intimate team, accept an occasional episode of sexual dysfunction as normal and as a lapse (a single event which is not overly significant), and commit to not allow it to be a relapse (a pattern perpetuated by anticipatory anxiety, tense sexual performance, and avoidance).

There are cognitive, behavioral, and emotional components of an individualized relapse prevention program. Cognitive components include reinforcing a pleasure rather than performance orientation, seeing the partner as his intimate friend, remaining receptive to stimulation and arousal, feeling genuinely satisfied with good-enough couple sex, and not feeling pressure to strive for perfect intercourse performance.

The behavioral components of relapse prevention of PE, for example, include maintaining a regular rhythm of sexual experiences, blending self-entrancement arousal and partner interaction arousal, pacing with use of the "arousal continuum," not transitioning to intercourse until the PM is relaxed, cooperating as a couple to allow the penis to acclimate to the vagina, treating an episode of fast ejaculation simply as a lapse alerting the man and couple to take more care to manage progressive arousal, and returning to structured arousal exercises (especially the "stop-start" exercise) to reinforce the psychosexual skills.

The emotional components of relapse prevention include continuing to value each other as intimate friends and reinforce a sense of acceptance and cooperation. Especially important is setting aside quality couple time to share feelings of intimacy and sexuality.

The couple is given a handout with a number of strategies to individualize a relapse prevention plan (McCarthy, 2001). They choose two to four to develop an individualized relapse prevention plan.

Painful Ejaculation, "Dry Ejaculation," And Ejaculation Without Orgasm

When a man repeatedly experiences painful ejaculation (e.g., pain in the tip of the penis during ejaculation, postejaculation headache), "dry" ejaculation (orgasm without ejaculate), or ejaculation without orgasm, a medical evaluation is warranted. Each could be a symptom of an acute medical illness. For example, pain in the tip of the penis during ejaculation may be a symptom of a prostate infection which can often be treated effectively with an antibiotic. From the integrative, biopsychosocial perspective, it is always wise to consider possible physiological or medical sources for such sexual concerns, as well as possible psychological and relationship stresses that might manifest with such sexual symptoms.

Integrating Medications into The Couple Sexual Style

Several antidepressant medications (e.g., selective serotonin reuptake inhibitors such as paroxetine, sertraline) and tricyclics (e.g., clomipramine) are sometimes prescribed "off label" to slow ejaculation speed. Several pharmacologic agents are also under study for possible FDA approval for ameliorating PE, and it is likely that agents to facilitate ejaculation for men with EI will also appear in the future.

An integrative approach to PE (and EI) emphasizes the use of all available resources, including ejaculation-inhibiting medications – especially when PE is of the physical (neurologic) system type. The medication must be integrated into the couple's sexual styles. As is evident from research and clinical experience with the pro-erection medications (e.g., sildenafil), these medications are rarely effective as stand-alone treatments. The drop-out rate is relatively high, perhaps 40% to 80% (McCarthy & Fucito, 2005). This is due to a failure to integrate medication with the partner, failure of the medication to alleviate low sexual self-esteem, medication side-effects, or disappointment that the drug was not the miracle cure as shown on the TV advertisements.

There are currently no proven medications to treat EI. Anecdotally, some sympathomemenics such as over-the-counter decongestant/cold medications taken prior to sex may help on a very limited basis, but there is no controlled study to support this impression. Health food stores promote agents that claim to cure delayed ejaculation, but they lack controlled, reliable scientific evidence to support such claims.

Medication is likely to succeed best when used along with the psychosexual skills program and integrated into the couple's sexual style of intimacy, pleasuring, and eroticism (McCarthy & Fucito, 2005). If the man depends on the medication to establish 100% ejaculatory control or ejaculation every time, he sets himself and the relationship up for failure. Sex is an interpersonal experience. Striving for perfect sexual performance subverts sexual function and satisfaction rather than promoting "Good-Enough Couple Sex."

Good-Enough Couple Sex

An important characteristic of satisfied couples is a realistic appreciation of the value of sex in their relationship. The concept of Good-Enough Couple Sex (Metz & McCarthy, 2004) challenges couples to set realistic expectations with intimacy as the ultimate focus, pleasure as important as function, mutual emotional acceptance, and at times sex experienced as mature playfulness. Good-Enough Couple Sex is not mediocre sex, but positive and genuine sex. The quality of "Good-Enough Couple Sex" in well-functioning, satisfied couples varies: "very good" quality approximately 20% to 25% of the time, "good" (at least for one partner) 40% to

60%, "okay" although not remarkable 15% to 20%, and "mediocre" or dysfunctional 1% to 15% of the time.

An indicator of Good-Enough Couple Sex is the occasional presence of playfulness because, for play to occur, other aspects of intimacy must be functioning well: trust, mutual acceptance, priority on pleasure, freedom to be yourself, and deep valuing of the relationship – a "special feeling." Playful experiences personalize the bedroom.

Sexuality is integrated into the couple's daily life, and their daily life is integrated into their sex life to create the couple's unique sexual experience. Living daily life provides the opportunity to feel sexual experiences in a subtly yet distinctively personalized and enriched way. One time, sex is for anxiety release through orgasm. Another time it is for physical pleasure or for escape and fun or for emotional healing. Another time it is for romance and intimacy. Or another time, sex is a spiritual experience such as having gentle sex for emotional comfort after a death in the family. Good-Enough Couple Sex "fits" the couple's genuine lifestyle.

Referral to a Sex Therapy Specialist

Sex therapy is a clinical subspecialty which is offered by several groups of professionals including psychologists, marital therapists, psychiatrists, social workers, and pastoral counselors. For a sex therapy referral, contact the American Association of Sexuality Educators, Counselors, and Therapists (AASECT) at www.aasect.org or write or call for a list of certified sex therapists in your area: P.O. Box 1960, Ashland, VA 23005-1960; (804) 752-0026. Another excellent resource is the Society for Sex Therapy and Research (SSTAR) at www.sstarnet.org. To develop your skills as a sex therapist it is essential that you establish a consultation relationship with an established, credentialed sex therapist who can teach and supervise your growth. Organizations like AASECT and SSTAR are an excellent resource for finding colleagues and consultants.

Understanding the Neurophysiology of Male Ejaculation and Orgasm

Knowledge about the neurophysiology of ejaculation can help you understand ejaculatory problems, as well as the rationale for the strategies to teach the man and couple such as whole-body physical relaxation, conscious focus on pleasure, and pelvic muscle relaxation.

The Anatomy and Physiology of Ejaculation

The process of ejaculation involves several events: erection, emission, ejaculation, and orgasm. These processes are integrated by a complex set of interactions between the neurological, hormonal, and vascular systems. *Erection* refers to the processes in the brain, nervous system, and vascular system leading to penile rigidity. *Emission* refers to the collection and transport of fluids from several glands that form the semen in preparation for ejaculation. Sperm from the testicles travel through the *vas deferens,* which joins in the *prostate gland* with the tube exiting the *bladder* to form the *urethra* tube. Then the urethra runs through the chestnut-sized prostate, then out through the penis. With arousal, the neck or exit of the bladder closes (that is why it is difficult to urinate when the man has an erection), the testicles draw up against the body, and semen collects in the *verumontanum,* a balloonlike chamber inside the prostate gland. When the man is highly aroused, the verumontanum fills with semen, enlarging to three times its normal size. This pressure triggers the sensation of "ejaculatory inevitability" and the reflex of ejaculation. Technically, ejaculatory control is actually emission control, because once emission occurs the man will ejaculate within seconds.

Ejaculation is the process of pushing the seminal fluids out of the verumontanum through the urethra and the penis. Ejaculation occurs when a critical level of nerve input reaches the spinal cord and causes the reflexive ejaculatory response. The pelvic muscles (PMs) are directly involved in ejaculation by rhythmically contracting to force the semen out. Learning to identify and relax the PM is a core psychosexual skill.

Orgasm refers to the subjective experience of pleasure associated with ejaculation. Orgasm is a natural, healthy extension of the pleasuring-arousal-intercourse process. Orgasm and ejaculation are experienced as one and the same, although physiologically they are two distinct processes. Orgasm is primarily an experience in the brain. Though emission, ejaculation, and orgasm are integrated events and seem simultaneous, technically, erection is not required for ejaculation, and ejaculation is not required for orgasm, because they are controlled by separate neurological mechanisms. On rare occasion, these events can be out of synchrony (especially with aging), usually caused by physical and/or emotional fatigue.

Ejaculatory Neurophysiology

How the nervous system (neurophysiology) brings about ejaculation is only partially understood. Although ejaculation is technically a biological reflex involving the verumontanum in the prostate, the brain interprets sensual information, which may either augment ("turn on") or inhibit ("turn off") his arousal. Signals from the brain to the lower spinal cord link with neurologic impulses from the verumontanum to signal the ejaculatory system, which results in emission and activation of the *pelvic floor muscles* resulting in 2 to 10 rhythmic contractions of ejaculation.

Knowledge of how the sexual body works can help the couple ground their sexual expectations on accurate knowledge. For example, for a young couple to expect 45 minutes of vigorous intercourse without ejaculation is physiologically unreasonable. Understanding physiologic features such as the role of the brain as an "interpreter," the role of conscious regulation of arousal and physiologic relaxation, and the role of the PM as the means of ejaculation, can aid management of ejaculation.

Sexual Dysfunction Diagnostic Decision Tree: Assessing the Types (Causes and Effects)

Michael E. Metz

INITIAL DIFFERENTIAL: (1) Is the onset of sexual dysfunction (SD) lifelong or acquired? If lifelong, go to Step 1; if Acquired, to Step 4.
(2) Is the context of SD generalized to all sexual situations or is it situational?

LIFELONG ONSET – IF LIFELONG ONSET AND GENERALIZED CONTEXT:

STEP 1.   Is there also history and evidence of a physiological condition associated with SD such as congenital, genetic, circulatory, neurologic, hormonal, or urologic system problem, and no evidence of psychopathology?

YES: PHYSICAL SYSTEM SD   Treatment: medical options, pharmacotherapy, and cognitive-behavioral sex therapy for adaptation.

NO: to Step 2

STEP 2.   Is there evidence of chronic psychopathology or a psychological character pattern that predisposes to SD such as bipolar, obsessive/compulsive, dysthymia, or generalized anxiety disorders, and so on?

YES: PSYCHOLOGICAL SYSTEM SD   Treatment: individual psychotherapy, psychotropic pharmacotherapy, and cognitive-behavioral sex therapy.

NO: to Step 3

IF LIFELONG ONSET AND EITHER GENERALIZED OR SITUATIONAL CONTEXT SD:

STEP 3.   Is there evidence of the person's cognitive and behavioral inability to physiologically relax during sexual arousal, focus on specific pleasure/arousal of one's own bodily sensations, and manage desire and arousal?

YES: PSYCHOSEXUAL SKILLS SD   Treatment: Cognitive-behavioral psychosexual skills training; judicious use of prosexual medications

NO: to Step 4

ACQUIRED ONSET – IF ACQUIRED ONSET AND GENERALIZED CONTEXT SD:

STEP 4.   Is there a current physical illness that is known to cause SD, such as one or more of the following?

Diabetes mellitus	Cardiac disease	Vascular disease
Multiple sclerosis	Sleep apnea	Peyronie's Disease
Hypothyroidism	Hypopituitarism	Hypogonadism
Polyneuropathy	Systemic lupus	Sexually transmitted disease (STD)
Lipid abnormalities	Chronic renal failure	Epilepsy
Prostatitis	Hypertension	Cancer (and its treatments)

YES: PHYSICAL ILLNESS SD   Treatment: medical treatment, if possible; consider cognitive-behavioral sex therapy to rebalance.

NO: to Step 5

STEP 5.   Has there been a physical injury, pelvic surgery, or neurologic trauma that may reasonably cause SD?

        YES: <u>PHYSICAL INJURY SD</u>   <u>Treatment</u>: medical treatment if possible; pharmaco-
                                              therapy; consider cognitive-behavioral
        NO: to Step 6   sex therapy.

STEP 6.   Has the person begun taking (or withdrawn from) a chemical agent known to cause SD such as an antihypertensive, psychotropic medications, or chemotherapy?

        YES: <u>DRUG SIDE EFFECT SD</u>   <u>Treatment</u>: discontinue agent if safe; try alternatives
                                            or antidotes; cogitive-behavioral
        NO: to Step 7   sex therapy.

STEP 7.   Are there physiologic lifestyle patterns that are known to precipitate detrimental effects on sexual function such as obesity, smoking, poor cardiovascular conditioning, marathon athletics, sleep deprivation, and so forth?

        YES: <u>PHYSIOLOGIC LIFESTYLE SD</u>   <u>Treatment</u>: address patterns with programs such as
                                            weight loss, physical conditioning, and
        NO: to Step 8   adaptation sex therapy.

IF ACQUIRED ONSET AND EITHER GENERALIZED OR SITUATIONAL CONTEXT SD:

STEP 8.   Is there history and objective psychological test evidence that the person is experiencing current psychological stress?

        YES: <u>PSYCHOLOGICAL DISTRESS SD</u> <u>Treatment</u>: psychotherapy; consider psychotropic
                                            medication; cognitive-behavioral
        NO: to Step 9   sex therapy.

STEP 9.   Is there interview, history, and relationship test evidence of relationship distress associated with SD such as emotional conflict, infertility stresses, and infidelity?

        YES: <u>RELATIONSHIP DISTRESS SD</u>   <u>Treatment</u>: relationship therapy and cognitive-
                                            behavioral sex therapy.

        NO: to Step 10

STEP 10.   Is there also a complaint of another SD with the person and/or partner?

        YES: MULTIPLE SEX DYSFUNCTION <u>Treatment</u>: Comprehensive treatment of the causes and
             ("Mixed SD"). Reconsider Steps 1,   effects of the multiple sex dysfunctions.
             2, 7, and 8.

        NO: If acquired SD, consider Step 3,
             Psychosexual Skills Deficit.
             Reconsider and reevaluate the case.

Name:_____   PESI Score: _____

Date: _____   File #: _____

Premature Ejaculation Severity Index (PESI)

(Metz & McCarthy, 2003)

Medical Factors: Describe any physical health problems:

List medications and doses you take:

Over the last 6 months, what is your average number of ejaculations **per month** of:

Sex with a partner _____   Masturbation _____   All other _____ (e.g., "Wet dreams")

Previous Treatment: Please describe how you have tried before to treat or overcome premature ejaculation? (For example: talked to Doctor, tried creams, condoms, "squeeze" technique, distraction, etc.).
   "I have tried. . . ."

(Circle the number that indicates what you typically experience for the questions below.)

1. HOW LONG HAS PREMATURE OR RAPID EJACULATION BEEN A PROBLEM FOR YOU?

10	9	8	7	6	5	4	3	2	1	0
Lifelong ("All my life.")					Intermittent ("Off and on") ("Now and then")					Recent or new problem ("Just started")

2. IN WHAT PERCENT OF ALL SEX ACTS ARE YOU UNABLE TO CHOOSE WHEN TO EJACULATE?

10	9	8	7	6	5	4	3	2	1	0
100%	90%	80%	70%	60%	50%	40%	30%	20%	10%	0%

3. WHEN DO YOU USUALLY EJACULATE?

10	9	8	7	6	5	4	3	2	1	0
Before penetration			At penetration			Shortly after penetration				After some intercourse

4. IF YOU CAN HAVE INTERCOURSE, HOW LONG IS IT BEFORE YOU EJACULATE?

10	9	8	7	6	5	4	3	2	1	0
Not able to enter	15 secs.	30 secs.	1 min.	2 mins.	3 mins.	4 mins.	5 mins.	10 mins.	15 mins.	More than 15 mins.

5. RATE THE INTENSITY OR VIGOR OF PHYSICAL STIMULATION AT THE TIME OF EJACULATION?

10	9	8	7	6	5	4	3	2	1	0

Very mild,
little,
or slow

Very intense,
vigorous,
or fast

6. HOW DIFFICULT IS IT FOR YOU TO CONTROL OR CHOOSE WHEN YOU EJACULATE?

10	9	8	7	6	5	4	3	2	1	0

Extremely
difficult
to control

Extremely
easy
to control

7. HOW UPSET IS YOUR SEXUAL PARTNER BECAUSE OF YOUR PREMATURE EJACULATION?

10	9	8	7	6	5	4	3	2	1	0

Extremely
troubled

Very
calm

8. HOW UPSET ARE YOU BECAUSE OF YOUR PREMATURE EJACULATION?

10	9	8	7	6	5	4	3	2	1	0

Extremely
troubled

Very
calm

9. HOW MUCH HAS YOUR PREMATURE EJACULATION AFFECTED YOUR LIFE IN GENERAL?

10	9	8	7	6	5	4	3	2	1	0

Major impact
(Ex: makes me shy, has
ruined relationships.)

No significant
effect

10. HOW OFTEN WHEN YOU HAVE SEX DO YOU ALSO HAVE ERECTION PROBLEMS?

10	9	8	7	6	5	4	3	2	1	0
100%	90%	80%	70%	60%	50%	40%	30%	20%	10%	0%

PREMATURE EJACULATION SEVERITY INDEX

(To determine your severity index, add PESI items 1-10, and enter score below and on top of first page.)

(TOTAL SCORE: _____)

100	90	80	70	60	50	40	30	20	10	0

EXTREME
SEVERITY

MILD
SEVERITY

Name:_____   EISI Score: _____

Date: _____   File #: _____

Ejaculation Inhibition Severity Index (EISI)

(Metz & McCarthy, 2003)

<u>**Medical Factors:** Describe any physical health problems:</u>

<u>List medications and doses you take:</u>

<u>Over the last 6 months, what is your average number of ejaculations **per week** of:</u>

Sex with a partner _____   Masturbation _____   All other _____ (e.g., "Wet dreams")

<u>Previous Treatment: Please describe how you have tried before to treat or overcome ejaculation inhibition?</u>
(For example: talked to doctor, tried lubricant, vitamins, fantasy, etc.).
   "I have tried. . . ."

(Circle the number that indicates what you typically experience for the questions below.)

1. HOW LONG HAS EJACULATION INHIBITION BEEN A PROBLEM FOR YOU?

10	9	8	7	6	5	4	3	2	1	0
Lifelong ("All my life.")				Intermittent ("Off and on") ("Now and then")						Recent or new problem ("Just started")

2. WHAT PERCENT OF ALL SEX ACTS ARE YOU UNABLE TO EJACULATE?

10	9	8	7	6	5	4	3	2	1	0
100%	90%	80%	70%	60%	50%	40%	30%	20%	10%	0%

3. WHEN DO YOU USUALLY EJACULATE DURING SEXUAL INTERCOURSE?

10	9	8	7	6	5	4	3	2	1	0
Never			After 45 minutes			After 30 minutes				Before 8 minutes

4. IF YOU CAN EJACULATE BY MASTURBATION, HOW LONG IS IT BEFORE YOU EJACULATE?

10	9	8	7	6	5	4	3	2	1	0
Never			After 45 minutes			After 30 minutes				Before 8 minutes

5. RATE THE INTENSITY OR VIGOR OF PHYSICAL STIMULATION AT THE TIME OF EJACULA-TION?

```
  10        9        8        7        6        5        4        3        2        1        0
```
Very intense,   Very mild,
  vigorous,   relaxed,
or extremely   or slow
    fast

6. HOW DIFFICULT IS IT FOR YOU TO CHOOSE WHEN YOU EJACULATE?

```
  10        9        8        7        6        5        4        3        2        1        0
```
Extremely   Extremely
 difficult   easy

7. HOW UPSET IS YOUR SEXUAL PARTNER BECAUSE OF EJACULATION DELAY OR ABSENCE?

```
  10        9        8        7        6        5        4        3        2        1        0
```
Extremely   Very
 troubled   calm

8. HOW UPSET ARE YOU BECAUSE OF YOUR EJACULATION DELAY OR ABSENCE?

```
  10        9        8        7        6        5        4        3        2        1        0
```
Extremely   Very
 troubled   calm

9. HOW MUCH HAS YOUR EJACULATION INHIBITION AFFECTED YOUR LIFE IN GENERAL?

```
  10        9        8        7        6        5        4        3        2        1        0
```
  Major impact   No significant
(Ex: makes me shy, has   effect
 ruined relationships.)

10. HOW OFTEN WHEN YOU HAVE SEX DO YOU ALSO HAVE AN ERECTION PROBLEM?

```
  10        9        8        7        6        5        4        3        2        1        0
 100%      90%      80%      70%      60%      50%      40%      30%      20%      10%      0%
```

EJACULATION INHIBITION SEVERITY INDEX

(To determine your severity index, add EISI items 1-10, and enter score below and on top of first page.)

(TOTAL SCORE: _____)

```
 100       90       80       70       60       50       40       30       20       10        0
```
EXTREME   MILD
SEVERITY   SEVERITY

CONTRIBUTORS

Michael E. Metz, PhD, is a Licensed Psychologist and Licensed Marital and Family Therapist in private practice, Meta Associates, St. Paul, Minnesota, and Adjunct Assistant Professor, Marriage and Family Therapy Program, Department of Family Social Science, University of Minnesota. He is the former director of the Marital and Sex Therapy Program and Post-Doctoral Clinical/Research Fellowship Program, Program in Human Sexuality, Department of Family Practice and Community Health, University of Minnesota Medical School, Minneapolis, MN. He received his PhD with distinction from the University of Pennsylvania, Philadelphia, with marital and sex therapy training at the Pennsylvania Center for Relationships (formerly the Marriage Council of Philadelphia), Family Studies Division, Department of Psychiatry, University of Pennsylvania Medical School. He is the author of more than 50 professional publications on marital and sexual therapy, couple conflict dynamics, sexual medicine, aging, and *The Styles of Conflict Inventory (SCI)* (for the psychometric assessment of couple conflict) published by Consulting Psychologists Press. He is also the author, with Barry McCarthy, of *Coping With Premature Ejaculation* (2003) and *Coping With Erectile Dysfunction* (2005), New Harbinger Publications. He is also a frequent and popular speaker and leader of professional and public workshops on various human relations topics. Dr. Metz may be contacted at 821 Raymond Avenue, Suite 440, St. Paul, MN 55114. E-mail: mmetzmpls@aol.com

Barry W. McCarthy, PhD, is currently a professor of psychology at American University and a partner at the Washington Psychological Center. He has published over 65 professional articles, 16 book chapters, and has coauthored nine books in the area of relationships and sexuality. Dr. McCarthy can be reached at the Washington Psychological Center, 5225 Wisconsin Avenue, NW, Suite 513, Washington, DC 20015. E-mail: mccarthy160@comcast.net

RESOURCES

American Psychiatric Association. (2000). *Diagnostic and Statistical Manual of Mental Disorders (DSM-IV-TR;* 4th ed. text rev.). Washington, DC: Author.

Grenier, G., & Byers, E. S. (2004). Premature or rapid ejaculation: Heterosexual couples' perceptions of men's ejaculatory behavior. *Archives of Sexual Behavior, 33*(3), 261-270.

Laumann, E. O., Paik, A., & Rosen, R. C. (1999). Sexual dysfunction in the United States: Prevalence and predictors. *Journal of the American Medical Association, 261*, 537-544.

Loudon, J. B. (1998). Potential confusion between erectile dysfunction and premature ejaculation: An evaluation of men presenting with erectile difficulty at a sex therapy clinic. *Sexual and Marital Therapy, 13*(4), 397-401.

McCarthy, B. W. (2001). Relapse prevention strategies and techniques with erectile dysfunction. *Journal of Sex and Marital Therapy, 27*, 1-8.

McCarthy, B. W., & Fucito, L. (2005). Integrating medication, realistic expectations, and therapeutic integration in the treatment of male sexual dysfunction. *Journal of Sex and Marital Therapy, 31*, 319-328.

Metz, M. E., & McCarthy, B. W. (2003). *Coping With Premature Ejaculation: Overcome PE, Please Your Partner, and Have Great Sex.* Oakland, CA: New Harbinger Publications.

Metz, M. E., & McCarthy, B.W. (2004). *Coping With Erectile Dysfunction: How to Regain Confidence and Enjoy Great Sex.* Oakland, CA: New Harbinger Publications.

Metz, M. E., & Miner, M. (1998). Psychosexual and psychosocial aspects of male aging and sexual health. *Canadian Journal of Human Sexuality, 7*(3), 245-259.

Metz, M. E., & Pryor, J. L. (2000). Premature ejaculation: A psychophysiological approach for assessment and management. *Journal of Sex and Marital Therapy, 26*(4), 293-320.

Metz, M. E., Pryor, J., Abuzzahab, F., Nesvacil, L., & Koznar, J. (1997). Premature ejaculation: A psychophysiological review. *Journal of Sex and Marital Therapy, 23*(1), 3-23.

Mosher, D. L. (1980). Three psychological dimensions of depth of involvement in human sexual response. *Journal of Sex Research, 16*(1), 1-42.

Perelman, M. A. (2004). Evaluation and treatment of the ejaculatory disorders. In T. Lui (Ed.), *Atlas of Male Sexual Dysfunction.* Philadelphia, PA: Current Medicine.

Rowland, D. L., & Slob, A. K. (1997). Premature ejaculation: Psychophysiological considerations in theory, research and treatment. In R. C. Rosen, C. M. Davis, & H. J. Ruppel, Jr. (Eds.), *The Annual Review of Sex Research* (Vol. 8., pp. 201-209. Mason City, IA: Society for the Study of Human Sexuality.

Zilbergeld, B. (1999). *The New Male Sexuality.* New York: Bantam.

Pedophilia and Other Paraphilias

Gene G. Abel, Markus Wiegel, and Candice A. Osborn

Sexual behavior is an immensely varied phenomenon that can range from the intimate and erotic to the pornographic, bizarre, and even illegal. Not all atypical and uncommon sexual behaviors are problematic, requiring intervention and treatment. An example is sadomasochistic sexual behavior when practiced between two adults within the bounds of the "safe, sane, and consensual." However, other forms of sexual behavior are extremely harmful to self and others, and the harmful effects to the survivors of child sexual abuse have been well documented (Beitchman et al., 1992). Evaluating the client seeking assessment for possible paraphilia (sexual deviation) requires some specific approaches, as well as awareness and sensitivity to specific issues. For example, there is a potential conflict of interest between protecting the client's confidentiality and state mandatory reporting laws in cases of child sexual abuse. This contribution is not meant to be a comprehensive discussion to cover all aspects of such evaluations but, instead, clarifies a number of areas that will assist the evaluator in the initial assessment of a client presenting with or potentially being involved in paraphilic sexual behaviors.

A BRIEF REVIEW OF THE PARAPHILIAS

This section will help the evaluator review the basic paraphilias he or she will be evaluating and some characteristics of each to keep in mind. In a study of 561 individuals who had collectively committed over 290,000 sex acts, the majority of the reported acts were exhibitionism, frottage, child sexual abuse of boys outside the family, and voyeurism (Abel & Bradford, 2005). Surprisingly, acts of rape, incestuous sexual molestation of boys, bestiality, sadism, sexual abuse of girls outside the home, public masturbation, and fetishism were infrequently reported. These data reflect what various clients reported doing and do not reflect what typically brings them in for evaluation or treatment. The most common reasons adult males seek evaluation is for accusations of child sexual abuse (32%), voyeurism (15%), and public exposure (11%). Adolescent males seek evaluation for accusations of child sexual abuse (58%); fetishism (23%); voyeurism (16%); obscene phone calls, frottage/rape, and phone sex (each 15%); and exhibitionism (11%). Adult females seek evaluation primarily for accusations of child sexual abuse (18%). Adolescent females seek evaluation for accusations of child sexual abuse (46%), making obscene phone calls (17%), fetishism (11%), and frottage/rape (10%). Although frottage (sexual touching of another without their permission) and voyeurism (window peeping) commonly occur, the individuals involved in this activity infrequently appear in the clinic for evaluation because voyeurs are infrequently apprehended, and frottage behavior is usually ignored because the police may view it as a nuisance crime (unless it involves the touching of a child). The paraphilias can be conceptualized as relating to inappropriate or problematic sexual target choice, as in pedophilia, fetishism, and bestiality; or as relating to misguided, inappropriate, or problematic courtship behavior, as in voyeurism, exhibitionism, obscene phone calls and letters, stalking, frotteurism, and sexual sadism (Freund, Seto, & Kuban, 1997). However, central to both categories is the concept of consent.

Pedophilia and Sexual Abuse of Minors

Because the majority of clients seek evaluation for accusations of sexually abusing a child or minor, it is essential that the evaluator have a clear understanding of the diagnostic criteria for pedophilia. The category of child sexual abuse is not an official psychiatric diagnosis (it is included as a "V" code) and simply refers to sexual touching of a child (individuals below age 18, in most states). Some individuals may have sexually abused a child but are not pedophiles, generally because they have not carried out this behavior for longer than 6 months and/or do not have sustained sexual interest in children. Most, but not all, pedophiles have actually carried out child sexual abuse. Pedophiles can meet the criteria for pedophilia, which is having sexual urges, desires, and fantasies involving sex with children, but have not actually sexually abused a child. Sexual abuse of a child in most cases involves fondling, with oral, vaginal, or anal intercourse (as well as intercrural intercourse, which is the male's penis between the child's legs) occurring at a much lower frequency. If the evaluee admits to sexual abuse, the evaluator needs to get as much detail as possible regarding the duration, frequency, and kinds of sexual acts reported, but must also keep state mandatory reporting laws in mind. It is helpful to clarify immediately in the interview process that there is no "off-the-cuff talk"; that is, the evaluator may write down everything that is reported.

Cases of suspected child sexual abuse necessitate the evaluator having a clear understanding of and ability to identify individuals with pedophilia. Pedophilia is exceedingly important, because recent research (Abel & Harlow, 2002) indicates that those who meet the criteria for pedophilia in the *Diagnostic and Statistical Manual of Mental Disorders* of the American Psychiatric Association (*DSM-IV-TR*; 2000) commit 95% of the acts of child molestation, against 88% of all the victims of child sexual abuse. In a large group of 4,000 adult child sexual abusers, 65% met the *DSM-IV-TR* criteria for pedophilia. Because this one psychiatric illness constitutes such a large percentage of the acts of child molestation, it is critical to identify potential pedophiles so that treatment can proceed rapidly, protecting potential victims and protecting pedophiles from themselves.

> Mr. A.* was a 37-year-old male who was referred for a sexual abuser-specific evaluation after he had been arrested for sexually abusing the 8-year-old daughter of his girlfriend. He denied the offense but was found to have significant sexual interest in prepubescent children on the Abel Assessment for sexual interest. Based on this, it was recommended that he participate in sex offender-specific therapy, but he declined the recommended therapy. In the intervening months before his charge was adjudicated, he sexually abused another prepubescent female and received a second charge for child molestation.

Fetishism

Only rarely do individuals with a sexual fetish present for treatment, because, in many cases, the pursuit of the sexual fetish does not cause them distress. Sexual fetishists usually come to an evaluator's attention in two ways. First, an individual's partner may find out about the fetish or the individual may attempt to convince his or her partner to participate in the fetish. When the partner either finds the sexual fetish upsetting or refuses to participate despite

---

* Names and identifying characteristics in all case examples have been changed to protect confidentiality.

repeated efforts by the client, the couple may present for couple's or sex therapy. Second, a sexual fetish may come to light in the course of assessing another sexual behavior for which the client is primarily seeking an assessment. One study found that sexual fetishism was a secondary diagnoses in 33% of individuals with a primary diagnosis of bestiality, 25% of individuals engaging in obscene phone calls, 22% of individuals with pedophilia, 20% of transvestites, and 11% of those involved in voyeurism (Abel & Osborn, 1992).

Theoretically, any object or body part can become the focus of a sexual fetish. However, sexual fetishes tend to focus on clothing, such as underwear or lingerie; certain materials, such as rubber or leather; and particular body parts (partialism), such as feet, legs, or hair (Laws & O'Donohue, 1997); but a fetish may also focus on more unusual items, such as jewelry, balloons, their partner smoking cigarettes during sex, and so on. Persons with a sexual fetish engage in a variety of behaviors with the fetish object to achieve sexual arousal and orgasm, including fondling, stroking, wearing, smelling, or sucking the object while masturbating or engaging in sexual activity with a partner. Some individuals require the presence of the fetish object, actually or in fantasy, in order to become aroused, and are not able to become sexually aroused or reach orgasm without the fetish object. Individuals with sexual fetishes have, in some studies, been found to have higher than average levels of sexual arousal or an increased capacity for developing conditioned sexual arousal (Bailey, 1991). Although most individuals do not come in contact with the legal system as a result of their fetish, when it does happen it is usually as a consequence of the person attempting to steal the fetish object. More frequently, the diagnosis of a sexual fetish, which according to *DSM-IV-TR* criteria requires distress or impairment of functioning, results in relationship conflicts arising from the person insisting that the fetish be incorporated into sexual activity with the partner.

Bestiality

Bestiality is frequently considered a laughable condition, but it should not be considered trivial. Of all of the various paraphilias, bestiality is the most likely to lead to other categories of paraphilias. This is probably because an individual who can maintain sexual arousal while having a sexual encounter with an uncooperative animal can ignore much of the realities of such activity. Therefore, they probably can ignore the consequences to victims of other types of sexual acts.

Compulsive Internet Sexual Behavior

The repetitive, excessive, and compulsive use of Internet pornography, sex chat rooms, and attempts over the Internet to meet and be sexual with underage individuals is exceedingly common, especially given the increased availability of the Internet. About 20% of all Internet users engage in some form of online sexual activity (Cooper, Delmonico, & Burg, 2000). For the vast majority of these individuals, Internet sexual behavior is mainly recreational or educational and does not cause problems. However, for about 17%, Internet-related sexual behavior becomes problematic and compulsive (Cooper et al., 2000). Much like individuals with other types of compulsive behaviors, these individuals were characterized by an increased appetite, desire, or tolerance for Internet sexual behaviors; denial or minimization of negative consequences; repeated unsuccessful attempts to stop or limit online sexual activities; continuing to engage in Internet sexual activities despite negative consequences; and interference in offline relationships, as well as feelings of distress, guilt, and shame. Individuals with compulsive Internet sexual behaviors reported spending an average of 15 to 25 hours per week pursuing online sexual activities (Cooper et al., 2000). As with all paraphilic sexual behaviors, men use the Internet for sexual activity more frequently than women (Cooper et al., 2002). However, women are also at risk for developing compulsive Internet sexual behaviors, particularly related to the use of Internet chat rooms. The opportunities for sexual expression over the Internet are constantly evolving, and further innovations in technology will bring with them new means and opportunities for engaging in Internet sexual behaviors.

On the one hand, the use of the Internet and computers for sexual pursuits can be conceptualized as applying new technology to common sexual behaviors. For example, use of chat rooms may replace use of newspaper personal ads or calling telephone-sex lines, and viewing online erotic materials and pornography may take the place of magazines and films or videos. Other paraphilic behaviors may also be expressed using this new technology, such as live Internet cameras, which can be used to expose one's genitals or watch others engaging in sexual behavior. On the other hand, certain characteristics of online sexual behavior may make it particularly liable to becoming problematic and compulsive. These Internet characteristics include a sense of anonymity, ease and affordability of access, the ability to present oneself as one wishes, and the availability of a wide range of ever-updated sexual materials (Beard, 2005).

Correspondingly, individuals with problematic Internet-related sexual behaviors can be classified into two types: (a) those individuals with a previously established pattern of problematic sexual behaviors, and (b) individuals who are vulnerable to developing compulsive Internet sexual behavior (Cooper et al., 2001). The first type, the sexually compulsive type, is already involved with paraphilic sexual behaviors or other types of problematic sexual behaviors, such as sexual activity with strangers, excessive offline pornography and erotica use, or frequent extrarelationship sexual behaviors (i.e., sexual affairs). When they become involved with sexual pursuits over the Internet, they transfer the focus of their preexisting difficulties to Internet-related activities (Cooper et al., 2001; Pratarelli & Browne, 2002). For example, men with pedophilic interests may frequent teen chat rooms, using Internet chat as a means of grooming their victim, eventually hoping to set up a face-to-face meeting with a minor. Unfortunately, due to the ease of access, greater anonymity, and availability of sexual stimuli and sexual opportunities associated with the Internet, their paraphilic or problematic sexual behaviors often escalate in frequency, as well as the associated distress and interference of other activities (Cooper et al., 2001). The second type, the at-risk or predisposed type, had no preexisting problems with compulsive sexual behaviors, but developed compulsive Internet-related sexual activities as a result of the interaction between their personal characteristics that predisposed them to develop compulsive behaviors and the specific characteristics of the Internet described previously. In particular, individuals who were prone to procrastination, experienced dysthymia or depression, were involved with pathological gambling, or had substance use problems were at risk for developing compulsive Internet-related sexual activities as a way to cope with stress (Beard, 2005; Cooper et al., 2000, 2001, 2004). Another characteristic found to increase the risk of developing compulsive Internet sexual behaviors was sexual and nonsexual sensation-seeking traits (Cooper et al., 2000). In addition, the ever-changing, continuously updated nature of sexual stimuli on the Internet facilitates and reinforces the periodic obsessive desire in some individuals to find the "perfect" image, story, or erotic material that fulfills a favorite or preferential sexual fantasy theme (Delmonico, Griffin, & Moriarty, 2001). However, even if the individual finds that perfect image or sexual stimuli, the satisfaction is frequently fleeting and quickly followed by a new search for some variation or escalation of that sexual fantasy theme.

The negative consequences resulting from online sexual activities, particularly when they take on compulsive qualities, can be devastating and far-reaching. One study found that of individuals who engage in Internet-related sexual behaviors, 5.8% access the Internet for sexual reasons exclusively from work, while another 12.7% reported accessing the Internet to engage in online sexual behaviors both from work and from home (Cooper et al., 1999). Thus, 20% of men and 12% of women are using work computers for at least some portion of their Internet sexual activities (Cooper et al., 2000). Individuals who view pornography at their work site are involved in a very problematic behavior, because most major companies have hired security personnel or installed computer software that scan the use of company computers to identify those looking at or exchanging erotica or pornography. Because this behavior is against company policy, immediate dismissal is very possible and, although most cases of Internet pornography are not criminal actions, the loss of a job and positive letters of reference can have significant repercussions for the individual. Use of Internet chat rooms to engage in "cybersex" or to arrange face-to-face meetings for sexual encounters, although not a specific paraphilia, can cause major disruption in the individual's relationships when discovered by their partner. "Recreational sex" outside of the committed relationship is often viewed as a predivorce behavior. Individuals whose preferred Internet sexual behaviors involved chat rooms experienced greater problems in their real-world relationships, compared to individuals who predominantly used the Internet to view online pornography and erotica.

When assessing someone with potential compulsive Internet sexual behaviors, it is important to quantify the number of hours an individual spends pursuing sexual activities via the Internet. Cooper and colleagues (1999, 2004) have found that individuals who spend 11 hours or more per week in sexual activities on the Internet experience greater distress and interference, and tend to be more sexually compulsive, than those who spend less than 10 hours per week. It is typical for clients who are confronted by a significant other about these nonparaphilic sexual compulsions to at first deny and minimize them and then to promise never to do the behavior again, but, months later, they frequently revert to their sexually compulsive behaviors. In addition, it is important to gather details about the types of online activities in which the client is involved (e.g., chat rooms, online erotica, newsgroups, etc.) as well as the content of online sexual stimuli.

> Mr. B. was an attorney in his early 30s who became involved in sex chat rooms, questioned women who were interested in sadomasochistic activity, and eventually became involved with women who would spank him. By his report, the result of his participation in the spanking led to his use of spanking fantasies during masturbation and sex with his wife and his seeking out more and more injurious behavior. Initially, he was exceedingly cautious about safe sex. However, by the time he was evaluated, he had been involved in over 100 encounters with different women who performed sadistic acts upon him (with his permission). He had started meeting individuals whom he knew nothing about, in environments that were strange to him, and had been disregarding protecting himself from sexually transmitted diseases. The frequency of this behavior and the expense involved in traveling around the United States for such encounters was impinging on his professional work.

Voyeurism

Voyeurism, exhibitionism, frotteurism, and rape represent increasingly intrusive forms of nonconsensual sexual interactions. Although most individuals find it arousing to watch a sexual partner undress or to look at a naked sexual partner, when this is done without the knowledge or consent of the other person it becomes problematic. The careful assessment of voyeurism is particularly important because it may represent a "gateway paraphilia" for some individuals. Although not all voyeurs engage in more severe forms of behavior, some research indicates that voyeurism tends to develop prior to other paraphilias such as exhibitionism or frotteurism (Abel & Rouleau, 1990; Freund & Watson, 1990). Individuals with voyeuristic sexual interests frequently prefer this to looking at pornography because voyeurism involves a relationship, albeit a one-sided or imagined one, with a real person (Laws & O'Donohue, 1997). Voyeurs rarely watch females who are known to them. The voyeuristic behaviors may be exciting to the client because it involves watching something personal and intimate, violating taboos, or the risk of getting caught. These individuals have been found to possess poor social skills, be less assertive, experience sexual dysfunction, and have deficits in sexual knowledge (Marshall, Eccles, & Barbaree, 1991).

Some degree of voyeuristic sexual fantasies and interest is common and normative; the assessment of voyeurism should therefore focus on the extent to which it has become a preoccupation or compulsive behavior. A diagnosis of voyeurism may be appropriate when it dominates a person's sexual fantasies and behaviors, supplants and interferes with the normal progression of courtship, or when it causes the person distress. The evaluator should assess the amount of time the client spends fantasizing about, seeking out opportunities for, and engaging in voyeuristic sexual behaviors. Clinicians can assess the degree of compulsiveness by asking whether the person has ever unsuccessfully tried to stop these behaviors. Paying careful attention to the antecedents and consequences of the voyeuristic behavior can provide some insight into the function of the behaviors for the person, such as emotion regulation, which is frequently associated with a behavior becoming compulsive. Lastly, an interest in voyeurism should not be dismissed as a victimless crime, but should serve as a warning sign to assess the degree to which it has escalated to other behaviors such as exhibitionism, frotteurism, stalking, and potentially rape.

Exhibitionism

Exhibitionism is the most commonly committed paraphilia but, relative to the numbers of exhibitionistic acts that are committed, only a small percentage of exhibitionists actually seek out evaluation. Like many other paraphilias, exhibitionism tends to begin during the mid-teen years or during the mid-twenties (Abel & Rouleau, 1990; Smukler & Schiebel, 1975). It tends to be predominantly a male disorder, although limited reports of female exhibitionists exist (J. P. Fedoroff, Fishell, & B. Federoff, 1999); however, the targets of exhibitionism tend to be exclusively female. Exhibitionists can expose their genitals from a variety of environments; some exhibit (generally only to a small number of individuals) in public settings, on foot or from their car, while others expose their genitals from their own home or from buildings. The reaction an exhibitionist expects from his victim can range from shock and fear to sexual approval and reciprocation (Laws & O'Donohue, 1997). Individuals who expose their genitals tend to have similar demographic backgrounds to persons in the general population. In addition, exhibitionists do not seem to have a specific psychological profile or evidence a distinguishable sexual arousal profile on objective measures (Marshall & Hall, 1995; Marshall, Payne, Barbaree, & Eccles, 1991).

When assessing exhibitionism, it is particularly important to determine the underlying motivations; that is, to assess the function of the behavior through its antecedents and consequences. The client's exposing his genitals can occur during a hypomanic or manic episode, result from organic brain deficits (in particular left frontal temporal lobe problems), function as a method of affect regulation, or serve as a misguided attempt at courtship. In addition, individuals with intellectual disabilities may also be prone to exhibitionism. Because exhibitionists have a very high frequency of exhibitionistic acts prior to their seeking treatment, they have a high recidivism rate posttreatment (Marshall, Eccles, & Barbaree, 1991). In general, a person with a lengthy history of a paraphilic behavior has a greater likelihood of recidivism than someone with a paraphilia whose frequency is low. The laws in most states are no longer treating exhibitionism as a nuisance crime because of the relative high frequency of acts of exhibitionism and significant recidivism rates posttreatment. The evaluator should also consider this paraphilia as serious, because re-arrest can have profoundly negative consequences to the community and the exhibitionist. In addition, it is important to assess individuals with this paraphilia carefully, because about 30% exhibit exclusively to children or minors and may be at risk for sexually abusing minors. There is also a high degree of overlap between exhibition and other paraphilias, including voyeurism, public masturbation, frotteurism, obscene phone calls, and child sexual abuse.

> Mr. C. had been exposing his genitals since his late teens. By the time he was evaluated, he had exposed his genitals over 200 times and had been arrested only twice. His usual exhibitionistic acts involved removing the license plate from his car, driving around the city until he was in a residential area with a number of females out walking, unbuttoning his pants and masturbating until he got an erection, and then, as a woman passed by his car, he would call to her while sitting back from the window so that she would see his erection. Irrespective of the woman's response to his exposing himself, he always interpreted it as the woman enjoying the experience. For example, if she frowned and walked away rapidly, he would interpret that to mean that she was so overwhelmed by her sexual feelings and responsiveness to seeing his erect penis that she had to leave. If she smiled and then walked away, especially if she turned back (probably to be sure he wasn't following her), he would conclude that she was very sexually interested in having sex with him and wanted to take another look because she enjoyed the experience so much. If the woman laughed at him or shrieked, he believed that she was surprised at her sexual responding at seeing his penis, so much so that she was laughing at herself. Her shrieks would be seen as clear evidence of her surprise and sexual enjoyment of seeing his penis. In other words, irrespective of the woman's response, his distorted thinking allowed him to rationalize and justify his behavior to support his contention that his exposing his penis to her was a thoroughly enjoyable experience for the woman.

Studies of the responses of victims of exhibitionists have found quite the contrary (Cox & McMahon, 1978). As is usually the case in individuals with paraphilias, exhibitionists conceal their sexual behavior from friends and family and do not talk to their victims; thus they do not appreciate how others see their behavior and, instead, interpret it in a way that is supportive of repeating the behavior.

Frotteurism

Frotteurism involves deriving sexual excitement from rubbing up against or touching other individuals without their knowledge, frequently in crowded places such as subways. Freund and colleagues (Freund et al., 1997; Freund & Watson, 1990) consider frotteurism as one of the courtship disorders. Individuals with frotteuristic sexual interest frequently are also involved in other paraphilic behaviors (Abel et al., 1987), and with voyeurism and exhibitionism, in particular (Freund et al., 1997). Like clients who engage in voyeuristic or exhibitionistic sexual behavior, clients engaging in frotteurism will have done so on numerous occasions. One study of 62 adult males with a primary diagnosis of frotteurism found that they had committed a mean number of 849.5 frotteuristic acts (Abel et al., 1987). The paraphilia frotteurism should be distinguished from more severe grabbing of female breasts, buttocks, and genitals that are better conceptualized as sexual assault or sexual harassment. Asking the client whether the persons he is touching are aware that his actions are for sexual arousal may be helpful in this respect. When assessing this disorder, it is important to obtain as clear a description of the frequency of such behaviors, the locations where they generally occur (on a bus or subway), and the types of behaviors involved (e.g., rubbing genitals against another person, touching another person's hair, genital area, etc.). Because a client may be reticent to fully admit the frequency of such behaviors, it may also be helpful to ask how frequently he rides the subway or bus, and to determine whether he is spending more time there than necessary to allow for additional opportunities to engage in frotteurism. It is also important to determine the degree to which these acts occur impulsively as opposed to being planned, as well as how frequently the activity is associated with substance use.

Sexual Masochism and Sadism

Most acts of masochism and sadism occur within the context of a committed relationship or as a result of Internet chat rooms bringing together individuals with these interests. When such behavior is mutually enjoyable and consensual between those involved, it does not constitute a problematic behavior. It is exceedingly unusual for masochism and sadism to be performed against an unwilling partner, although sadistic acts are extensively reported in the media.

Consensual forms of Bondage/Discipline/Sadomasochism (B&D, S&M) need to be distinguished from sadistic rape, lust murders, and sexually sadistic criminal behavior. Only 5% to 10% percent of rapists meet the diagnostic criteria for sadism (Abel et al., 1988). Most rapists are not sadists and use only as much force and violence as is needed to gain compliance from their victims, albeit in their own distorted perception (Freund & Watson, 1990; Prentky & Knight, 1991). In addition to issues of anger, power, and dominance, most cases of rape, including acquaintance or date rape, are characterized by a lack of inhibition of arousal in response to outward signs of distress and suffering by the rape survivor, rather than an increased arousal to the suffering of the victim (Lohr, Adams, & Davis, 1997). The distinguishing characteristic in lust murders is the fact that the sexual arousal is derived from the killing. Sexually sadistic criminals, who are often the subjects of high-profile reports in the media, tend to be rare. Data from 30 cases collected by the FBI indicate that, in nearly all of the cases, the offenses were carefully planned (Dietz, Hazelwood, & Warren, 1990). Commonly, victims were abducted, held captive for more than 24 hours, tortured, and, in 73% of the cases, were murdered. The preferred sexual activities included sexual bondage, anal rape, forced fellatio, and insertion of foreign objects. In many such cases, the individuals have profoundly narcissistic personality traits and many meet criteria for antisocial personality disorders. Sexually sadistic criminals and stalkers tend to be particularly dangerous, and it is strongly suggested that the average therapist not attempt to assess or treat this type of individual. Such individuals should be referred to a qualified and experienced forensic psychiatrist.

Mr. D. was a 17-year-old male who had been arrested and charged with assaulting and attempting to rape his 19-year-old sister. He had tied her up, beaten her, and would have raped her if their parents had not come home and disrupted the assault. He made numerous threats against his sister and, even after he had been mandated to move out of the family home, he returned, broke into the house, and attempted to rape her a second time. Fortunately, she had called the police while he was breaking into the house and he was arrested before he was able to rape her. During his evaluation, he admitted to gaining significant pleasure from terrifying and assaulting his sister, and reported engaging in sadistic sexual fantasies during masturbation. After the first assault on his sister, his parents attempted to minimize his actions and attributed them to his being frustrated that she was more successful than he at school. Additionally, they denied that he had any sexual intent in his actions and believed he could continue to live in the family home. It was only after he attempted to rape his sister a second time and they discovered his stash of sadistic pornography that his parents realized the extent of their son's sadistic sexual interests. At this point they accepted that their son was at significant risk to reoffend. He was subsequently referred to a forensic psychiatrist for treatment.

EVALUATING CLIENTS WITH PARAPHILIAS

Evaluation of a client who presents with potential problematic sexual behaviors or paraphilias requires a comprehensive assessment involving a number of topic areas. Beyond assessing the specific alleged problematic or paraphilic sexual behavior with which the client presents, the evaluation needs to include obtaining informed consent, identifying all additional deviant as well as nondeviant sexual behaviors, objectively measuring sexual interests and arousal, mapping cognitive distortions, and assessing the client's general sexual functioning and sexual knowledge. Additionally, it is important to include an assessment of the client's social and assertiveness skills, Axis I clinical disorders, Axis II disorders, substance use issues, relationship functioning, and medical/physical history at some point in the overall evaluation. Many of the aforementioned topics can be assessed provisionally while obtaining a thorough and comprehensive initial history from the client. A crucial difference between an assessment of paraphilic sexual behaviors and other forms of psychopathology is the need to obtain information from clients who are most often defensive, angry, isolated, filled with self-reproach, and motivated to minimize, distort, and misrepresent their sexual behaviors. As a result, it is crucial to review all possible collateral materials carefully prior to the first interview with the client, and the evaluator should request, in writing, all available materials regarding the accusations. In most evaluation settings, time for conducting clinical interviews is limited, and employing questionnaires and psychological tests, such as the Millon Clinical Multiaxial Inventory-III (MCMI-III; T. Millon, Davis, & C. Millon, 1997), can facilitate completing a thorough assessment in a limited amount of time. Evaluation of sexual arousal and sexual interests may also require the use of specialized objective measures, such as visual reaction time (VRT) measures or penile plethysmography. Not all clinicians and evaluators have the necessary training, knowledge, or experience to conduct such an assessment competently or effectively. Evaluating one's own level of training and experience and when it is appropriate to refer a client to a sex-specific therapist or evaluator is part of the ethical practice of psychology (Ethical Standards: 2.01, Boundaries of Competence; American Psychological Association, 2002).

Obtaining Informed Consent

Obtaining a proper consent for assessment and history gathering is particularly critical because many clients seeking assessment have not only been accused of some paraphilic behavior, but also, in over half the cases, the accusation involves child molestation (Abel & Bradford, 2005). Following the enactment of the 1974 Child Abuse Prevention and Treatment Act (CAPT), all 50 states have mandatory reporting laws that, by and large, indicate that if a mental health worker suspects that a client has sexually touched or abused a specific child, this must be reported to child protective services. Failure to disclose sexual molestation could result in criminal action being taken against the evaluator. In most states the law specifies that the evaluator must know or strongly suspect who the alleged victim is. Of course, if clients report that they have sexually abused a child without identifying which child they have victimized or give insufficient information to strongly suspect who that victim might be, the evaluator is not justified in reporting such cases to child protective services. Many evaluators obtain the client's history without clarifying the mandatory reporting laws prior to starting the assessment and only afterward inform unsuspecting clients that they must make a report to child protective services or the criminal justice system. Ethically, however, the evaluator should clarify this to clients presenting with a potential paraphilia prior to starting the evaluation process, using a written consent form that clarifies that confidentiality must be broken if a specific child sexual abuse victim is identified (see a sample informed consent form on p. 173).

Dealing With Denial

In contrast to most clinical evaluations, clients who are involved with problematic or illegal sexual behaviors are frequently threatened by the idea of an assessment or motivated to conceal their behavior because of the serious sanctions that could result should their paraphilic behavior become known, including possible incarceration, disruption of their family, loss of employment, and the necessity of hiring legal representation, as well as feelings of shame and guilt regarding their paraphilic behavior. The evaluator is faced with having to navigate all of these issues as soon as the evaluation is started, and the evaluator is put in the difficult position of identifying the reason for the referral while dealing with the client's frequent denial and lack of motivation to seek out an assessment or comply with a court-ordered assessment. It is important to be constantly attentive to the factors and antecedent events that motivated clients to come forward and to participate in the precarious activity of an evaluation of their potential paraphilia. The challenge to the evaluator is, while simultaneously clarifying the limits of confidentiality, to also motivate clients to be forthcoming by helping them understand that a well-informed evaluator leads to a much better assessment.

The typical denying paraphiliac will most often try to put the examiner in the immediate position of either accepting his or her denial or coming into conflict with the client, who has come forward for a proper evaluation. It is recommended that the evaluator not take sides regarding whether the accusations or the client's denial is valid. Instead, the evaluator informs the client that the factors that contributed to the accusation of inappropriate sexual behavior await the result of a proper assessment. So, although the client initially asks the evaluator to join his or her side in denial of the accusation, the objective evaluator must clarify that answering such questions must follow the proper assessment, not precede it. Nonetheless, paraphiliacs will often attempt to take a strong position of denying the accusation promptly after the assessment begins. If the client spends the first 30 minutes of the evaluation process taking the strong position of denying the accusation, it makes it more difficult for the evaluator to question the legitimacy of the accusations against the client. Therefore, if the client takes the strong position of denial, the evaluator should immediately change the subject to a less emotionally ridden topic and, instead, gather historical elements dealing with his or her family constellation, relationships within the family, educational and work history, and so on. After the client "cools down," the evaluator once again poses the question of what has led to the referral.

Clients frequently have clear information that justifies their being improperly accused and want to explain in great detail the factors justifying their position. Under these conditions the evaluator questions if others may have "misunderstood" or "misperceived" the actions of the accuser. This allows the client to explain the events that led up to the accusation, but within the context of potential explanations (or rationalizations by the client) for the accusations. If the client once again moves promptly into a strong position of denial, then the evaluator must again switch the topic from the emotionally laden claim of false accusations to an emotionally more neutral topic to allow the client to "cool off." Again, if the evaluator permits the client to give extensive details that support his or her denial, it becomes much more difficult for the client to eventually look at the potential misunderstandings that surround the accusation.

Creating a Neutral Environment

The goal of the evaluator is to allow clients the opportunity to discuss the details of their possible inappropriate sexual behavior in an emotionally neutral environment. This means that the evaluator must be able to tolerate listening to clients report horrendous and sometimes frightening sexual behavior without reacting emotionally. Clients are very aware of the strong sanctions that society will impose should these inappropriate sexual behaviors be found out. In contrast, the evaluator cannot react to clients reporting behavior that might seem exceedingly gross by telegraphing the shame and guilt typically reflected by society. Those who cannot maintain objectivity without showing disdain for the client or the client's behavior should not be evaluating potential paraphiliacs. The evaluator wants to know everything, including all the details, so as to organize a proper diagnosis and potential treatment plan or referral to a sex-specific therapist. Telegraphing the community's outrage for inappropriate sexual behavior will not allow clients to be forthcoming about their behavior and, therefore, will block them from receiving proper diagnoses and recommendations.

Evaluating Deviant and Nondeviant Sexual Behaviors

A common error for evaluators is assuming that the only sexual problem that the client has is the one that the client initially discusses. However, research has confirmed that paraphiliacs frequently become involved in a variety of different paraphilic acts, directed against females and males, across a variety of ages, involving victims within and outside of the family (Abel et al., 1988). In interviewing, assume that the client has been involved in a variety of inappropriate sexual behaviors. Don't ask, "Are there any other types of sexual behaviors you have carried out?" Instead, say, "Tell me about the other types of sexual behaviors that you have been involved with." It is vital to ask about and assess all the categories of paraphilic behavior, and it is helpful to have a list of the various paraphilias and go through them one at a time. As the evaluator goes through the list, rather than asking whether the client has ever engaged in the sexual behaviors, it is more productive to ask, "How old were you when you first. . . ?" or "Approximately how many times have you. . . ?" When the evaluator has finished going through the list, the final catch-all question is, "What other kinds of sexual behavior have you been involved in that could be problematic if others were aware of them?" Special attention should focus on behaviors in which a victim is not easily identified and yet become problematic for the client (sexual compulsive behavior involving multiple sexual partners, multiple affairs during a committed relationship, preoccupation with Internet erotica and/or sex chat rooms, as well as acquiring and distributing erotica). Pornography is defined as sexual activity involving an individual who cannot give consent or involving sexual behavior that is injurious to the victim. The use of Internet pornography, although frequently defined by the client as a victimless crime, becomes devastating when the individual loses his or her job because of the use of company computer equipment and Internet access to look at pornography, arrange for sexual contacts with others, and so forth.

In a small percentage of cases, the evaluator will have to take immediate action for the protection of clients and/or others in their environment. For example, ongoing child molestation of a child in the client's current environment, sadomasochistic activity that is well beyond consenting participation by the client's partner, autoasphyxiation in which clients strangle themselves in order to increase sexual excitement, or unprotected sexual activity with partners unknown to the client all require the evaluator to get an immediate consultation with a specialist in evaluating paraphiliacs. The client's immediate removal from access to potential victims, implementation of medication to quickly reduce sexual drive, rapid institution of cognitive-behavioral treatment with a strong relapse prevention component, and prompt discussion with individuals in the client's environment can prove exceedingly effective at protecting the client and potential victims.

Sexual Interest and Arousal

Another important aspect of evaluating sexual behavior problems is the use of objective means to measure the client's sexual interests and/or sexual arousal to a variety of stimuli. Such assessments are often beyond the scope of the typical evaluator and require referral to a sex-specific therapist. The two most commonly employed objective measures of sexual interest are penile plethysmography (also referred to as phallometry) and measures of visual reaction time (VRT).

Penile plethysmography (PPG) has long been used as an objective measure of sexual interest. Conceptually, PPG is based on the assumption that sexual arousal, as measured by penile circumference or volume change, to a stimulus (e.g., image, film, or audiotaped scenario) is evidence of sexual interest in the type of person or activity represented by the stimulus. Penile plethysmography (PPG) refers to a methodology for measuring penile tumescence response (penile circumference or penile volume) rather than a specific instrument.

Visual reaction time is based on the assumption that the longer a person views (i.e., attends to) a stimulus (usually an image) the greater his or her interest in the type of person or activity represented by the stimulus (Rosenzweig, 1942). The Abel Assessment for Sexual Interest (AASI; Abel et al., 2001) refers to a specific assessment instrument developed by Abel Screening, Inc. to evaluate pedophilic sexual interest. The AASI utilizes visual reaction time to various images in addition to a detailed questionnaire. Both VRT data and self-report data are used to assess respondents' sexual interest and calculate probability values that reflect the likelihood that a respondent has sexually touched a child or that he or she matches the characteristics of individuals who have sexually abused a child but attempted to conceal this during the evaluation (Abel & Harlow, 2002; Abel et al., 2001). Both the AASI and PPG have advantages and disadvantages based on the specific methods used.

The absence of paraphilic sexual interests and arousal, as measured by VRT or penile plethysmography, is diagnostically not informative because individuals may engage in paraphilic sexual behaviors without having a sustained sexual interest in that behavior. However, the presence of such paraphilic sexual interests and arousal, particularly in the case of child sexual abuse, is significant and an important consideration. Without the use of objective measures, paraphilic sexual interests, especially sexual attraction to children, might be missed because clients rarely volunteer such information.

A further integral aspect of evaluating the client's sexual interests, which does not require specialized equipment, involves assessing the client's sexual and/or masturbatory fantasies. This means obtaining the details of sexual fantasies during intercourse, masturbation, or just attending to sexual themes during the day. Such information can be exceedingly helpful because it allows the evaluator to potentially hear, in clients' words, the frequency of their various sexual themes when sexually aroused. The content of sexual fantasies is a very personal topic and may be difficult for clients to discuss. As a result, sometimes it is more productive to inquire about sexual and masturbatory fantasies later in the assessment, once rapport has firmly been established. The evaluator can usually ask about such sexual fantasies and the typical client will initially report rather benign heterosexual or homosexual fantasies as being a large part of their sexual interest. The evaluator should then ask, "What other sexual fantasies do you have?" When the clients have exhausted their list of the various categories, the evaluator then asks for a more quantitative report of the client's fantasies in the various categories. The client, for example, may report that 80% of his or her sexual fantasies are of consensual heterosexual interaction, that 15% fall within the category of dominance or control, and the remaining 5% involve adolescent females. Being able to quantify the various fantasy categories helps the evaluator appreciate all of the client's problematic sexual interests.

Miscellaneous Areas of Assessment

Specific sexual interest in and sexual arousal to paraphilic sexual behaviors may not be the only etiologically important factors. For example, a distinction is made between individuals who meet the diagnostic criteria for pedophilia and those who have sexually abused minors without sustained sexual interest in children. Sexual abuse of a minor can also be related to substance intoxication, it can occur in the course of hypomanic and manic episodes with symptoms of hypersexuality, and it can be related to antisocial personality traits or intellectual disabilities. Thus, an assessment of paraphilic sexual behaviors must also be able to rule in/ rule out other associated Axis I and II disorders. Gathering information about the client's strengths and weaknesses, as well as the degree of social support from the client's family and friends, will facilitate treatment planning.

EVALUATING ADOLESCENTS

Adolescents (14-17 years of age) commit 20% of all rapes and 50% of all child sexual abuse. The average age of child molesters in the United States, according to a government study, is age 14 (Snyder, 2000). This does not mean that adolescents involved in inappropriate sexual behavior absolutely become adult sexual offenders. It is suspected that 5% to 8% of adolescent sex abusers will continue abusing, but the vast majority of these adolescents stop their inappropriate sexual behavior before reaching adulthood. *DSM-IV-TR* diagnostic criteria for pedophilia do not allow adolescents to be considered for the diagnosis of pedophilia unless they have sustained sexual interest, urges, or behavior in children under the age of 13; the adolescent must be at least 16 years of age or older; and the victim must be at least 5 years younger than the adolescent. The reason for this is to exclude cases in which an adolescent becomes sexually involved with someone relatively close in age to the adolescent. The American Psychiatric Association, by their diagnostic criteria, was attempting to identify pedophiles as individuals who had a persistent, ongoing sexual interest in children, certainly not based on a single episode of a sexually abusive act or experimental sexual activity between children.

It is common knowledge that adolescents learn about sex primarily from experimenting with other adolescents and, therefore, because younger individuals are always present and are relatively easy to engage in sexual activity, it should not be surprising that adolescents frequently get involved in sexual abuse of younger children. In part, the ease of abuse of younger children emanates from younger children not being appreciative of with whom they should be sexual. They instead believe what older individuals tell them and are willing to accept an adolescent's or older child's comments that such activity is acceptable. It isn't until age 12 to 14 that children begin to appreciate that there are standards of sexual behavior that give them the right to choose with whom they are sexual and when they are sexual, rather than that being determined by statements that older individuals make.

Adolescents engage in sexual activity with much younger children as part of sexual experimentation and because of their proximity to younger children, their lack of appreciation of the potentially severe consequences of such behavior, the lack of sex education in our culture, and the ease of effectively concealing such behavior from others (by the older adolescent demanding that the younger child not tell because the younger would be punished by their parents). Other factors that contribute to an adolescent engaging in sexual activity with a much younger child include his or her proximity to groups or gangs where it is culturally accepted to sexually aggress on others and the use of alcohol or recreational drugs that facilitate sexual impulsivity. Additionally, adolescents with Attention-Deficit/Hyperactivity Disorder, which appears to be modestly correlated with impulsive acts, including sexually impulsive acts, are at higher risk for sexual involvement with children. The possibility that adolescents could be actual pedophiles, where sexual interest develops at an early age and continues throughout adulthood, must not be ignored as a possibility, especially in cases where there have been molestations of more than one child. Referral to a sex-specific treatment provider should definitely be considered for repetitive adolescent sexual abusers.

REFERRING CLIENTS TO A SEX-SPECIFIC THERAPIST

When the evaluator determines that a client needs to undergo sexual abuser-specific therapy for a serious sexual problem, it is important to know the difference between traditional therapists and sex-specific therapists. Traditional therapy is not particularly effective at dealing with serious chronic paraphilias (Abel & Harlow, 2002). Sexual abuser-specific therapists have unique training, qualifications, and evaluative and treatment skills not only for working with clients, but also to protect the general public from individuals with paraphilias who pose a significant risk. Table 1 (p. 171) outlines the difference between sex-specific therapists and traditional therapists, as it applies to clients involved in sexual abuse of minors. When referring a serious sex offender to a sexual abuser-specific therapist, it is critically important to verify that the therapist has the qualifications necessary to deal with more serious paraphiliacs. There are six characteristics that a sexual abuser-specific therapist should have. First, the therapist should have the necessary experience treating the type of paraphilia being referred. A rule of thumb would be selecting a therapist who works with at least 50 individuals with paraphilic or problematic sexual behaviors per year. Second, a sexual abuser-specific therapist should have the ability to include (and should regularly use) objective measures of sexual interest and arousal as part of the initial assessment, as well as to evaluate treatment outcomes. If the therapist does not have the necessary training or equipment to do objective sexual interest testing, the therapist should have a working relationship with another evaluator who can provide such testing. Similarly, if the therapist is not a psychiatrist, there should be a working relationship with a medical doctor who can prescribe medications such as selective serotonin reuptake inhibitors (SSRIs) and Provera, which directly target sexual drive or desire. If the person is able to prescribe psychopharmacological treatments, the therapist should be comfortable and knowledgeable about issues involved with prescribing medications to reduce sexual drive and desire (e.g., monitoring of hormone levels or liver functioning). Fourth, in addition to using medication to reduce paraphilic sexual arousal and interests, the therapist should employ behavioral treatments that directly reduce such sexual interests, such as covert sensitization, aversion, or satiation therapies. Fifth, the therapist's treatment package should also contain cognitive-behavioral and relapse prevention therapy modules and skills training. And last, the therapist should be a member of the Association for the Treatment of Sexual Abusers (ATSA). Professional organizations establish ethical guidelines specific to the field and generally publish practice guidelines. Therapists who are members of ATSA are more likely to have had the continued training and experience required to successfully treat sexual abuser clients with more complex clinical presentations.

Resolving the questions raised by the referral agent needs to be accomplished as rapidly as possible. Many times the evaluator does not have the experience or testing material and equipment available to objectively evaluate clients' specific sexual interests. Therefore, when the risk is high for future victims and for clients themselves, immediate referral is critical. The Association for the Treatment of Sexual Abusers (http://www.atsa.com)* maintains a listing of experts in the field of evaluating individuals with potential paraphilias. The Child Molestation Research and Prevention Institute (http://www.childmolestationprevention.org), Stop It Now (http://www.stopitnow.com), and the Safer Society (http://www.safersociety.org) can all provide referrals to sex-specific evaluators and therapists in the immediate area.

---

* Although all websites cited in this contribution were correct at the time of publication, they are subject to change at any time.

TABLE 1: Contrast – Traditional Versus Sexual Abuser Specific Therapist*

Traditional Therapist	Sex-Specific Therapist
Offers dynamically oriented therapies (talking therapies) that do not directly reduce sexual interest in children.	Offers sexual abuser-specific treatments that use cognitive-behavioral techniques to drastically reduce or eliminate a patient's sex drive toward children.
Knows little about the development of a sex drive toward children and frequently reacts emotionally to a patient with this disorder.	Trained to deliver sex-specific therapies to patients with sex drives toward children and to maintain objectivity.
Not trained to proceed with those sexual abuser patients who habitually lie, deny, conceal, and state that they do not want or need therapy.	Trained to proceed with the assessment and treatment of sexually abusive patients irrespective of their denial.
Has one focus: the patient's welfare.	Has a double focus: The children who must be protected and the patient's extinction of sexual interest in children.
Trained to assess whether a patient is a danger to himself or herself (suicide risk) or to others (murder risk).	Trained to assess murder risk, suicide risk, and the risk that the patient will sexually abuse a child or minor.
Usually delivers outpatient therapy that begins and ends in the therapist's office.	Organizes a plan to monitor the patient's activities outside the treatment setting.
Tests: Rarely uses objective measures to monitor treatment success.	Tests: Uses objective measures to prove treatment is effective for reducing paraphilic sexual interests.
Medicines: Not trained in use of SSRIs and Provera to alter sex drive.	Medicines: Trained in use of SSRIs and Provera to alter sex drive.
Success: Partial degrees of recovery are acceptable.	Success: Sex-specific therapy must significantly reduce sexual desire for children and protect potential victims.
Patient determines when the therapy ends.	Therapist determines when therapy ends.

* Adapted with permission from The Child Molestation Research and Prevention Institute website: http://www.childmolestationprevention.org.

CONCLUSION

These are exceedingly difficult times for individuals with paraphilias seeking assessment and/or treatment. The scandals in volunteer organizations and religious organizations have been followed by attempts to change the laws against sex offenders requiring lifetime registration, long periods of incarceration, and sometimes incarceration for life. These changes throughout the United States and Canada require all mental health providers to be knowledgeable about the initial assessment of the potential paraphiliac for ensuring the safety of the public and the safety of the client.

The most difficult aspect of evaluating individuals with paraphilias concerns the harsh attitudes that society, other therapists, and the evaluator's friends and family generally hold toward this population. The evaluator needs to be able to not be prejudiced by the widely held views that individuals with paraphilias are evil people and that all of them need to be incarcerated. Paraphiliacs carry out highly inappropriate behavior that can be very upsetting to the evaluator, but the difficult task of the evaluator is to not be contaminated by societal attitudes so that he or she can maintain objectivity to help a human being with a difficult sexual problem and, at the same time, protecting the community in an environment that may view such efforts as problematic.

Consent Form for
Evaluation of Sexual Interest

I understand that I am being asked to give my permission to participate in a screening procedure that will evaluate, beyond my awareness, my sexual interest. I will be asked to complete paper-and-pencil questionnaires regarding my attitudes and experiences with 21 categories of sexual interest. I will also be asked to undergo psychological testing to identify problems I may have that might be relevant to my evaluation and/or possible treatment. My physiologic response to a series of images of males and females of various ages will be measured, beyond my awareness. I will be asked to rate my level of sexual attraction to each slide using the number keys on a computer keyboard, as I view the images.

The interviews and self-report tests will ask intimate details about my life and behavior. Revealing such intimate information produces temporary anxiety, nervousness, depression, and/or emotional upset in approximately 80% of individuals. Should these emotional upsets persist, the staff will counsel me to help me deal with this discomfort. If I develop any anxiety, nervousness, depression, and/or emotional upset that may have resulted from this evaluation, I should contact the *Organization*.

All information obtained from this evaluation will become part of my psychiatric record and, as such, is confidential. However, there are three conditions under which information about me may be revealed to others. These are:

1. I reveal that I might harm myself.
2. I reveal that I plan to harm someone else.
3. The greatest problem resulting from this assessment is that I may reveal that I have committed sex acts that must be reported by state law.

Most state laws require that when individuals reveal to a professional that they have victimized specific children, this must be reported to the appropriate protection agencies, and it could lead to my being charged with the commission of a sex crime. I understand that I may choose not to answer any questions if to do so would reveal information that must be reported to the authorities. As to any other questions, I understand that I am answering them subject to the risks described in this paragraph.

The benefits of this evaluation are that the evaluators may be able to identify specific sexual interest that I have in inappropriate sexual behavior. Such information will help the evaluator recommend to me what kind of treatment would be indicated in my case.

The information that I provide the evaluator will be kept in my file, unless mandatory reporting is required by state law. This information will also be incorporated into a database at Abel Screening, Inc. under a special code and used, not only for understanding my case, but also for research regarding the understanding of sexual behavior in general. This information placed in Abel Screening, Inc. database for research purposes will <u>not</u> have my name associated with it.

My signature below indicates that any questions I had regarding my evaluation have been answered to my satisfaction. My signature also indicates that I have read and understand the inherent risks and benefits of such an evaluation as described in this consent form, and that I agree to participate in the evaluation of my sexual interests conducted by the *Organization*, in the manner described above. I hereby release the *Organization* and/or its employees, agents, or any other treatment participants for any loss, damage, or injury to me that may occur from any cause whatsoever as a result of my participation in this evaluation.

_____   _____

Signature   Date

_____   _____

Witness   Date

CONTRIBUTORS

Gene G. Abel, MD, is currently Medical Director of the Behavioral Medicine Institute of Atlanta and a full Professor of Clinical Psychiatry at Emory School of Medicine and Morehouse School of Medicine in Atlanta, Georgia. He has been researching the evaluation and treatment of individuals and paraphilias since 1969 and has over 140 publications. He has had six NIMH grants related to the evaluation and treatment of perpetrators and victims of sexual abuse. Dr. Abel was awarded the Masters and Johnson Award by the Society for Sex Therapy and Research and the Significant Achievement Award by the Association for the Treatment of Sexual Abusers. He currently supervises the evaluation and treatment of over 200 sex offenders, evaluates and treats professionals involved in professional sexual misconduct, and is co-founder of the Child Molestation Research and Prevention Institute, a nonprofit organization to help families deal with the issues of child sexual abuse. Dr. Abel may be contacted at the Behavioral Medicine Institute of Atlanta, 1401 Peachtree Street, N.E., Suite 140, Atlanta, GA 30309. E-mail: geneabel@mindspring.com

Markus Wiegel, MA, is a PhD candidate at Boston University whose dissertation focuses on the characteristics of female child sexual abusers of children. He currently is part of the research and development department at Abel Screening, Inc. He has conducted research and published in the areas of child sexual abusers, sexual dysfunction, and anxiety disorders. Prior to joining the Abel Screening, Inc. research team, Mr. Wiegel was the Assistant Director of the Sexuality Research and Treatment Program at the Center for Anxiety and Related Disorders at Boston University. Mr. Wiegel can be reached at ASI, 1280 Peachtree Street N.W., Suite 100, Atlanta, GA 30309. E-mail: Markus@abelscreening.com

Candice A. Osborn, MA, LPC, is currently Director of Sex Offender Services at the Behavioral Medicine Institute of Atlanta in Atlanta, Georgia. Before moving to Georgia, she was the Grants Manager of a research project to evaluate various treatment methodologies for child sexual abusers, funded by the National Institute of Mental Health, conducted at Florida Mental Health Institute in Tampa, Florida. Ms. Osborn previously evaluated Mentally Disordered Sexual Offenders at Atascadero State Hospital in California. Prior to this, she worked at Memphis Mental Health Institute and the New York Psychiatric Institute on a NIMH grant to evaluate and treat rapists. Ms. Osborn may be contacted at the Behavioral Medicine Institute of Atlanta, 1401 Peachtree Street, N.E., Suite 140, Atlanta, GA 30309. E-mail: cando001@msn.com

RESOURCES

Abel, G. G., Becker, J. V., Cunningham-Rathner, J., Mittelman, M. S., & Rouleau, J. L. (1988). Multiple paraphilic diagnoses among sex offenders. *Bulletin of the American Academy of Psychiatry and the Law, 16*, 153-168.

Abel, G. G., Becker, J. V., Mittelman, M. S., Cunningham-Rathner, J., Rouleau, J. L., & Murphy, W. D. (1987). Self-reported sex crimes of nonincarcerated paraphiliacs. *Journal of Interpersonal Violence, 2*, 3-25.

Abel, G. G., & Bradford, J. M. W. (2005, May). *The Assessment of Child Sexual Abusers.* Paper presented at the 156th annual meeting of the American Psychatric Association, Atlanta, GA.

Abel, G. G., & Harlow, N. (2002). *The Abel and Harlow Stop Child Molestation Prevention Study* (rev. text ed. April 2002). Retrieved November 1, 2005, from the Child Molestation Research and Prevention Institute website: http://www.childmolestationprevention.org/pdfs/study.pdf

Abel, G. G., Jordan, A. D., Hand, C. G., Holland, L. A., & Phipps, A. (2001). Classification models of child molesters utilizing the Abel Assessment for Sexual Interest. *Child Abuse and Neglect, 25*, 703-718.

Abel, G. G., & Osborn, C. A. (1992). The paraphilias: The extent and nature of sexually deviant and criminal behavior. *Psychiatric Clinics of North America, 15*, 675-687.

Abel, G. G., & Rouleau, J. L. (1990). The nature and extent of sexual assault. In W. L. Marshall, D. R. Laws, & H. E. Barbaree (Eds.), *Handbook of Sexual Assault: Issues, Theories, and Treatment of the Offender* (pp. 9-12). New York: Plenum.

American Psychiatric Association. (2000). *Diagnostic and Statistical Manual of Mental Disorders* (*DSM-IV-TR*; 4th ed. text rev.). Washington, DC: Author.

American Psychological Association. (2002). Ethical Principles of Psychologists and Code of Conduct. Retrieved November 30, 1995, from http://www.apa.org/ethics/code2002.html#preamble

Bailey, K. (1991). Human paleopsychopathology: Implications for the paraphilias. *New Trends in Experimental and Clinical Psychiatry, 7*, 5-16.

Beard, K. W. (2005). Internet addiction: A review of current assessment techniques and potential assessment questions. *CyberPsychology and Behavior, 8*, 7-14.

Beitchman, J. H., Zucker, K. J., Hood, J. E., DaCosta, G. A., Akman, D., & Cassavia, E. (1992). A review of the long-term effects of child sexual abuse. *Child Abuse and Neglect, 16*, 101-118.

Cooper, A., Delmonico, D. L., & Burg, R. (2000). Cybersex users, abusers, and compulsives: New findings and implications. *Sexual Addiction and Compulsivity, 7,* 5-29.

Cooper, A., Delmonico, D. L., Griffin-Shelly, E., & Mathy, R. M. (2004). Online sexual activity: An examination of potentially problematic behaviors. *Sexual Addiction and Compulsivity, 11,* 129-143.

Cooper, A., Griffin-Shelly, E., Delmonico, D. L., & Mathy, R. M. (2001). Online sexual problems: Assessment and predictive variables. *Sexual Addiction and Compulsivity, 8,* 267-285.

Cooper, A., Morahan-Martin, J., Mathy, R. M., & Maheu, M. (2002). Toward an increased understanding of user demographics in online sexual activities. *Journal of Sex and Marital Therapy, 28,* 105-129.

Cooper, A., Scherer, C., Boies, S. C., & Gordon, B. (1999). Sexuality on the Internet: From sexual exploration to pathological expression. *Professional Psychology: Research and Practice, 30,* 154-164.

Cox, D. J., & McMahon, B. (1978). Incidents of male exhibitionism in the United States as reported by victimized female college students. *International Journal of Law and Psychiatry, 3,* 453-457.

Delmonico, D. L., Griffin, E. J., & Moriarty, J. (2001). *Cybersex Unhooked: A Workbook for Breaking Free from Compulsive Online Sexual Behavior.* Center City, MN: Hazelden Educational Press.

Dietz, P. E., Hazelwood, R. R., & Warren, J. (1990). The sexually sadistic criminal and his offenses. *Bulletin of the American Academy of Psychiatry and the Law, 18,* 163-178.

Fedoroff, J. P., Fishell, A., & Fedoroff, B. (1999). A case series of women evaluated for paraphilic sexual disorders. *The Canadian Journal of Human Sexuality, 8,* 127-140.

Freund, K., Seto, M. C., & Kuban, M. (1997). Frotteurism and the theory of courtship disorder. In D. R. Laws & W. O'Donohue (Eds.), *Sexual Deviance: Theory, Assessment, and Treatment* (pp. 111-130). New York: Guilford.

Freund, K., & Watson, R. J. (1990). Mapping the boundaries of courtship disorder. *Journal of Sex Research, 27,* 589-606.

Laws, D. R., & O'Donohue, W. (Eds.). (1997). *Sexual Deviance: Theory, Assessment, and Treatment.* New York: Guilford.

Lohr, B. A., Adams, H. E., & Davis, J. M. (1997). Sexual arousal to erotic and aggressive stimuli in sexually coercive and noncoercive men. *Journal of Abnormal Psychology, 106,* 230-242.

Marshall, W. L., Eccles, A., & Barbaree, H. E. (1991). The treatment of exhibitionists: A focus on sexual deviance versus cognitive and relationship features. *Behaviour Research and Therapy, 29,* 129-135.

Marshall, W. L., & Hall, G. C. N. (1995). The value of the MMPI in deciding forensic issues in accused sex offenders. *Sexual Abuse: A Journal of Research and Treatment, 7,* 205-219.

Marshall, W. L., Payne, K., Barbaree, H. E., & Eccles, A. (1991). Exhibitionists: Sexual preferences for exposing. *Behaviour Research and Therapy, 29,* 37-40.

Millon, T., Davis, R., & Millon, C. (1997). *Millon Clinical Multiaxial Inventory-III Manual* (2nd ed.). Minneapolis, MN: National Computer Systems.

Pratarelli, M. E., & Browne, B. L. (2002). Confirmatory factor analysis of Internet use and addiction. *CyberPsychology and Behavior, 5,* 53-64.

Prentky, R. A., & Knight, R. A. (1991). Identifying critical dimensions for discriminating among rapists. *Journal of Consulting and Clinical Psychology, 59,* 433-443.

Rosenzweig, S. (1942). The photoscope as an objective device for evaluating sexual interest. *Psychosomatic Medicine, 4,* 150-158.

Smukler, A. J., & Schiebel, D. (1975). Personality characteristics of exhibitionists. *Diseases of the Nervous System, 36,* 600-603.

Snyder, H. N. (2000). *Sexual Assault of Young Children as Reported to Law Enforcement: Victim, Incident, and Offender Characteristics.* Pittsburgh, PA: National Center for Juvenile Justice. (NCJ No. 182990)

Sexual Addiction/Compulsion – Diagnosis and Treatment

Dennis P. Sugrue

An alarming number of clients are presenting in clinicians' offices with a sexual complaint that is nowhere to be found in the *Diagnostic and Statistical Manual of Mental Disorders* (*DSM-IV-TR*; American Psychiatric Association, 2000) yet is having a devastating impact on their health, career, and family life. They complain that their sexual behavior is out of control and ruining their lives, but professionals cannot agree on its cause or treatment, or even on what to call the condition.

In the early professional literature, out-of-control, high-frequency sexual behavior was referred to as nymphomania, satyriasis, erotomania, and Don Juanism. Today researchers, writers, and clinicians, unable to achieve a consensus on a label or conceptual model, refer to this problematic behavior as compulsive sexual behavior, sexual addiction, sexual impulsivity, or hypersexuality.

Patrick Carnes, a pioneer in the sexual addiction field, estimates that 8% of men and 3% of women in the general population suffer from sexual addiction (Carnes, 1983). Critics of the sexual addiction model challenge the magnitude of these estimates, insisting that the criteria for sexual addiction are overly inclusive (Klein, 2003). Regardless of theoretical orientation, however, most mental health professionals agree that people do lose control over their sexual behavior and experience dire consequences as a result (Sugrue, 2003).

For this contribution, it is not my intention to wade into the ongoing debate about the merits and weaknesses of conceptualizing problematic hypersexual behavior as either a sexual addiction or a sexual compulsion. In truth, both labels have their limitations (Bancroft & Vukadinovic, 2004). For the sake of impartiality, I will use the label *sexual addiction/compulsion*. Rather than critiquing sexual addiction and sexual compulsion as theoretical constructs, this contribution will focus on the practical tasks encountered in the clinical setting – namely, identifying and treating out-of-control sexual behavior.

WHAT IS (AND ISN'T) A SEXUAL ADDICTION/COMPULSION?

Does daily masturbation constitute a sexual addiction/compulsion? What about masturbation twice a day, every day? Is a man's plea, "I have a sexual addiction," after getting caught having an affair a valid cry for help or a clever way of deflecting responsibility? Is a person who has a boot fetish or who is heavily involved in the sadomasochistic community a sexual addict/compulsive? Does a woman who visits online adult chat rooms or a man who views pornographic pictures on an adult website have a sexual addiction/compulsion? All of the above questions have the same answer – it depends.

In our culture people tend to be suspicious of high-frequency sexual behavior – The underlying assumptions ranging from "Too much of anything can't be good for you" to "Sex is dangerous and corrupting." Even if masturbation is okay, the reasoning goes, certainly masturbating more than once a day cannot be healthy. Kafka (1997), a frequently cited researcher in the field, goes so far as to suggest that anyone who orgasms more than six times a week over a minimum duration of 6 months should be suspected of having a sexual addiction/compulsion.

On the other hand, it can be argued that high-frequency sexual behavior does not necessarily indicate an addiction/compulsion. The clinician needs to consider a number of variables such as the degree of behavioral control, consequences, organic factors, and psychological agenda when determining whether high-frequency sexual behavior is indeed an addiction/compulsion.

Consider Table 1 (below) and how various forms of high-frequency sexual behavior can differ from each other. Some people, for example, can have a very robust, healthy sexual drive. They enjoy sex and have frequent sexual opportunities. They exercise good judgment and control in their sexual behavior and, as a result, neither exploit others nor do they put themselves in jeopardy. Their sexual behavior has no agenda other than pleasure or pleasure and intimacy.

TABLE 1: High-Frequency Sexual Behavior

	TYPES OF HIGH-FREQUENCY SEXUAL BEHAVIOR				
	Healthy	**Neurotic**	**Characterological**	**Organic**	**Addictive/ Compulsive**
Pleasure	Normal	Limited	Normal	Absent to Normal	Limited
Brain Function	Normal	Normal	Normal	Impaired	Normal to mildly impaired
Control	Yes	Yes	Yes	Limited	Limited
Exploitative or Risk to Self	No	Yes	Potentially	Potentially	Yes
Psychological Agenda	No	Yes	Possibly but not necessarily	No	Yes

Some people engage in frequent sexual behavior because they have an underlying psychological agenda. Sex serves as a means to an end – perhaps attention, acceptance, or love. Their neurotic quest runs the risk of adverse outcomes like sexually transmitted infections (STIs), unwanted pregnancies, or serial dysfunctional relationships. They do not experience their behavior as out of control but, rather, as a matter of choice. Unfortunately, however, they continuously make bad choices in their quest to prove something, undo something, or soothe something. Because their core agenda remains unrealized, they keep returning to the self-defeating sexual behavior.

Some people have control over their sexual behavior and pursue sexual gratification whenever possible with little or no concern about the consequences. Because of a flawed character structure, exploitation of others or exposure to potential risk does not deter them; sometimes the domination or risk taking actually adds to the sexual excitement and gratification. In some cases sexual behavior may be driven by a psychological agenda (power, self-validation, sadism), but most often sexual behavior for these individuals is an unrestricted pursuit of gratification. They act when they can get away with it and have the ability to restrict their behavior when necessary. This pattern of sexual behavior is frequently observed in narcissistic and antisocial personalities.

Sexual control can be compromised due to organic factors. Substance abuse, a brain lesion, or mania could result in high-risk, out-of-control behavior. The behavior is not driven by a psychological agenda but is largely the result of some organic malfunction or influence.

Sexual addiction/compulsion shares some features in common with each of the previous categories, but also differs in important ways. Unlike healthy, neurotic, or characterological high-frequency sexual behavior, a person with a sexual addiction/compulsion experiences limited sexual control. The sexual addict/compulsive either has given in to hopelessness and no longer attempts to restrict sexual behavior or has a long cyclical history of swearing abstinence, only to return to the behavior at a later time.

Like the neurotic pattern of high-frequency sexual behavior, the underlying agenda for sexual addiction/compulsion is all-important. Because the behavior is driven in the service of an underlying agenda, pleasure is severely limited. The agenda may be stress reduction, affect regulation, or recapitulation of past trauma. Unlike the neurotic pattern, sexual behavior for the sexual addict/compulsive does not feel like a string of bad choices but, rather, a compulsion spinning out of control. Sexual addicts/compulsives often find themselves falling into a deteriorating cycle that begins with negative affect. Desperate efforts to anesthetize the uncomfortable feelings with sex leads to guilt, shame, self-loathing, and an even stronger urge to deaden the pain by further acting out.

Although the psychological agenda is a critical component of sexual addiction/compulsion, organic factors may also contribute to the out-of-control pattern. Sexual addiction/compulsion may have a biological profile similar to an obsessive-compulsive disorder (OCD). Like the treatment efficacy for OCD patients, selective serotonin reuptake inhibitor (SSRI) antidepressants have been reported to be effective in the treatment of sexual addicts/compulsives (Kafka, 1996; Kafka & Prentky, 1992; Stein et al., 1992.) On another front, researchers are attempting to determine whether neurological processes associated with sexual arousal differ for individuals with a sexual addiction/compulsion compared to the normal population (American Foundation for Addiction Research [AFAR], n.d.).

The critical features required for making the diagnosis of a sexual addiction/compulsion are (a) high frequency of sexual behavior and/or sexual preoccupation; (b) inability to maintain control over the behavior and/or preoccupation; (c) a high risk for negative consequences; and (d) the behavior and lack of behavioral control are not due to an identifiable organic condition. An underlying psychological agenda, a critical feature of sexual addiction/compulsion, is not always immediately apparent and, therefore, is not required to make the initial diagnosis.

Notice that the criteria listed previously do not take into consideration the specific type of sexual behavior. Because of the unusual or even bizarre nature of some sexual behaviors, clinicians may be tempted automatically to diagnose paraphilic behavior as a sexual addiction/compulsion. This position, however, conflicts with clinical experience and our core understanding of what constitutes an addiction/compulsion.

Paraphilic behaviors are sexual behaviors that not only fall outside accepted norms, but also are required or at least highly preferred in order to achieve sexual arousal. Both normative and nonnormative behavior can become compulsive, but because a behavior is paraphilic does not automatically make it compulsive. For example,* a woman who is active in the sadomasochistic (S/M) community and relies exclusively on S/M cues for sexual arousal may consistently engage in safe, sane, consensual sexual behavior. Given the appropriate control of her sexual behavior, a diagnosis of a sexual addiction/compulsion would hardly be justified.

A more dramatic example of this distinction between paraphilia and sexual addiction/compulsion would be a pedophile whose sexual behavior is under control. His primary source of arousal may be children, but he exercises sufficient control not to act on the impulse. Instead,

---

* Names and identifying characteristics in all case examples have been changed to protect privacy.

he resorts to fantasy and masturbation for sexual release. Even if on occasion he relapses, the relapse, as socially repugnant as the behavior might be, is not qualitatively the same thing as sexual behavior spiraling out of control. Keep in mind that sexual behavior by its very nature is marked by moments of a strong – albeit usually controllable – impulse to act. Because a person's arousal landscape is skewed toward nonnormative sexual behavior does not mean that a desire to act on an aberrant sexual urge or even an isolated aberrant behavior is compulsive per se.

ASSESSMENT OF SEXUAL ADDICTION/COMPULSIVE BEHAVIOR

When a patient presents with complaints that his or her sexual behavior is out of control, a thorough assessment is important both to establish a correct diagnosis and to develop the optimal treatment plan. Shame is often an overwhelming emotion associated with sexual acting out, making a nonjudgmental therapeutic posture essential. In most cases, a therapist's visible shock or voyeuristic press for details would heighten the patient's shame and embarrassment. In some cases, however, a patient may actually derive secondary gain from a full disclosure – a form of exhibitionism. In either event, the therapist's accepting, respectful, matter-of-fact approach will be essential.

The assessment of a patient presenting with problematic sexual behavior, on the one hand, will be similar to the comprehensive assessment performed for any psychological complaint but, on the other hand, will require particular attention to the areas described below.

The Sexual Concern

The Behavior

In what sexual behaviors does the patient engage? Is the problematic behavior normative sexual behavior or paraphilic? What is the patient's attitude about the behavior; that is, does the patient find the behavior acceptable, disgusting, and so on?

In some cases sexual addicts/compulsives display a pattern similar to the tolerance and escalation observed in chemical addiction. Has there been a progression in behaviors; that is, have there been other problematic sexual behaviors in the past that have evolved into the current pattern of behavior?

Frequency of the Behavior

How frequently does the behavior occur? Is it episodic or continuous? Does it take on a cyclical quality, with each cycle causing greater distress and a stronger impulse to repeat the behavior? When not acting on the behavior, is the patient preoccupied with thoughts about the sexual behavior?

Look for binge-purge patterns – periods of sexual acting out followed by periods of sexual withdrawal or avoidance. A patient with a sexual addiction/compulsion may present for an evaluation not with complaints of high-frequency sexual behavior but, rather, low desire, sexual aversion, or sexual avoidance. In such cases the patient is in a purge phase of the disorder, or what Carnes refers to as *sexual anorexia* (Carnes, 1997, 1998).

Circumstances, Precursors, Triggers Associated With the Behavior's Occurrence

Often emotional states or specific circumstances serve as precursors of or triggers for the problematic sexual behavior. Identification of these precursors and triggers can be useful when helping the patient develop strategies to control the behavior. Pay particular attention to sexual fantasies, which often initiate or accelerate addiction/compulsive behavior.

Behavioral Control

Control is a critical diagnostic feature. Some patients will state they have control over their behavior but, when pressed, will acknowledge that they have attempted to discontinue the behavioral pattern in the past only to revert to it. Regardless of rationalizations or denial, a patient's acknowledgment that he or she is frequently engaging in sexual behaviors despite high risk of negative consequences is strong evidence of diminished control.

The Behavior's Aftermath, Risks, and Consequences

How has this behavior impacted the patient's life? Has the behavior put the patient into physically dangerous situations? Has the patient contracted an STI? Has the sexual behavior jeopardized employment, taken time away from the family, created distance in significant relationships, or led to financial or legal problems?

Sexual Status

A thorough understanding of the patient's sexuality and sexual history is an essential part of treatment planning. Many sexual addicts/compulsives have developmentally failed to achieve sexual maturity.

Trauma

A history of trauma is highly prevalent in this population and often serves as a significant etiologic factor for sexual addiction/compulsion (Carnes, 1991). One common dynamic is the recapitulation of past trauma – the patient recreates sexual situations symbolically similar to the original trauma in a desperate attempt to rewrite history and triumph rather than be victimized. For other trauma victims, compulsive exploitative behavior may be the result of identification with the original aggressor – a twisted attempt to defend against feelings of powerlessness, helplessness, and vulnerability. Even if there is no overt history of sexual abuse, look for covert sexual abuse – inappropriate emotional enmeshment between the parent and child (Adams, 1991).

Sexual Relationship History

Intimacy disorders are common for this population. Has the patient ever experienced healthy sexual interactions? Is the patient able to integrate love and sex? A history of healthy sexual relationships serves as a favorable prognostic indicator.

Sexual Response/Dysfunctions

How does the patient describe his or her libido? Is the patient only interested in the compulsive behavior? Are there any sexual performance problems – erection difficulty, premature ejaculation, delayed ejaculation, inability to orgasm, and so on? Do these problems occur all the time or only under certain circumstances?

Sexual Interests/Turn-Ons

Once a sexual boundary has been crossed, additional boundary crossings become more likely (Abel & Osborn, 1992). Inquire regarding the full range of sexual behaviors, especially looking for nonnormative and problematic sexual behaviors. Make no assumptions regarding sexual orientation but, instead, seek clarification regarding the gender of sexual partners, present and past. Does the patient engage in cybersex relationships or make use of adult websites, pornography, or phone sex? Does he frequent strip clubs, massage parlors, or prostitutes? Has he ever exposed himself in public or does he look for opportunities to spy on others in compromised situations? Has the patient engaged in any sexual behaviors that most people would consider unusual?

Family-of-Origin History

Although it is not clear whether it is due to genetic or environmental factors, sexual addiction/compulsion appears to have a strong familial component (Carnes & Wilson, 2002). Addiction in general appears to have a genetic link, and sexual addiction/compulsion often occurs in the addiction population (Gordon, Fargason, & Kramer, 1995; J. P. Schneider & B. H. Schneider, 1991). Is there a family history of substance abuse or compulsive eating, spending, or gambling? Did either parent have a history of affairs or multiple relationships?

Childhood experiences can influence sexual health in adulthood. Was pornography in open view as the patient was growing up? Was the patient exposed on an ongoing basis to explicit sexual behavior in the household? Or, on the other hand, did sex negativism, authoritarian parenting, or oppressive religiosity characterize the home environment as the patient was growing up? Both extremes have been observed in the sexual addiction/compulsive population (Carnes & Wilson, 2002).

Psychiatric History/Comorbid Conditions

Sexual addiction/compulsion rarely occurs in isolation. Other compulsive disorders, posttraumatic stress disorder (PTSD), substance abuse, anxiety disorders, mood disorders, and attention deficit disorder (ADD) are often found in this population (Black et al., 1997; Kafka & Hennen, 2002; Kafka & Prentky, 1998; Raymond, Coleman, & Miner, 2003). For a successful outcome, comorbid conditions have to be addressed as part of the overall treatment for problematic sexual behavior.

Relationship Status

Secrets, betrayal, and shame, by-products of sexual addiction/compulsion, significantly impact relationship dynamics and often lead to devastating results. How has the sexual addiction/compulsion affected the patient's partnered relationship? How much does the partner know? Is the partnered relationship in danger of terminating? How committed is the patient to the relationship? What is the status of sexual intimacy in the relationship? Is unprotected sex exposing the partner to the risk of contracting an STI? What are the strengths and weaknesses of the relationship? What other core issues challenge the relationship's stability?

Online Sexual Activity

Because of the meteoric increase of online sexual activity (OSA) in recent years and the diagnostic challenges OSA presents, special consideration of this topic is warranted.

A 2005 survey by the Pew Internet and American Life Project (Pew, 2005b) suggested that 72% of American adults (approximately 145 million people) use the Internet, which is more than a 50% increase over survey findings in 2000 (Pew, 2000). Based on another survey by the same organization, of the estimated 145 million adult Internet users in the United States, 13% (5% of the women and 21% of the men) have visited an adult website (Pew, 2005a). Other researchers have estimated that as many as 20% of Internet users have visited adult websites (Cooper, Delmonico, & Burg, 2000).

With anywhere between 19 and 29 million American adults visiting adult websites, it is not surprising that clinicians are encountering a growing number of patients and their partners who present with concerns about online sexual activity. A common clinical scenario is a partner's discovery that the spouse visited an adult website, leading the partner to question the spouse's fidelity, integrity, and sexual health. Another common scenario is a patient presenting for an evaluation after being suspended or fired due to OSA at the workplace.

Due to the boundless opportunities to explore both the conventional and the darker side of one's sexuality, adult websites are a magnet for sexual addicts/compulsives and a potent precipitant for people at risk for developing this disorder. People spending long hours engaged in OSA are more likely to experience distress, shame, and other symptoms suggestive of a sexual addiction/compulsion (Cooper et al., 1999). Nevertheless, research suggests that the vast majority of people visiting adult websites are recreational users who do not appear to be at risk for a sexual addiction/compulsion (Cooper et al., 1999). For these recreational users, OSA may be prompted by curiosity, a quest for novelty, and/or a desire to enhance autoerotic behavior.

OSA requires careful assessment to determine whether it is problematic or benign. How much time does the patient spend online? What type of adult websites does the patient frequent? How much money does the patient spend on OSA? Has the patient ever contacted or met with people encountered on an adult website or in a chat room? Has the patient ever accessed an adult website while at work? How does the patient feel about his or her OSA? Has the patient tried but failed to stop OSA? Is the patient's partner aware of the OSA? If not, how does the patient think the partner would react?

TREATMENT

The treatment of sexual addiction/compulsion calls for a multimodal, multiphasic approach. Treatment modalities often include a combination of cognitive-behavioral therapy, insight-oriented therapy, relationship therapy, psychoeducation, group therapy, 12-step support groups, residential care, and pharmacotherapy. The treatment focus and interventions are sequenced in phases that at times overlap. Table 2 (below) presents the phases of treatment and their objectives.

TABLE 2: Treatment Phases and Objectives

PHASE	OBJECTIVES
Phase I: Stabilization	Perform crisis intervention
Phase II: Assessment	Identify the problematic behavior, antecedents, and consequences Assess patient's history and overall adjustment
Phase III: Control	Facilitate behavioral control Address comorbid conditions
Phase IV: Uncovering/ Repairing	Uncover the underlying psychological agenda Facilitate reparative work
Phase V: Enrichment	Heal the primary relationship Promote healthy sexuality Promote psychological well-being
Phase VI: Relapse Prevention	Develop relapse-prevention strategies

Phase I: Stabilization

When a patient finally seeks treatment for out-of-control behavior, crisis is often the motivation. Arrest, a spouse threatening divorce, public embarrassment, financial ruin, job loss, infection – all common consequences of a sexual addiction/compulsion – can lead to desperate cries for help. Under such circumstances, the patient may be struggling with shame and a sense of hopelessness.

The first phase of treatment is stabilization of the crisis situation. As stated earlier, the therapist's attitude will be critical in this process. Without minimizing the significance of the acting-out behavior or the gravity of the current crisis, the therapist needs to communicate respect for the patient, an understanding of how decent people are capable of troubling behaviors, and optimism that the patient will be able to survive the current crisis and rebuild his or her life. The potential for suicidal gestures, substance abuse relapse, or other behaviors manifesting self-loathing requires careful and ongoing monitoring.

Phase II: Assessment

Once the immediate crisis has been evaluated and stabilized, a comprehensive assessment of the problematic sexual behavior, its antecedents and consequences, and the patient's history and overall adjustment is essential. The focus of the assessment is described previously in this contribution.

Phase III: Control

Because of the potential of dire consequences, the problematic sexual behavior has to be brought under control as quickly as possible. Establishing early control of the behavior not only minimizes the risk of further negative outcomes, but also demonstrates to the patient that there is hope for a more successful future.

An underlying psychological agenda fuels sexual addiction/compulsion. The agenda may be to soothe or escape an uncomfortable affective state, seek affirmation, prove mastery, or a host of other unconscious motivations. Although addressing the underlying agenda is important for long-term remission, in most cases it is not required for establishing initial control over the problematic sexual behavior. In other words, behavioral control can be and often needs to be established before we have the luxury of delving into the underlying agenda.

Multiple therapeutic modalities and intervention techniques can assist with this immediate objective of establishing behavioral control.

Clarifying Acceptable, Unacceptable, and At-Risk Behaviors

For patients to gain control of their sexual behavior, it is important for them to have a clear understanding of which behaviors are acceptable and which behaviors should be avoided. When dealing with chemical dependency, total abstinence is an important part of establishing and maintaining sobriety. When it comes to sexual addiction/compulsion, however, total abstinence is neither practical nor desirable. The drive for sexual gratification is both normal and powerful; to totally thwart it could set a patient up to fail. Instead, it is important for the patient to identify not only which behaviors have been out of control, but also which sexual behaviors are healthy and acceptable.

The list of acceptable and unacceptable behaviors should be individualized for each patient. For example, a patient who compulsively masturbates will at least initially need to avoid all masturbatory behavior. For a patient who compulsively cruises for anonymous sexual partners, masturbation may prove to be not only an appropriate sexual outlet but may help decrease the intensity of the drive to act out. A patient who masturbates during compulsive use of Internet pornography – masturbatory behavior that may be hours in duration – may find masturbation without pornography nondisruptive and an effective sexual outlet.

Sexaholics Anonymous (SA) uses a helpful graphic: three concentric circles. In the center circle, the person lists out-of-control sexual behaviors; in the middle ring, potentially at-risk behaviors; and in the outer ring, acceptable sexual behaviors. This simple graphic or some similar exercise can help the patient to clearly define appropriate and problematic sexual behaviors.

Identify When At Risk

Triggers/antecedents for the problematic behavior should be clearly spelled out. For example, a man who spends hundreds of dollars every time he goes to a strip bar may discover that the draw to the strip bar is strongest when he is angry with his wife. Armed with this awareness, he can take preventative steps to minimize the risk of relapse whenever a conflict arises at home.

In addition to anger, hunger, loneliness, fatigue, anxiety, and depression are other common emotional antecedents to relapsing into problematic behaviors. Additional antecedents can be substance use, work failures, erotica, specific fantasy themes, or encountering an attractive person.

Stimulus Control

It is critical for the sexual addict/compulsive to develop strategies to remove or distance himself or herself from stimuli to act out. Installation of software that blocks or monitors access to adult websites, for example, can help prevent compulsive OSA. Canceling subscriptions to suggestive magazines and avoiding strip bars may help someone who is inclined to solicit prostitutes after exposure to highly sexualized situations.

It is helpful to conceptualize acting-out behavior as the end product of a chain of events or factors. The closer the person is to the actual sexual situation, the more easily judgment and impulse control can be compromised. The patient therefore needs to "go upstream" when applying stimulus control strategies. The further removed he or she is from the sexual behavior, the greater the likelihood of making appropriate choices.

> Frank has spent thousands of dollars at local massage parlors. The route home from the factory takes him past a string of adult bookstores and massage parlors, which serve as a powerful temptation. When pulling out of the parking lot at the end of the workday, he has a better chance of exercising control and making good choices than when he is actually passing a massage parlor. His stimulus-control strategy therefore focuses on the time when he is leaving work, when, for example, he can choose to take an alternate route home.

Sometimes stimuli cannot be avoided, but they can be managed.

> Peter is a middle-aged man with a strong attraction to young females just starting to show breast development. Every time he encounters a teen in public, he looks for ways to admire her from afar. Afterwards he goes online seeking out teen porn sites and masturbates for hours. Peter will not be able to avoid encountering teens in public, but he can adopt the *3-second rule*. Whenever he encounters a teenage girl, he will break off visual contact within 3 seconds, thereby limiting the possibility of stirring up arousal and, in turn, compromising his resolution to control his problematic behavior.

Cognitive Interventions

Distorted cognitions invariably accompany sexual acting out. "I'm not hurting anyone," "I'm broken, worthless," "I'm never successful, so why even try to control this," and "I've got it under control so there's no harm indulging once in awhile," is just a small sampling of the rationalizations, denials, and distortions that pave the way for further self-defeating behavior. It is important to help the patient identify maladaptive beliefs and cognitions, test and challenge their accuracy, and develop constructive alternative ways of viewing self-worth, competence, responsibility, and behavioral choices.

Breaking the Trance

Patients with a sexual addiction/compulsion will often report that the actual sexual behavior leading to orgasm is not as important as is the whole ritual leading up to climax. A man can spend hours jumping from website to website with incredible focus and intensity as he views, sorts, savors, and saves explicit pictures and videos. When he finally gets around to masturbating to orgasm, there is a sense of letdown and disappointment. A man who frequents strip bars finds the drive to the bar, entry, checking out the dancers, small talk, negotiating a lap dance, finding another dancer, paying for yet another lap dance, and so on as a string of behaviors that completely engulfs him and temporarily removes him from life stressors and conscious awareness of internal distress.

Many individuals, when going through a similar chain of behaviors, will describe their state of mind as *trance-like*. Any motivation or resolve to stop the behavior once in this trance-like state is minimal at best. If the patient fails in exercising stimulus-control strategies to avoid the behavioral chain in the first place, it will take rather drastic measures to snap him or her out of this trance-like state.

One helpful strategy for breaking or avoiding the trance-like state is having the patient carry vitamin B tablets (300 mg tablets of vitamin B1 work well). Vitamin B in tablet form is meant to be swallowed whole, but when a person bites into a tablet, it produces an incredibly nasty taste. The disgusting shock of the vitamin B tablet can serve as a powerful "slap in the face" that breaks the trance-like state. Many patients report that it becomes difficult, if not impossible, to focus on anything erotic when one's mouth suddenly mimics a toxic waste site.

Aversive Conditioning

Vitamin B tablets can also be used as an effective noxious stimulus that, after repeatedly being coupled with the compulsive sexual behavior, can diminish the allure of the compulsive ritual.

Henry visited high-priced call girls once or twice every week. He would contact these women through an escort website. The website not only served as the portal for sex but as a trigger for compulsive behavior. Each time he entered the website, he began a process of increasing sexual preoccupation that could only be dissipated by an actual encounter with a call girl. In attempts to utilize aversive conditioning to neutralize the power of the website, Henry's therapist instructed him to log onto the website daily, each time with a vitamin B tablet in hand. As soon as he encountered the website's home page, he immediately bit into the tablet. Not only did the immediate temptation to act out pass, but within a few weeks, he reported that viewing the website elicited a gag response.

Imagery can also be an effective tool for aversive conditioning. For example, a patient can be instructed to develop a clear image of the compulsive sexual ritual and then shift to an image of being discovered by his or her children, or of some other traumatic scenario. For this technique to be effective, it is important for the therapist to identify what imagery or scenario is most powerful for the client. Aversive imagery is not universal; because the therapist might consider a particular scenario catastrophic does not mean that the patient would react in the same way.

12-Step Group Support

Many patients with a sexual addiction/compulsion find the structure and support of a 12-step program a valuable adjunct to their treatment. The acceptance of a group can serve as a powerful elixir for the shame that often accompanies and even fuels sexual acting out. Sex Addicts Anonymous (SAA), Sexaholics Anonymous (SA), and Sexual Compulsives Anonymous (SCA) are popular 12-step programs for this condition. Although these programs share the 12-step format, there are differences worth noting. For Sexaholics Anonymous, sexual sobriety includes abstinence from all sexual behavior except sex with one's spouse. Under no circumstance is masturbation condoned, and if the participant is not married, complete sexual abstinence is expected. Boundaries for members of Sex Addicts Anonymous are more individualized and are determined with the guidance of a person's sponsor and other group members. Sexual Compulsives Anonymous takes perhaps the most liberal position:

> Members are encouraged to develop their own sexual recovery plan, and to define sexual sobriety for themselves. We are not here to repress our God-given sexuality, but to learn how to express it in ways that will not make unreasonable demands on our time and energy, place us in legal jeopardy – or endanger our mental, physical or spiritual health. (SCA, n.d., ¶ 2)

The 12-step format is not effective for everyone. Even within the same organization, the group experience can vary widely due to the unique composition of each group's membership. Some groups are overtly religious or take on a distinct Christian identity, which may be objectionable for atheists, agnostics, and non-Christians. Although some people seek and benefit from the structure provided by a 12-step program, others are put off by the formal openings and closings, time limits on sharing, the prohibition of cross talk, prayers, and so on.

Referral should be made only after careful assessment, and the impact of 12-step participation should be monitored closely. Of particular concern is when unrealistic behavioral restrictions and sex misinformation and negativism are promoted by an overzealous member or sponsor. The work in the 12-step program should complement, not contradict, the overall treatment plan.

Group Therapy

A more traditional group-therapy format for sexually addicted/compulsive patients can be a very useful alternative or adjunct to a 12-step program. Participating in a group with other sex addicts/compulsives helps lessen shame by highlighting that the patient is not unique. The patient can learn from others what works and what does not when trying to control problematic behavior. Fellow group members can also effectively see through and confront the patient's excuses, rationalizations, and distorted thinking.

Addressing Comorbid Conditions

Anxiety, depression, ADD, PTSD, and other addictions are common comorbid conditions that can prompt the need to act out sexually, diminish impulse control, or neutralize any motivation to resist the self-defeating behavior. Addressing the comorbid conditions is therefore essential for restoring behavioral control.

Pharmacotherapy

Selective serotonin reuptake inhibitor (SSRI) antidepressants may play a valuable role beyond treating comorbid conditions: in some cases they may directly impact the drive to act out sexually. It has been hypothesized that the effectiveness of SSRIs in the treatment of sexual addiction/compulsion is due to the common side effect of these antidepressants: decreased libido. But SSRIs have also been used effectively in the treatment of OCD, giving rise to the hypothesis that the serotonergic action of this class of antidepressants directly impacts the compulsive mechanism of out-of-control sexual behavior (Coleman, 2003; Kafka, 1996).

In extreme cases where the sexual acting out is treatment-resistant and the consequences are severe, the use of an antiandrogen may be considered (Bradford, 2000; Coleman, 2003). Depo-Provera, for example, has been used with out-of-control sex offenders, its efficacy due to the resulting reduction in the patient's sex drive (Kafka, 1996). Although the severity of the patient's sexual acting out may at times necessitate such a dramatic intervention, the clinician needs to keep in mind that the elimination of sexual interest does not necessarily alter the underlying dynamics. When using cognitive-behavioral techniques or SSRIs to bring the behavior under control, if internal conflict must find expression or an outlet, relapse is a potential "safety valve." When you essentially eliminate that safety valve via "chemical castration," however, the patient can be left defenseless if he has not yet developed alternative coping mechanisms. It is therefore essential to closely monitor the patient's adjustment when on an antiandrogen regimen, especially watching for self-destructive behavior.

Residential Treatment

When the crisis, comorbidity, or sexual acting out cannot be brought under control in an outpatient setting, residential treatment should be considered. A number of treatment facilities across the United States offer intensive, multimodal treatment in a safe, controlled environment.

Phase IV: Uncovering/Repairing

Unlike normal, healthy sexual behavior, sexual addiction/compulsion is not pleasure-motivated. Whatever the pleasure experienced, it is limited and quickly overshadowed by guilt, shame, and self-loathing that often cascade into consiousness. If not pleasure, what drives problematic sexual behavior?

Research continues to explore whether biological abnormalities account for the development of sexual addiction/compulsion. Clinical experience, however, has made it clear that regardless of any biological substrate, a psychological agenda helps drive the maladaptive pattern of behavior. Careful analysis of the behavioral pattern, triggers, circumstances, and history can provide important clues regarding the underlying agenda. Consider the following examples:

Craig is 35 and single and has a very restricted social life. He's a lawyer at a prestigious law firm and on the cusp of making partner. Whenever pressure mounts to bill more hours, complete complex briefs for the state court of appeals, or to contend with some other difficult challenge, Craig resorts to his secret life for escape and survival. Late at night he leaves his office and heads off to a discreet bathhouse or cruises gay bars for a quick encounter in a bathroom stall or the back seat of his car. He despises his behavior almost as much as he despises his hidden sexual orientation but feels powerless in the face of overwhelming stress.

Perhaps the most common agenda for a sexual addiction/compulsion is stress reduction and affect regulation. In many cases the addict/compulsive has failed to develop healthy internal mechanisms for dealing with conflict and stress and resorts to sexual ritual to distract, calm, or soothe. The reparative work of therapy is not only building stress reduction skills and enhancing affect tolerance, but also helping the patient to internalize confidence in being able to cope with life stressors.

Leanne's father was an authoritarian figure who was highly invested in his sons but had little time or use for his daughters. Leanne has been married and divorced three times. Her infidelity contributed to each of the three breakups. Her pattern is unvary-ing – she meets a man and becomes infatuated, feels challenged to seduce him, and readily tires of him should he make the fatal error of becoming smitten with her. During the past year this pattern has escalated to a point at which Leanne feels compelled to seduce any man she encounters. An unrelenting series of one-night stands and "anonymous fucks" has left her HIV-positive and alone.

Repairing old injuries or overcoming earlier disappointments is another common underlying agenda for sexual addictions/compulsions. Reparative work for Leanne begins with insight into the futility of her attempts to win paternal validation. The profound disappointment over no man being capable of providing what she so sorely wanted as a child has to be fully experienced and grieved over. Only then can work begin on helping her to internalize self-validation and discover how to relate to significant others in an honest, self-actualizing way as opposed to the manipulative, self-serving manner of the past. The therapist/patient relationship can be an invaluable mechanism to help the patient learn experientially new and healthier ways of relating.

Robert and Carol's 18-year-marriage has been in trouble for years. Hurt and angered over his long-standing sexual avoidance, Carol was infuriated when she learned that he was secretly masturbating. Robert acknowledged that his masturbation was at times out of control, causing him to be late for work, miss deadlines, and avoid opportunities to be more involved in his children's activities. He repeatedly resolved to control his masturbation, but kept relapsing. Upon closer examination, it became clear that most, if not all, of his masturbatory binges followed heated conflict with his wife.

Anger is a common dynamic found in cases of sexual addiction/compulsion. Patients like Robert are often threatened by their anger and fear some unknown catastrophic outcome if the anger is not kept in check. For Robert, masturbation provides not only a passive/aggressive outlet for his anger ("Screw you, I can get my needs met without you") but also a powerful means to deflect awareness from the anger and all it represents. The task of therapy is to help the patient to become aware of this underlying pattern and to alter his core belief that anger must be defended against at all costs.

Phase V: Enrichment

Healing Primary Relationships

Sexual addiction/compulsion takes a tremendous toll on relationships, especially marital relationships. Partners often feel betrayed and disillusioned. They may question whether to stay in or leave the relationship. Indeed, many relationships break up due to the sexual acting out. If partners choose to stay in the relationship, they may torment themselves with thoughts like, "What does it say about me that I won't leave after such a horrendous betrayal?"

Just as a high percentage of sexual addicts/compulsives have a history of sexual, physical, and emotional abuse, so also is true of their partners (Carnes, 1991). Partners of sexual addicts/compulsives often have difficulty with self-esteem, affect recognition, autonomy, and conflict resolution. Similar to sex addicts/compulsives, partners tend to search out fellow trauma survivors who are seeking to compensate for earlier emotional abandonment. Laaser (2002) described partners in such relationships as "heat-seeking missiles attracted to the perceived emotional warmth or nurturing abilities of their partners" (p. 126).

Healing the relationship will often require healing for both individuals. While always making it clear that the partner is not responsible for the sexual acting out – the patient alone must assume responsibility for the negative behavior – the therapist must help the couple understand how their own unresolved issues, especially trauma, create a toxic environment for both of them.

In general terms, relationship work focuses on building or rebuilding trust and emotional intimacy. More specifically, the couple will need help with communicating at an affective level and resolving conflict in a win-win fashion. They need to rediscover qualities they once valued in each other and learn to be playful and at peace in each other's presence. Sexual barriers, including dysfunction, fear, and inhibitions, have to be identified and addressed.

One of the most difficult questions when addressing sexual addiction/compulsion is how much should be disclosed to the partner. Certainly if the partner is at risk of being unknowingly exposed to possible STIs because of the patient's out-of-control behavior, he or she is entitled to that information. In such cases, the therapist must challenge the patient to take steps to protect the partner. But what about cases where the spouse is not at risk and has no idea about the extent of the patient's acting out?

> For the past 6 months, Larry has been visiting a local massage parlor once or twice a week. The urge continues to grow stronger and his ability to resist weaker. Racked with guilt and struggling to hide the financial strain caused by his acting out, he has nevertheless managed to keep his problematic behavior a secret from his wife. Because he and his wife have not been sexual for over 3 years and because he does not consider his compulsive behavior at risk for an STI (the sex worker manually stimulates him to ejaculation, so there is no exchange of body fluids), he refuses to disclose his behavior. On the contrary, he is convinced that his wife would be crushed if she learned of his infidelity and would, in all likelihood, file for divorce.

In many cases, disclosure is a nonissue because it was the spouse's discovery of the problematic behavior that forced the patient to seek treatment. When the spouse is in the dark, however, the risk that the relationship might not survive the outcome of discovery or disclosure is real. Domestic violence is another potential danger, especially when a husband learns of his wife's infidelity. Given these dangers, is voluntary disclosure ever advisable?

Core dynamics in a relationship can usually best be addressed only after the problematic behavior is out in the open. When aware of current infidelity, a therapist cannot in good conscience work with a couple on relationship issues until the infidelity either stops or is disclosed. Only when the partner is aware of the sexual addiction/compulsion can the couple address systemic issues that may be supporting or contributing to the sexual acting out. The spouse's awareness of the behavioral pattern may also make it much more difficult for the patient to act out, which assists in the critical goal of behavioral control.

In a survey of sex addicts/compulsives and partners of sex addicts/compulsives, a significant majority of both the patients and partners reported that the decision to disclose compulsive infidelity was the correct one, even in those cases where the couple ended up separated or divorced (J. P. Schneider, Corely, & Irons, 1998). The patients reported that the disclosure represented honesty, an end of denial, and hope for the future. For the partners, clarity, validation, and hope for the future were viewed as the positive outcome of disclosure.

This dilemma has no clear-cut, one-size-fits-all answer. It is important for the therapist on a case-by-case basis to evaluate risks and potential gain coming from disclosure. The actual timing of the disclosure and the level of detail to be disclosed also have to be considered carefully.

Promoting Healthy Sexuality

The goal of treatment for sexual addiction/compulsion is not to eliminate sexual behavior but to replace problematic with healthy sexual behavior. This transition does not happen automatically simply because the sexual acting out is brought under control. For this population, sexual health is neither self-evident nor intuitive. On the contrary, for the sexual addict/

compulsive, sexuality is a highly distorted concept that implies pain and escape, power and powerlessness.

A broad-based sex education must therefore take place, providing accurate information not only about sexual response and interaction, but also about the nature of healthy sexuality. The patient needs to view and experience sexual behavior as safe, boundaried, victimless, respectful, honest, consistent with one's values, emotionally connected, playful, sensual, and authentic.

Promoting Psychological Well-Being

A patient's overall psychological health and stability is essential for establishing and maintaining control over self-defeating sexual behavior. Work on social skills training, assertiveness, conflict resolution, anger management, affect recognition, frustration tolerance, stress management, and communication skills will help the patient to experience greater success in life, increase self-esteem, and decrease the potential for resorting to sexual acting out in order to reduce stress and regulate affect.

Phase VI: Relapse Prevention

Once control of the problematic sexual behavior is achieved, relapse prevention becomes the primary lifelong objective. All of the interventions above (psychotherapy, pharmacotherapy, relationship work, skill building, sex education, etc.) will help the patient to establish and maintain behavioral control, but one can never do too much to prevent future relapse. It is valuable for the patient to have a structured plan of proactive behaviors and fallback strategies to prevent future crises or, if crises should arise, to prevent relapse.

An example of a structured relapse-prevention plan is on page 194. What follows is a brief description of each of the components of this sample plan.

Sexual Behaviors in the Inner Circle (Compulsive Behaviors I Must Stop)

Making use of the three concentric circles described earlier in this contribution, the patient lists specific sexual behaviors in the inner circle, sexual behaviors that have been out of control.

Sexual Behaviors in the Middle Circle (Dangerous Behaviors I Must Avoid)

As a result of therapy, the patient should be aware of sexual behaviors that might be nonproblematic for others but for the patient have the potential of becoming problematic or leading to behaviors in the inner circle. The patient should be very clear on which behaviors to avoid and encouraged to be firm and unbending in adherence.

What's at Stake if I Don't Control My Sexual Behavior?

Have the patient make an exhaustive list of what is at stake: the marriage, children's respect, financial stability, career, health, and so on. For optimal relapse prevention, there can be no ambiguity regarding the importance of behavioral control.

What I Have to Gain by Maintaining Control of My Sexual Behavior

It can be valuable to have the patient write down and keep in mind a positive image of what life can be like if free of the sexual addiction/compulsion. This image should be ever-present in the patient's mind because it serves as an important positive motivator.

Ways to Take Better Care of Myself

Have the patient make a list of health-positive behaviors (diet, exercise, hobbies, etc.) that promote not only physical and mental health but also a sense of self-mastery.

Ways to Take Better Care of My Relationships

As described above, much effort will be required to heal and strengthen significant relationships after a history of sexual addiction/compulsion. Based on insights derived from therapy, the patient should make a list of resolutions (e.g., being more attentive, honest, tolerant, communicative, etc.) for strengthening the marriage or other significant relationships.

Behaviors and Situations I Must Avoid

Some behaviors and circumstances can trigger sexual acting out. Alcohol, driving through a particular neighborhood, and associating with certain individuals or groups are examples of behaviors and situations the patient must avoid in order to maintain adequate control over sexual behavior.

Circumstances That Should Put Me on Alert

Some potential triggers may be unavoidable (hunger, anger, stress, presence of attractive people, media advertisements, etc.), but the patient needs to be aware of them and prepared to go on "full-alert" when encountering them.

Early Signals of Pending Relapse

Relapse seldom occurs without precursors. The patient needs to identify behavioral patterns or psychological states of mind that signal pending relapse. Early signals could include failure to follow through on prevention steps listed previously, pessimism about maintaining control, increasing preoccupation with sexual acting out, or planning how to act out without getting caught.

In Case of an Emergency

If the impulse to act out becomes overwhelming or if relapse has indeed occurred, the patient has to act quickly and decisively to counteract the tendency to capitulate completely. Having a series of emergency procedures planned out in advance increases the chances of the patient regaining behavioral control before irreparable harm occurs. Examples include:

- *My Mantra.* Based on the cognitive work done during therapy, what message or statement does a patient need to continuously repeat internally when facing imminent or recent relapse? "I'm better than this," "I'm a person of worth," "I'm not broken," and "I can succeed one day at a time" are examples of possible mantras.
- *Whom to Call.* If relapse is imminent, who would be the best person to call for encouragement and support: the 12-step sponsor, the therapist, a clergyman, or a friend? Usually it is not advisable to have the spouse serve in this role because the spouse should not be burdened further with a sense of responsibility for the patient's behavior and because it is difficult for any spouse not to personalize the patient's temptation to relapse.
- *My Most Effective Control Techniques.* Based on experience in therapy, what strategies proved to be most effective in controlling the urge to act out: vitamin B, a potent mental image, or a particular cognitive reframe?
- *My First-Aid Kit.* Have the patient carry a "first-aid kit" that can be readily accessed in the event of an emergency (Carnes, 2001). The kit might include a vitamin B tablet, a picture of a loved one, the phone number of a support person, an inspirational or scriptural quote, and/or a letter written to oneself during an earlier time when determination was stronger and vision was clearer about the importance of maintaining control.

CONCLUSION

In order to understand and treat sexual addiction/compulsion effectively, we have to evaluate our own attitudes, beliefs, and fears about sex. Sexuality is a wonderful and powerful dimension of our humanity that draws us out of a solitary existence, fuels bonding, and provides pleasure. Sexuality does have a dark side, to be sure, which unfortunately has contributed to the schizophrenic attitude our culture has long harbored toward it. But this dark side (compulsion, exploitation, etc.) does not warrant or justify societal attempts to repress sexual health. Failure to educate our children about sexuality or insisting that admonitions against premarital sex constitute adequate sex education; attempts to overregulate sexual expression in the media, Internet, or the arts; or intolerance of sexual diversity will not prevent sexual addiction/compulsion or other sexual problems. Such pervasive sex negativism only intensifies the lethal association of sex with shame.

It is important for all clinicians, not just specialists, to be well versed regarding sexual issues. When encountering nonnormative sexual behavior, clinicians must be objective and nonjudgmental. They need to validate rather than pathologize sexual behavior that is safe, consensual, and nonexploitative. When encountering patients with a sexual addiction/compulsion, clinicians must be prepared for the long, challenging task of helping the patient gain control over the behavior, repair the impact of developmental disruption and trauma, and develop skills and prevention strategies to ensure healthy sexual expression and successful living.

Personalized Relapse-Prevention Plan

Sexual behaviors in the inner circle (compulsive behaviors I must stop):

Sexual behaviors in the middle circle (dangerous behaviors I must avoid):

What's at stake if I don't control my sexual behavior:

What I have to gain by maintaining control of my sexual behavior:

Ways to take better care of myself:

Ways to take better care of my relationships:

Behaviors and situations I must avoid:

Circumstances that should put me on alert:

Early signals of pending relapse:

In case of an emergency:

- My mantra:

- Whom to call:

- My most effective control techniques:

- My first-aid kit:

CONTRIBUTOR

Dennis P. Sugrue, PhD, is an Adjunct Clinical Associate Professor of Psychiatry at the University of Michigan Medical School and has a private practice in Bloomfield Hills, Michigan. Prior to his current position, he was the founder and Co-Director of The Henry Ford Center for Human Sexuality. Dr. Sugrue is a Diplomate in Sex Therapy and a past President of the American Association of Sexuality Educators, Counselors, and Therapists (AASECT). He is a coauthor of the acclaimed book *Sex Matters for Women*. Dr. Sugrue may be contacted at 74 W. Long Lake Road, Suite 104, Bloomfield Hills, MI 48304. E-mail: dsugrue@umich.edu

RESOURCES

Abel, G. G., & Osborn, C. (1992). The paraphilias. The extent and nature of sexually deviant and criminal behavior. *Psychiatric Clinics of North America, 15*(3), 675-687.

Adams, K. (1991). *Silently Seduced: When Parents Make Their Children Partners: Understanding Covert Incest.* Deerfield Beach, FL: Health Communications.

American Foundation for Addiction Research (AFAR). (n.d.). *Promising Early Results in Vanderbilt Study.* Retrieved November 25, 2005, from http://www.addictionresearch.com/promising_early_results.cfm

American Psychiatric Association. (2000). *Diagnostic and Statistical Manual of Mental Disorders* (*DSM-IV-TR*; 4th ed. text rev.). Washington, DC: Author.

Bancroft, J., & Vukadinovic, Z. (2004). Sexual addiction, sexual compulsivity, sexual impulsivity, or what? Toward a theoretical model. *The Journal of Sex Research, 41*(3), 225-234.

Black, D. W., Kehrberg, L. D., Flumerfelt, D. L., & Schlosser, S. S. (1997). Characteristics of 36 subjects reporting compulsive sexual behavior. *American Journal of Psychiatry, 154*(2), 243-249.

Bradford, J. M. (2000). Treatment of sexual deviation using a pharmacologic approach. *Journal of Sex Research, 37*(3), 248-257.

Carnes, P. (1983). *Out of the Shadows: Understanding Sexual Addiction.* Minneapolis: CompCare.

Carnes, P. (1991). *Don't Call It Love: Recovery From Sexual Addiction.* New York: Bantam.

Carnes, P. (1997). *Sexual Anorexia: Overcoming Sexual Self-Hatred.* Center City, MN: Hazelden.

Carnes, P. (1998). The case for sexual anorexia: An interim report on 144 patients with sexual disorders. *Sexual Addiction and Compulsivity, 5*(4), 293-309.

Carnes, P. (2001). *Facing the Shadow: Starting Sexual and Relationship Recovery.* Wickenberg, AZ: Gentle Path Press.

Carnes, P., & Wilson, M. (2002). The sexual addiction assessment process. In P. Carnes & K. Adams (Eds.), *Clinical Management of Sex Addiction* (pp. 3-19). New York: Brunner-Routledge.

Coleman, E. (2003). Compulsive sexual behavior: What to call it, how to treat it? *SIECUS Report, 31*(5), 12-16.

Cooper, A., Delmonico, D., & Burg, R. (2000). Cybersex users and abusers: New findings and implications. *Sexual Addiction and Compulsivity, 7*(1-2), 5-29.

Cooper, A., Scherer, C., Boies, S., & Gordon, B. (1999). Sexuality on the Internet: From sexual exploration to pathological expression. *Professional Psychology: Research and Practice, 30*(2), 154-164.

Gordon, L. J., III, Fargason, P. J., & Kramer, J. J. (1995). Sexual behaviors of patients in a residential chemical dependency program: Comparison of sexually compulsive physicians and nonphysicians with non-sexually compulsive physicians and nonphysicians. *Sexual Addiction and Compulsivity, 2*, 233-255.

Kafka, M. P. (1996). Therapy for sexual impulsivity: The paraphilias and paraphilia-related disorders. *Psychiatric Times, 13*(6). Retrieved November 25, 2005, from http://www.psychiatrictimes.com/p960627.html

Kafka, M. P. (1997). Hypersexual desire in males: An operational definition and clinical implications for males with paraphilias and paraphilia-related disorders. *Archives of Sexual Behavior, 26*(5), 505-526.

Kafka, M. P., & Hennen, J. (2002). A DSM-IV Axis I Comorbidity Study of Males (n = 120) with paraphilias and paraphilia-related disorders. *Sexual Abuse: Journal of Research and Treatment, 14*(4), 349-366.

Kafka, M. P., & Prentky, R. A. (1992). Fluoxetine treatment of nonparaphilic sexual addictions and paraphilias in men. *Journal of Clinical Psychiatry, 53*(10), 351-358.

Kafka, M. P., & Prentky, R. A. (1998). Attention-deficit/hyperactivity disorder in males with paraphilias and paraphilia-related disorders: A comorbidity study. *Journal of Clinical Psychiatry, 59*(7), 388-396.

Klein, M. (2003). Sex addiction: A dangerous clinical concept. *SIECUS Report, 31*(5), 8-11.

Laaser, M. (2002). Recovery for couples. In P. Carnes & K. Adams (Eds.), *Clinical Management of Sex Addiction* (pp. 125-136). New York: Brunner-Routledge.

Pew Internet and American Life Project. (2000, March). *March 2000 Tracking Survey.* Retrieved December 15, 2005, from http://www.pewinternet.org/trends/UsageOverTime.xls

Pew Internet and American Life Project. (2005a, May-June). *May-June 2005 Tracking Survey.* Retrieved December 15, 2005, from http://www.pewinternet.org/trends/UsageOverTime.xls

---

* Although all websites cited in this contribution were correct at the time of publication, they are subject to change at any time.

Pew Internet and American Life Project. (2005b, September). *September 2005 Tracking Survey*. Retrieved December 15, 2005, from http://www.pewinternet.org/trends/User_Demo_12.05.05.htm

Raymond, N. C., Coleman, E., & Miner, M. H. (2003). Psychiatric comorbidity and compulsive/impulsive traits in compulsive sexual behavior. *Comprehensive Psychiatry, 44*(5), 370-380.

Schneider, J. P., Corely, M. D., & Irons, R. R. (1998). Surviving disclosure of infidelity: Results of an international survey of 164 recovering sex addicts and partners. *Sexual Addiction and Compulsivity, 5*, 189-217.

Schneider, J. P., & Schneider, B. H. (1991). *Sex, Lies, and Forgiveness: Couples Speak on Healing From Sex Addiction*. Center City, MN: Hazelden.

Sexual Compulsives Anonymous (SCA). (n.d.). Retrieved December 15, 2005, from http://www.sca-recovery.org/

Stein, D. J., Hollander, E., Anthony, D. T., Schneier, F. R., Fallon, B. A., Liebowitz, M. R., & Klein, D. F. (1992). Serotonergic medications for sexual obsessions, sexual addictions, and paraphilias. *Journal of Clinical Psychiatry, 53*(8), 267-271.

Sugrue, D. P. (2003). Giving problematic sexual behavior the serious attention it requires. *SIECUS Report, 31*(5), 4.

Innovative Methods of Treating Patients With Sexual Trauma

Stephen L. Braveman

Sexual trauma has been, and continues to be, treated by means of traditional psychotherapy methods. These methods include everything from Rogerian Client Centered empathic approaches to Eye Movement Desensitization and Reprocessing (EMDR). Psychodynamic insight-oriented approaches may be the most common methods used by therapists today. However, many of my patients reported a lack of reaching a level of full recovery through these methods alone. Quite a few reported they have participated in traditional group therapy sessions year after year wondering when they would truly feel better. Patients who received only EMDR sometimes reported that something was missing in the healing process and frequently found that their symptoms resurfaced within a short period after treatment was terminated.

My treatment experiences indicate that innovative methods, in conjunction with classic approaches, greatly enhance the patients' prognosis so they may experience a full recovery within a couple of years or sooner, and that this recovery holds for them many years down the road. This contribution explores basic elements of sexual trauma, addresses classic treatment approaches, and examines some innovative methods that have positive results in helping sexual abuse survivors heal.

Classic methods of psychotherapy, when combined with modern innovative methods, provide sexual abuse survivors with a therapeutic recipe that works. For example, Bass and Davis recognized how important an Adlerian, or psychoeducational, approach is to treating sexual trauma patients. Their two groundbreaking books, *The Courage to Heal: A Guide for Women Survivors of Child Sexual Abuse* (1994) and its accompanying workbook (Davis, 1990), were strongly influenced by the Adlerian approach. Lew's groundbreaking book on the sexual victimization of males, *Victims No Longer* (1990), took a similar approach, though it lacked the dynamic step-by-step approach toward healing that appeared in the books by Bass and Davis. Davis continued the Adlerian approach in her book for couples dealing with the healing of sexual trauma in the relationship: *Allies in Healing: When the Person You Love Was Sexually Abused as a Child* (1991).

All of the psychoeducational books on sexual victimization include information that the layperson, the survivor, the survivor's loved ones, and therapists unfamiliar with the topic need to know about sexual abuse and the healing process. At first glance, much of this information appears basic and targeted toward a very young and immature audience. However, it is evident that the majority of Americans, including trained and experienced therapists, lack this basic knowledge. Having patients review this basic information by reading one of the books mentioned above or a handout in the therapist's office provides them with a much needed reality check that they are not "crazy" and not "alone" in their experiences. Reading these materials also assists the therapist in structuring discussions with patients while keeping the topic of abuse on the forefront.

BASIC INFORMATION PROVIDED IN CLASSIC TREATMENT APPROACHES

Most resources on sexual abuse provide basic information. They typically describe various types of sexual abuse, not just the popularly held view that sexual abuse equals violent rape. For example, many people are surprised to learn that sexual abuse includes nonphysical incidents such as being a witness to indecent exposure, receiving obscene phone calls, being the subject of voyeurism, being exposed to pornography, being a nonphysically touched subject of pornography, and living in an overly sexualized, emotionally incestuous, or verbally inappropriate setting (Davis, 1991). It is not uncommon to find female patients who feel traumatized by a father's frequent verbal references to her mother's breasts or a boy who has been repeatedly insulted about the short length of his penis.

Most people are not surprised to learn that sexual abuse may include physical touch. After all, it is the violent rape scenes depicted in movies and on television, those that include forced vaginal or anal penetration, that typically come to mind for most when thinking about sexual abuse. Of course these violent scenes do occur. Touching, fondling, and caressing the victim's genitals, or having the victim do these kinds of things to the perpetrator, is common and also not too surprising. However, physical sexual abuse also occurs in ways that many may not think of as abuse. This includes such things as a parent experiencing orgasm while spanking a child on his or her naked buttocks for things most would not consider punishable or insisting on wiping a child's anus clean after a bowel movement up until the child is as old as 12. In fact, according to the T.A.S.K. (Take A Stand for Kids) national website, kissing a child when he or she does not want to be kissed is considered to be a form of sexual abuse.

One of the reasons people may not recognize behavior as being sexually abusive is that the behavior truly appears to be innocent and fun. For example,* one man described how, when he was between the ages of 3 and 5, his mother played a game with him. The mother lay on the bed with her legs spread open and her skirt pulled up. She told the young boy that he came from her vagina and then encouraged him to climb back in head first. The man remembers this play as having been odd but somewhat okay until his father caught the two at this game one day and severely shamed them both. The young man has suffered from all the classic symptoms of a sexual abuse survivor ever since.

The image of what a sexual perpetrator looks like has been changing. Men have, and continue to be, the main culprit in most people's minds. The denial that a female could sexually offend has been very strong. Many people, especially males, have suffered tremendously due to this denial. Many males have been denied appropriate treatment because of the false belief that females cannot abuse males. In fact, many of my male patients have reported that they were diagnosed with a psychotic disorder, put on psychotropic medications, institutionalized, and even given electroshock therapy as a result of the professional therapeutic field joining in this denial between the 1940s and mid-1980s.

We now recognize that, although at a lesser rate than males, females do commit sexual offenses. Mothers, sisters, aunts, and even grandmothers sometimes molest children (Abraham, 1997) and at a rising rate (Bureau of Justice Statistics, 2002). A fairly common occurrence is a female babysitter who explores a young boy's body while changing him and putting him to bed at night (Lew, 1990). Similarly, it is not uncommon for me to hear female patients report that they were sexually abused by an older female under the guise of initiating the young girl into lesbian love. Of course, just as with males who molest males, females who molest females are doing this not due to homosexual desire but rather a desire for power and control over the victim.

---

* Names and identifying characteristics have been changed to protect confidentiality.

Common symptoms occur in the sexually traumatized person which are strongly related to the developmental stage when the abuse first took place (Dunlap, Golub, & Johnson, 2003). Of course, it is important to recognize that not all children who display these symptoms have been abused. Infants and toddlers who are, or have been, abused sometimes display behaviors such as excessive clinging, avoidance of certain people, stiff body, difficulty sleeping, difficulty eating, colicky behavior, passivity, withdrawal, and fussy behaviors. In young children we may see sexualized behavior, inserting objects into the vagina or anus, excess masturbation, inability to relate to peers, overly seeking out or avoiding adults, parentified activities, manipulative behavior, easily becoming distracted, poor self-esteem, eating disorders, and school problems (Bass & Davis, 1994). In teens we may see sexualized behavior and acting out, such as promiscuity or prostitution, defiance or compliance to an extreme, isolation, fear and anxiety, self-mutilation, suicidal gestures, obsessive cleanliness, pseudomaturity, drug and alcohol abuse, delinquent behaviors, and running away (Gartner, 1999).

In adults who were sexually abused as children, there sometimes are various forms of disassociation; sexual difficulties in the form of shutting down, acting out, or both; distrust of others; a pervasive sense of guilt and shame; restriction of emotion; drug and alcohol abuse; poor self-esteem; withdrawal; running away from relationships; frequent relocations; inability to form lasting friendships; and under- or overachievement (Herman, 1997; Van der Kolk, 1987).

INNOVATIONS TO THE CLASSICS

New views, added to old information, frequently bring the facts to life and make them relevant for the sexual abuse survivor. Such is the case when looking at the various theories that exist as to why people molest or rape others. Some describe different kinds of perpetrator profiles. These profiles describe everything from the "naive experimenters" who did not know better and stopped, filled with remorse, when educated about the results of their actions, to the "antisocial personality disordered" person who would just as well commit murder, hold up a bank, or blow up a building, all on a whim. Although examining and understanding these various profiles and theories is helpful to some survivors, most find it little more than educational.

The relatively new "sick versus evil" theory (cited as "author unknown" by Kokish and published in the California Coalition on Sexual Offending's quarterly newsletter, *Perspectives*, Spring 2000) examines the notion that if sexual perpetrators committed their offense because they are "sick," and because we have no cure for this illness, then the perpetrators cannot really be blamed for their actions. We also should have pity on the perpetrators and acknowledge that the best we can do is lock them up to protect them from reoccurrences of their illness: sexually violating again. The theory contrasts this "sickness" model with a notion that sexual offenders are, instead, "evil." If they are "evil," then they committed the offense because it felt good, they wanted to do it, and they had little regard for the harm it would bring to the victim, the victim's family, and society. Furthermore, if we view offenders as "evil," and acting in an "evil" manner is a choice, then the perpetrator is responsible and can change the behavior.

Although the "sick versus evil" theory greatly helps the sexual abuse survivor see the perpetrator in a new light, one in which the perpetrator should not receive sympathy and forgiveness for what he or she has done, but instead be held fully accountable, for many people a new problem arises from the terminology. Discussing "evil" means we must consider its opposite, "good," and the source of both. This leads us into religion, an area few therapists find appropriate to expound upon. In this case religion is not only a difficult issue for the therapist, it is also a very difficult issue for many sexual abuse survivors, because many wonder how God could allow such terrible things to happen to such nice and innocent people. By replacing the word "evil" with "selfish," we not only avoid the issue of religion, we also solidify the concept of taking responsibility for one's actions. After all, many sexual abuse survivors are in therapy to begin with because someone is telling them to take responsibility for their behaviors, or what we typically refer to as symptoms.

CREATIVE CONFRONTATION

Confrontation is one of the most empowering methods a survivor of sexual abuse can utilize. When people confront, they are essentially saying that the secret is out, that what happened to them was not okay, and that they are fighting back. The process of confrontation typically leaves victims feeling more like survivors as they see that they can be in charge of their life, especially their body.

Classic confrontation for sexual abuse survivors may involve writing letters to the perpetrator or speaking to the person on the phone or in person. As all of these may carry great risks, therapists usually help prepare survivors by exploring the intended purpose of the confrontation; helping survivors decide what they want from the perpetrator; seeing that success is in the confrontation and not in the perpetrator's response; reviewing letters survivors may write long before they are sent, if they are sent; assuring that survivors have adequate support in place before, during, and after the confrontation; and role-playing the many possible scenarios that can occur during and after the confrontation.

Although direct confrontation with a perpetrator may be beneficial, many survivors find that they cannot take such action because the perpetrator is dead or lives too far away or the perpetrator is unknown to the survivor. Others do not confront the perpetrator, despite all the support they can get from the therapist, because they feel that they simply do not want to, their religion has taught them to forgive and forget, the perpetrator is old and too fragile and such a confrontation might kill him or her, or that the truth is too much for the family to handle and if discussed the family would collapse.

When reasons to avoid a direct confrontation between the survivor and the perpetrator exist, the therapist can help the patient find other ways to achieve the same healing results expected from a direct confrontation. The confrontation may be big or small, requiring what appears to be little or great effort and time. The important thing is that it is significant to the survivor and leads to the empowerment already mentioned and a sense that one is actually doing something to combat the abuse.

CONFRONTATION ISSUES UNIQUE TO THE MALE SURVIVOR

At the Monterey Rape Crisis Center in California, participants in the Men's Adult Survivors of Childhood Sexual Abuse Group have been confronting the perpetrators in their lives by confronting abuse itself. This has come in a variety of ways. Some confront by participating in the fundraising activities the center puts on. Others do so by guest speaking in local sex education college courses, telling their stories to others with the hope that someone who needs to hear about the healing process will come forward and receive their own healing.

Challenging commonly held beliefs and myths about sexual abuse is a significant method of confrontation. This is especially true for male survivors as the myths are well held by society and very damaging to survivors. Belief in these myths is dangerous. If survivors believe these myths, they may likely feel shame and anger and reinforce the notion that it was their fault.

Many male survivors have found reading, discussing, and comprehending myths about male sexual victimization to be one of the most significant elements in healing. These myths include:

1. Men are tough and cannot be sexually abused. They should be able to protect themselves, even as boys. This myth fails to recognize that the perpetrator is usually much bigger, older, and employs bribes, rather than force, for instance, to coerce the boy into unwanted sexual activities.
2. If the boy gets an erection, ejaculates, or even has an orgasm, then he was a willing participant. This myth places blame on the child for experiencing simple and predictable body functions in response to physical stimulation. It also falsely removes the fact that adults, or older children, are the ones responsible for inappropriate sexual activities with younger children even if those children do, in fact, enjoy the contact.
3. Boys are less traumatized by sexual abuse than are girls. This myth fails to recognize that girls are socialized to expect abuse from males while, at the same time, boys are socialized to protect themselves and brave whatever comes their way. The added pressure of not living up to expectations may, in fact, lead boys to feel more traumatized rather than less traumatized. In addition, comparing whose trauma is worse rarely bares fruit for anyone.
4. Boys who are sexually abused by males will become homosexuals. The reality is that it is impossible to make someone homosexual or heterosexual. Boys who are sexually abused are frequently left confused about their sexual orientation as a result of this myth.
5. Boys cannot be sexually abused by females. This myth feeds into the double standard in regard to sexual activity between the genders; childhood sexual contact between a man and a girl is seen as abuse, but childhood sexual contact between a boy and a woman is considered "luck" on the part of the boy. In truth, boys are sometimes sexually abused by mothers, grandmothers, sister, aunts, female teachers, and female babysitters. While the boy may not see the sexual contact as abusive at the time, he may very well grow up with many of the common symptoms of an adult molested as a child and may well come to recognize the contact as abusive if he examines it more closely when he has suffered with the symptoms long enough to cause substantial pain.
6. Males who are sexually molested as children will grow up to become child molesters themselves. This is perhaps the most damaging of all the myths about males molested as children because holding onto this belief can cause men to avoid working with children, or having children of their own, out of the fear that it is only time until they will cross the sexual boundary line with children in their care. Others frequently see the male survivor in the same way and, therefore, avoid having children with him or let him be around their children.

Challenging these myths is difficult. Few survivors can successfully accomplish such a task on their own. Joining forces as a team becomes essential. However, male sexual abuse survivors typically have a very difficult time bonding with other men, especially if they were abused by a male. Therefore, it is important to introduce bonding exercises early in treatment. Reading out loud handouts such as "Lessons from Geese" (Arrien, 1991) and learning to "honk" together and for each other, helps male survivors bond with peers and find strength to do the healing work they likely would not otherwise find. After reading and discussing "Lessons from Geese," men in the group stand up, hold hands, and literally "honk" for each other as loud as they can. Borrowing from other groups who have successfully employed such methods, such as the army and sporting teams, this not only provides the men with a sense of common purpose and support, it also allows others in neighboring rooms, or just outside the building, to get a clear message that there is a group of strong men here who mean business.

As mentioned before, successful confrontation comes in a variety of ways. Full recovery for male sexual abuse survivors rarely occurs if they do not get actively involved in the healing process. For some, this means going public with their opinions. Therefore, many write articles, commentaries, and reports and submit them to public newspapers. When they see their writings in print, and obtain positive feedback from family, friends, and community members, men typically report that this experience is a great catalyst toward full and final healing.

Others find that direct confrontation with the perpetrator fills them with the satisfaction they need to finish their healing. As is the case with many of the men in our groups, one man went through ups and downs in his healing. Along the way he was prompted to empower himself by first deciding what he really needs in order to heal and then going after it. A decision was made; he decided he needed to see justice served in the form of having the perpetrator be held responsible for his actions. The road was not easy. It involved role-playing, sample letter writing, making reports to Child Protective Services, being rudely rejected by Child Protective Services, and bouncing back from that defeat and moving on to a cooperative and knowledgeable team of District Attorneys and Police Investigator Detectives. A sting operation was planned and executed, one that took a year to complete and one that brought up much pain.

As a result of this man's efforts, a major arrest was made. The sting operation he participated in bore much fruit. The perpetrator provided more then enough evidence to warrant his arrest and charge him with many counts of child molestation and possession and distribution of child pornography. Within just a few days of the arrest, 15 other survivors came forward and reported that they too had been molested by the perpetrator. It appears that the perpetrator was a "career pedophile," one who most likely groomed and molested dozens of boys over a period of at least 30 years! Now he is behind bars awaiting trial. Now, many victim survivors will get the help they need, too. Even better, there now will be fewer new victims created.

Although our group participant is a clear hero for taking on, and sticking with, such a struggle for justice, he is by far not the only hero in our men's groups. Indeed, every time a man comes forward, defies society's myths about men who have been sexually abused, and takes some action, he becomes a hero too in the fight against child sexual abuse. Regardless of the individual action chosen, whether a police report, an honest sharing of the facts with a spouse or partner, or a sharing with our volunteers as part of a training, these men become heroes!

Recently the men's group at the Monterey Rape Crisis Center took confrontation to a larger audience. It started with a decision to make a film to send a personal message about male sexual victimization to a national audience who would be hearing a presentation on this subject to therapists and sex therapists. The men felt that they could reach the audience on film in a way that the therapist just could not do even when backed by facts and years worth of experience. They wanted to bring the pain of suffering, and the joy of healing, with hope that some of the attendees would go on to help other men. They were right. The short film they made led many to tears and many to seek out information about starting their own men's group, something much needed across the United States.

When the men in the group heard of the brief film's success, they decided to go further and produce three films. One was meant to be a 1-minute public service announcement to be aired locally, informing the general public of services available to male survivors in their community. The second was a 3-minute film for well-known television talk shows to "get the word out." The third was a 1-hour film meant for therapists and rape crisis centers across the country to educate people about the plight and possible healing of male sexual abuse survivors. So far a local television news broadcast has produced and aired a story about the making of the film, and the men are in full swing confronting sexual abuse by working on seeing these projects through to completion.

HEALING THE COUPLE:
THE SURVIVOR AND THE PARTNER

Survivors of sexual abuse typically find they cannot establish and maintain a healthy romantic, interpersonal relationship until they have completed significant individual and group psychotherapy. If they have been in a relationship, it has most likely suffered tremendously. Healing for the couple comes through a means similar to that for the individual. Education and confrontation are essential. For example, it is important for both the survivor and the partner to recognize that the partner has now been victimized in the process of being in the relationship; not by the victim but by the victimization of the victim. Together they have learned how pervasive the damage of sexual abuse can be. Together they can learn how to be partners in the healing.

It is especially useful to discuss the most common issues a partner of a sexual abuse survivor has to face when living with a survivor. These issues include:

1. Believing the survivor and expressing this belief in a manner in which the survivor accepts.
2. Being clear that the abuse was not the survivor's fault.
3. Learning about sexual abuse and the process of healing from it.
4. Choosing to interact, or not, with the perpertrator if the perpetrator is still in the survivor's life.
5. Understanding and being patient with the length of time it takes for the survivor to heal.
6. Adapting to the changes in the relationship as the survivor heals.
7. Seeing the survivor as a whole person and not just a victim.
8. Learning what triggers the survivor's abuse memory and avoiding these triggers when possible and when appropriate.
9. Recognizing the survivor's need for control.
10. Becoming a partner, a part of the team, in the healing process.

The therapist can help the couple identify which of any of these issues the couple still needs to face and can develop much of the remaining treatment plan based upon the results. As the work progresses, classic and innovative "couple's methods of treatment" may be employed.

TANTRA: OBTAINING SEXUAL
HEALTH AND SATISFACTION

The final step in the healing process for most victims of sexual trauma is reclaiming, or for some claiming for the first time, a healthy sex life. To reach this goal, many survivors find that learning Tantra does the trick.

Tantra primarily comes from India and predates the evolution of Hinduism. The word *Tantra* literally means *weaving* and refers to the weaving of *mind, body, and spirit*. Tantra is a spiritual practice in which one, on his or her own, practicing *White Tantra*, can find much healing and spiritual enlightenment. To Westerners, Tantra appears to be very similar to Hatha Yoga in that it blends a focus on the breath, the body, and meditative exercises. However, White Tantra goes further in that it allows one to also embrace ecstatic sexual pleasure by way of moving energy through the various Chakras, resulting in incredible orgasm without ever touching the genitals. In contrast, *Red Tantra* involves the coming together of two people in a mind, body, and spirit connection that includes utilizing sexual energy and frequently involves sexual touch. It is this Red Tantric approach which, when taught to sexual abuse survivors and their partners, can bring about the reclaiming, or claiming for the first time, of sexual health and a satisfying sex life which we want to see happen at this final stage of healing from sexual trauma.

The first step in teaching Tantra to survivors and their partners is to explain to them that they do not need to become a Hindu, a Buddhist, or, in fact, be spiritually focused at all to benefit from these methods. Tantric practices can be well assimilated into any religious or spiritual practice as the methods are well within the teachings of almost any religion. Tantra focuses on approaching one's partner with the deepest respect (Namaste), seeing the holy in one's partner, and finding a deep, close spiritual connection with one's partner during sexual encounters. Furthermore, if couples have a negative reaction to religion or spiritual practice and choose not to incorporate this part of Tantra into their sex life, they may still benefit from the basic methods and principles of Tantra as these principles mirror sound clinical Western medical approaches to treating sexual dysfunction and difficulties.

Another important issue to explain to the survivor and the partner about Tantra has to do with the time it takes to master these methods. Many of the books and videos on Tantra suggest practicing the exercises for as long as 5 hours a day. Of course few of us, including those who teach Tantra, have time to meet this recommendation. Similarly, some of the benefits of Tantra, such as prolonged multiple orgasms and female ejaculation, are typically achieved only after years of practice. After all, Tantra in its purest state is a lifelong journey and process. Therefore, it is vital to explain to the couple that they will not master these methods overnight and that they need not practice Tantra for hours at a time. For most, if they embrace as little as 5% of what they are taught, they will benefit tremendously and likely reach the goals they were seeking in the first place.

As a clinician, you may be wondering at this point how one can teach patients Tantra, a spiritually based practice that involves sexual touch, and remain within the laws and ethics that most clinicians are bound by. This is not an uncommon dilemma. However, by following some simple guidelines, teaching patients Tantra within the clinical setting is quite possible and is a powerful method to have as part of the clinician's therapeutic toolbox.

Typical "Introduction to Tantra" workshops offer well-functioning couples a basic understanding of Tantric history and many practical Tantric basics. Unfortunately, though, they tend to have too many attendees to address reactions that a survivor might have that need to be processed. In addition, many Tantra workshops teach specific touch by having partners work with a stranger and then bring that touch back to the partner. For many survivors, this learning of sexual touch with a stranger first, then trying to combine the touch with a truly intimate partner, is what they have been dealing with for years. As a result, many survivors abandon the workshops when issues of trust, safety, and risk taking surface, replicating the dysfunctional pattern they have been stuck in at home. Few complete the full workshop and even fewer are able to apply any of the techniques they have been taught as, once again, intimacy has been mixed with fear, anxiety, and a sense of failure.

Specialized "Introduction to Tantra for Sexual Abuse Survivors and Their Partners" workshops offer a well-received alternative in which the couple can safely learn the Tantric methods that will work for them without being overwhelmed. This is accomplished by first restricting the group to only survivors and their partners and keeping the amount of change small. Changing the composition of the facilitator team from two Certified Tantra Educators to one Certified Tantra Educator and one Licensed Marriage and Family Therapist/Certified Sex Therapist greatly increases the odds that the survivor will successfully complete the workshop and get his or her needs addressed. The facilitators introduce the topic of sexual abuse, how such history may have affected both the survivor and the partner, and repeatedly connect the exercises to the healing process. Couples only touch each other as opposed to engaging in physical contact with strangers that is common in other Tantra workshops. Furthermore, the level of graphic, explicitly sexual demonstration and actual touch is reduced to make the experience far more focused on building the trusting connection in the couple and making it more palatable to the sensitive attendees. For example, no nudity and no genital contact occur in these workshops.

Simple Tantric methods can be taught to patients during workshops and within the clinical hour without having to breech any professional boundaries, by verbally walking couples through exercises, providing them with handouts, and having them watch videos. In couple's therapy these homework assignments can be discussed in detail and any refinements can be suggested.

Hand on Heart and *Eye Gazing* are two such methods which couples can easily learn, immediately go home and practice, and benefit from significantly. For this exercise, the therapist prompts the couple to turn to each other, have each one place his and her right palm on the partner's heart, cup the partner's hand over the other's heart with the left hand, and gaze into each other's eyes. While instructing the couple to do this, the therapist is urged to pay special attention to the placement of the couple's right hand and instruct the couple to note that this hand placement is about feeling their partner's heart, not breast, so positioning the hand in an upright, center-of-the-chest position is ideal. This instruction alone typically helps the survivor and the partner feel increased safety and reassures them that the goal is a true emotional, loving connection and not about grabbing body parts. While in this hand-on-heart position, the therapist may guide the couple in imagining a loving energy flow, or an electrical current, running out of one's heart, down the right arm and hand, into the partner's heart and sequentially back again. Giving the suggestion that the loving energy increases every time it passes through one of their hearts helps deepen the experience for many. Similarly, the therapist may guide the couple through simultaneous breathing exercises, such as synchronized breath and alternating breath. Meanwhile, the eye gazing helps the couple, especially the survivor, feel connected and present with the partner. This helps alleviate the worry many survivors have that their loved one is off fantasizing about someone else, essentially just using his or her body, while having a sexual encounter.

Once the couple understands and feels comfortable with Hand on Heart and Eye Gazing, they may be instructed to use this technique to overcome some similar and some different obstacles survivors and their partners commonly have with sex. For example, if the couple has reported that they have not had sex with each other in a long time, the therapist may help them change that by having a safe and appropriate sexual encounter right there in the office. This is accomplished by having the couple assume the Hand on Heart and Eye Gazing position, breathe together, then close their eyes and go on a nonverbal sexual fantasy with each other. Instructions may be given to invite the couple to find the partner in a safe and private place, free of all potential difficulties that can be imagined, and enjoy an unencumbered encounter. After a few minutes the couple may open their eyes, come back to the room, and verbally share the experience with each other. When couched in a supportive manner, many couples agree that this is in fact quite a sexual experience and that it opens the door to more explicit encounters at home now that they have broken the stretch of abstinence.

CONCLUSION

The concept that "once a person is a victim, he or she will always be a victim" is out of date for those who have been sexually abused. Survivors of sexual abuse can and do find healing when treatment combines classic methods, such as empathy, with more dynamic methods, such as confrontation, and innovative methods, such as having patients become active participants in their own healing. Sexual abuse survivors can have safe, healthy, and sexually satisfying interpersonal romantic relationships when traditional approaches are utilized in couple's therapy and combined with tailor-made sex therapy approaches such as Tantra. This contribution presented a few innovative methods for treating sexual trauma and invites clinicians to be bold and create more innovative methods of their own.

CONTRIBUTOR

Stephen L. Braveman, MA, LMFT, DST, is a Licensed Marriage and Family Therapist, AASECT Certified Diplomate of Sex Therapy, and a Gender Specialist with a full-time private practice in Monterey, California. His specializations include the treatment of sexual abuse survivors, gender issues (extensively serving the transsexual community), and Tantra. He currently serves as Western Regional Representative for AASECT (American Association of Sexuality Educators, Counselors, and Therapists) and runs *Especially for Men: A Group for Adult Male Survivors of Childhood Sexual Abuse* at the Monterey Rape Crisis Center. Mr. Braveman is a Past-President of the California Association of Marriage and Family Therapists, Monterey Chapter. His work has been highly recognized by the National Organization on Male Sexual Victimization for co-leading the first national retreat for male sexual abuse survivors and his innovative methods. Mr. Braveman is also a consultant for the national Human Rights Campaign Coming Out Project. He is a regular expert contributor to the Ifriends relationship site, GLBTWORLD.net, and many local publications. With a rich history of therapeutic work, teaching experience, and workshop presentations, his work has appeared in many journals, such as *Treating Abuse Today*, books, and magazines such as *Men's Health*. Mr. Braveman may be contacted at 494 Alvarado Street, Suite A, Monterey, CA 93940 or via his website at www.bravemantherapy.com. He welcomes questions and comments.

RESOURCES

Cited Resources

Abraham, S. (1997). Yes, women do abuse. Retrieved from MenWeb - *Men's Voices Magazine* (http://www.menweb.org).

Arrien, A. (1991). *Lessons from Geese*. Transcribed from a speech at the Organizational Development Network and based upon the work of Milton Olson.

Bass, E., & Davis, L. (1994). *The Courage to Heal: A Guide for Women Survivors of Child Sexual Abuse* (3rd ed.). New York: HarperCollins.

Bureau of Justice Statistics. (2002). *Sexual Assault, Child Sexual Abuse Statistics* (FBI - National Incident-Based Reporting System). Washington, DC: U.S. Department of Justice, Office of Justice Program.

Davis, L. (1990). *The Courage to Heal Workbook: For Women and Men Survivors of Child Sexual Abuse*. New York: HarperCollins.

Davis, L. (1991). *Allies in Healing: When the Person You Love Was Sexually Abused as a Child*. New York: HarperCollins.

Dunlap, E., Golub, A., & Johnson, B. (2003). Girls sexual development in the inner city: From compelled childhood sexual contact to sex-for-things exchanges. *The Journal of Child Sexual Abuse, 12*(2), 73-96.

Gartner, R. B. (1999). *Betrayed as Boys: Psychodynamic Treatment of Sexually Abused Men*. New York: Guilford.

Gil, E. (1992). *Outgrowing the Pain Together*. New York: Dell.

Herman, J. (1997). *Trauma and Recovery: The Aftermath of Violence from Domestic Abuse to Political Terror*. New York: Basic Books.

Kokish, R. (2000). Why adults molest children: An opinion piece - submitted by Ron Kokish from his website - author unknown from the California Coalition on Sexual Offending quarterly newsletter, *Perspectives*.

Lew, M. (1990). *Victims No Longer*. New York: HarperCollins.

Van der Kolk, B. (1987). *Psychological Trauma*. Washington, DC: American Psychiatric Press.

Additional Resources

Geffner, R. (2003). *Journal of Child Sexual Abuse*. Canada: The Haworth Maltreatment and Trauma Press.

Hunter, M. (1990a). *Abused Boys: The Neglected Victims of Sexual Abuse*. New York: Faucett, Columbia.

Hunter, M. (1990b). *The Sexually Abused Male – Vol. 1: Prevalence, Impact and Treatment*. New York: Lexington Books.

Hunter, M. (1990c). *The Sexually Abused Male – Vol. 2: Application of Treatment Strategies*. New York: Lexington Books.

Steen, C. (2001). *The Adult Relapse Prevention Workbook*. Brandon, VT: Safer Society Press.

Section III: Sex Theapy With Special Populations

This section of *Innovations* provides information on how to provide sexual health information and treatment to members of special populations. Four groups are addressed – sexual minority clients, clients with chronic illness and disability, ethnic-racial minorities, and seniors.

In the first contribution, Benjamin Haffey, Frederick L. Peterson, Jr., Jill W. Bley, and Kathleen D. Glaus provide guidance to clinicians who wish to increase their knowledge and skills in assessment and treatment for clients who identify as gay, lesbian, bisexual, and transgendered. Relevant treatment guidelines are described and two case examples are presented. Brief coverage is provided on asexual individuals as well. A self-awareness exercise designed to expand understanding of diversity in sexual identity is presented in the next section of this volume (THERAPIST GUIDES AND PATIENT HANDOUTS) and is entitled "The Complexity of Sexual Diversity: Sexual Identity Cube and Self-Awareness Exercise."

A major illness or injury can have profound effects on sexual functioning. Kathleen M. Gill and Sigmund Hough discuss the adjustment process to injury or illness and its impact on sexual functioning with a goal of bringing clients to a new appreciation of sexuality and sexual behavior. They point out some specific issues that are faced by clients with various types of illness and injury.

The next contribution, by Frederick L. Peterson, Jr., James Dobbins, Florence Coleman, and Jouhaina Razzouk, is designed to assist clinicians in developing their awareness of key principles of culturally competent care with regard to sexual health. The authors describe a new model for building cultural competence and apply it to the treatment of sexual problems. An important companion piece is found in the next section of this volume (THERAPIST GUIDES AND PATIENT HANDOUTS) and is entitled "The Complexity of Sexual Diversity: Sexual Identity Cube and Self-Awareness Exercise."

Our society is very youth focused and promotes the stereotype that older men and women are uninterested and uninvolved in sexual activity. In the last contribution in this section, Larry M. Davis dispels this myth. From his perspective as a sex therapist, he sees an increasing number of couples in their 50s and older who seek a new personal awareness and sexual connectedness. He shares the therapeutic process of guiding older men and women in taking their sexuality to a new and deeply satisfying level.

Addressing Sexual Health Concerns of Sexual Minority Clients

Benjamin Haffey, Frederick L. Peterson, Jr.,
Jill W. Bley, and Kathleen D. Glaus

This contribution provides guidance to mental health therapists who wish to increase their knowledge and skills in providing assessment and treatment services for sexual health concerns to clients who identify as lesbian, gay, bisexual, or transgendered (LGBT). A brief review of key points from the literature is followed by discussion of an assessment protocol used by the authors. Relevant treatment guidelines are described. Two case examples are presented to illustrate key points and principles. In addition, a brief discussion is included on another group of people that some include as a sexual minority: asexual individuals. A self-awareness exercise designed to expand understanding of the tremendous diversity in sexual identity is presented in a separate section of this book. It is entitled "The Complexity of Sexual Diversity: Sexual Identity Cube and Self-Awareness Exercise" (see pp. 297-300). A brief description of the Sexual Identity Cube appears below.

Multiple forces converge on the therapist who is presented with the challenge and opportunity of working with clients who identify as lesbian, gay, bisexual, or transgendered and who are seeking help with a sexual health concern. Some of these forces include attitudes, knowledge, and values as they relate to sexual expression, gender expression, relationships, and social context.

Standards of ethical practice require knowledge and understanding of the particular issues that impact the lives of the LGBT community (American Psychological Association, 2000). This contribution is intended to add to that knowledge and understanding, specifically as they apply to sexual health concerns. Many issues addressed in sex therapy remain the same regardless of the orientation or gender identity of the client; however, some differences exist, including frequency of certain diagnoses, sexual identity issues, variety of sexual practices (Nichols, 2000), and the effects of oppression on sexual identity. As a caveat, the danger of considering the differences between sex therapy with heterosexual clients and sex therapy with LGBT clients is that it may implicitly communicate that heterosexuality is "normative" and other forms of sexual and gender expression must be understood in relation to heterosexuality. In contrast to this notion, this contribution discusses those issues that are specific to sex therapy with LGBT persons with the assumption that the reader simply may be less familiar with them, not with the assumption that they are defined by points of departure from, or congruence with, some heterosexual norm. Before addressing these specific issues to LGBT clients, a broader perspective of the diversity of sexual identity is needed for context.

THE COMPLEXITY OF SEXUAL DIVERSITY: SEXUAL IDENTITY CUBE

In a separate section of this volume, Peterson presents an exercise entitled "The Complexity of Sexual Diversity: Sexual Identity Cube and Self-Awareness Exercise" (pp. 297-300). It is based on the work of Alfred Kinsey, John Money, and Sandra Bem and presents three dimensions of sexual identity: Gender Orientation, Sexual Orientation, and Gender Role Orientation. The spatial arrangement of these three dimensions into a cube yields a 27-cell identity cube, with each of the 27 compartments called an identity or ID cube. The identity cube represents the entire set of human sexual identities, ranging from "heterosexual masculine males" to "bisexual androgynous transgendered" individuals. The sexual identities represented in this typology are based upon a person's self-identification. Readers are invited to complete the exercise and share it with clients as appropriate.

A discussion of all the possible permutations represented in the identity cube is beyond the scope of this contribution. The identity cube emphasizes the incredible sexual mosaic we are as people, and may be used as a teaching tool with students and clients. However, as discussed later, in the section entitled Sexual Health Assessment Protocol, sexual identity does need to be evaluated and understood by both the client and therapist for effective intervention to enhance the sexual health of an individual.

In addition to understanding the diversity of sexual identity, it is necessary to state here that it is important to avoid the tendency to classify clients or aspects of their identity by using dichotomous categories. Social scientists have warned, beginning with Kinsey, Pomeroy, and Martin's (1948) heterosexual-homosexual rating scale, that binary categories are rarely useful and are often harmful because they perpetuate stereotypes.

Kinsey proposed seven gradations of sexual orientation whereby a score of 0 represents exclusive heterosexuality, a score of 3 represents equal attraction to either sex, and 6 represents exclusive homosexuality. Kinsey's empirically based conceptualization of sexual orientation on a continuum, rather than dichotomy, was just one of many contributions that led to one overarching conclusion: There is a tremendous diversity of sexual expression among people and there is no empirical basis to pathologize variations in expression simply because they diverge from a cultural norm.

Recently, questions have been addressed by experts regarding the existence of *asexuality* as an authentic sexual orientation. Some researchers argue that some people have no interest in sex and no distress as a result of having no interest in sex. They argue that those who identify themselves as asexual should be accepted as they are and do not require treatment for sexual aversion disorder or hypoactive sexual desire disorder. Others argue that asexuality is not a sexual orientation, but that the lack of interest in sexual expression masks a trauma history or other medical or psychiatric conditions, or even represents a "pseudo-issue" manufactured by the media. Others reserve judgment and suggest that more research and exploration needs to be done on this issue (Melby, 2005). Melby offers an excellent brief review of the topic.

SOCIAL AND CULTURAL INFLUENCES ON SEXUAL MINORITIES

The mental health field has seen significant progress in understanding the needs of sexual minorities in the last three decades since homosexuality was removed from the *Diagnostic and Statistical Manual of Mental Disorders* (*DSM*; American Psychiatric Association [APA], 1972); however, the legacy of bigotry and misinformation has continuing effects of which therapists need to remain mindful. When therapists operate from a point of reference in which heterosexuality is normative, some common pitfalls may arise when working with LGBT clients. Issues such as how sexual dysfunction is defined, the impact of internalized oppression, the client's beliefs about monogamy, the presentation of cover stories, and the presence or threat of HIV status should be considered when seeking to effectively intervene with LGBT clients in sex therapy.

Defining Sexual Dysfunction

The current diagnostic nomenclature utilized by the *DSM-IV-TR* (APA, 2000) has been criticized for defining sexual dysfunction as primarily a problem associated with a man and a woman having intercourse. Although heterosexual couples encounter problems related to intercourse or mutual orgasm, these may not be of concern for the LGBT client. For example, problems that impede penetration with a lesbian couple may be less disconcerting than an oral sex aversion (Ritter & Terndrup, 2002). Similarly, for gay men, an often-overlooked problem is pain that prevents anal intercourse, or *anodyspareunia* (McNally & Adams, 2000).

Internalized Oppression

In treatment, it may be helpful to be aware of the oppression faced by the LGBT community, but draw on the strengths forged through these experiences rather than seeing them as deficits only. For instance, Hall (2001) asserted that Narrative Therapy with lesbians allows them to use skills learned as they redefined their identity during the coming-out process or as they were forced to rewrite their own erotic narrative. The skills necessary to negotiate these and other requisite tasks uniquely prepare them to rewrite and redefine other aspects of their identity or experience that may be causing sexual problems.

By virtue of their sexual identity being marginalized and pathologized, gay men may separate their sexuality from the rest of their identity. This may lead to a state where sexual and emotional intimacy cannot coexist. Consequently, some men may be unable to achieve erections or achieve orgasm with an emotionally intimate partner (Ritter & Terndrup, 2002).

Another consequence of internalized homophobia may be strong feelings of guilt or shame, perhaps related to religious training, surrounding sexual expression. Of course, feelings of guilt and shame can lead to problems with desire, arousal, erection/lubrication, and penetration regardless of sexual orientation, but in an LGBT client the prevalence and intensity of negative messages about sexuality are likely to be much greater.

Monogamy

For therapists who believe (whether or not it is acknowledged) that monogamy is the healthiest approach to a committed relationship, it may be helpful to consider ways in which they can assist couples who have chosen a sexually open relationship (Ritter & Terndrup, 2002). Therapists may be able to help the couple establish boundaries and minimize issues related to jealousy (Nichols, 2000) and risks of sexually transmitted infection (STI). Those who pursue nonmonogamous relationships may not have seen anyone model a similar, successful arrangement, so the therapist can assist them in navigating uncharted waters.

Cover Stories

When entering treatment, the LGBT client may offer the therapist a cover story, which allows the client to test the waters of the psychotherapeutic context without fully revealing the reasons for seeking treatment. This type of approach likely represents an adaptive response to an intolerant culture and is likely to wane should the client become more comfortable with and trusting of the therapist.

HIV Status

Given that AIDS was once called Gay Related Immune Deficiency Syndrome by the Centers for Disease Control (CDC; Nichols, 2000), it is not hard to imagine that the impact of this disease on the sexual functioning of LGBT clients is significant. Among gay men, sex frequently became seen as toxic, and problems with sexual desire and arousal naturally developed (Nichols, 2000). Carballo-Dieguez and Remien (2001) discussed issues that arise when treating couples with mixed or serodiscordant HIV status. Among them are ethical questions about confidentiality, increased risk of sexual dysfunction for HIV-positive persons, and the emotional issues for the HIV-positive and HIV-negative partner. They suggested that the therapist take a contextual and integrative approach in which HIV-related issues are neither ignored nor allowed to monopolize therapy (Carballo-Dieguez & Remien, 2001).

APA Guidelines for Lesbian, Gay, and Bisexual (LGB) Clients

Should the clinician working with a gay adolescent have an understanding of the special problems and risks faced by gay youth, or is it acceptable to have the client educate you on his or her experiences? The American Psychological Association provides an answer to this question in the form of its *Guidelines for Psychotherapy With Lesbian, Gay, and Bisexual Clients* (American Psychological Association, 2000). The guidelines first address *attitudes toward homosexuality and bisexuality*, stating that psychologists should recognize their own attitudes toward homosexuality and bisexuality, understand that homosexuality is not indicative of mental illness, and acknowledge that social stigmatization impacts mental health and the therapy process. The guidelines also state that psychologists should know about and respect homosexual and bisexual *relationships and families*, understand the pressures on LGB parents, recognize that LGB family members may not be biologically or legally related, and understand the impact of sexual orientation on one's family of origin. The third area addresses *issues of diversity*. Psychologists are encouraged to recognize the impact of multiple forms of oppression experienced by many LGB people based on their race, ethnicity, age (both young and old), and ability. Additionally, psychologists are encouraged to recognize the unique challenges of bisexual individuals, including negative attitudes coming from both the heterosexual and homosexual communities. Finally, the guidelines address *education*, stating that psychologists should educate themselves through professional training, supervision, and consultation and should make "reasonable efforts" to be familiar with educational and community resources for their LGB clients.

THE SEXUAL HEALTH ASSESSMENT PROTOCOL

As mentioned in the contribution in this volume by Candace Risen entitled "How to Do a Sexual Health Assessment" (see pp. 19-33), the evaluation of sexual health matters often takes more than one session. The protocol for doing evaluations with individuals and couples that we use is a multiple session format that typically involves at least three meetings with the client. The protocol is briefly reviewed here with special attention to LGBT clients. This model of assessment evolved in a hospital setting with strong influence from the Masters and Johnson approach to assessment (a private clinic setting), from the Kinsey Institute approach to assessment developed by Bancroft (a university center setting), and a consultative model of assessment shared by Siefer, past-president of the American Association of Sexuality Educators, Counselors, and Therapists (AASECT). It is successfully employed by both Dr. Peterson and

Dr. Bley (with some variation) in a fee-for-service, no-insurance, private practice setting. In short, this model is applicable to both private practice and clinic settings.

Before they make a decision to begin treatment, clients need to understand (and accept) that they will be expected to participate in three meetings (prior to the commencement of treatment) that are focused entirely on completing a comprehensive evaluation.

Session One

The first session consists of a standard clinical interview which covers the presenting complaint, any comorbid psychiatric diagnoses, medical history including medications, and social functioning. During the first meeting the therapist also provides information regarding rules of confidentiality, therapist qualifications, fees, and other office policies and procedures and discusses cultural factors related to differences between the therapist and client in gender, gender orientation, sexual orientation, ethnic backgrounds, and so on (see contribution on cultural competency in this volume [see pp. 245-260]), and obtains basic client contact information, signatures for informed consent, and Release of Information. The couple explains the presenting problem while together. Essentially, the first meeting is to get an understanding of the "big picture" of the couple and to set the stage not only for an effective evaluation but for the treatment that may follow.

Session Two

The second meeting is devoted to obtaining an in-depth sexual developmental history from the individual or the couple. Although the second session is focused on eliciting information about the client's sexual development history and functioning, it is also used to model accurate terminology and a nonjudgmental approach to sexuality and may act as a helpful didactic experience for the clients that can increase their comfort and disclosure. Whenever possible, a sexual development history is recorded from each person – both men, both women, or the man and woman. (An excellent guide to gaining the sexual story of each client can be found in the contribution by Candace Risen in this volume [see pp. 19-33].) Of special interest with LGBT clients are the origins of their awareness concerning their sexual and gender orientations. Understanding the client's perception of sexual identity is of particular significance.

Two special notes about sexual orientation are important. First, sexual orientation is not defined only by whom a person selects as a sexual partner. Second, sexual orientation has three components that must be evaluated: (a) the positive visceral physiological response one has to men, women, or both; (b) the content and nature of the sexual fantasy an individual enjoys when masturbating (similar to Money's concept of lovemaps; 1986); and (c) the sexual behavior in which the person engages and with whom he or she engages.

There are at least eight dimensions of gender status to consider when conducting an assessment with a transgendered individual: (a) chromosomal make-up, (b) prenatal hormonal development, (c) internal reproductive system, (d) external genitalia, (e) pubescent hormonal development, (f) gender the person was assigned at birth, (g) gender the person was raised as, and (h) gender identity. Of course, some of these dimensions cannot be assessed directly, but they sometimes may be inferred from other data, or may require specialized procedures such as DNA analysis or an MRI. This level of specification in assessment is often not advisable due to lack of interest of the client or lack of resources to pay for them. Hence, some of these dimensions, such as DNA, are inferred to be either male or female in development for the purposes of counseling.

Psychological testing is completed by the client following the interviews. We use screening tools to identify contributing factors to sexual dysfunction or disorders, such as depression, anxiety, and personality disorders. In addition, inventories for male and female sexual function are employed to specifically measure the nature and extent of the presenting problem(s).

Session Three

The final session of the assessment phase is the "results sharing conference" in which the client is presented with a four- to five-page "Draft Treatment Agreement" (see contribution on pp. 301-306) that contains the results of the interviews and the psychological testing, desired treatment outcomes, treatment goals, specific treatment strategies, a list of criteria for ongoing evaluation (e.g., frequency of satisfactory erections, Beck Depression Inventory [BDI] scores), client responsibilities, and consent for treatment. It is made clear that the document is a draft. Client input is strongly encouraged, and the document is revised as needed throughout treatment. This draft treatment agreement is used as a compass to guide therapist and client. The results sharing conference concludes the assessment process, and the client then decides whether to continue into a treatment phase.

CLINICAL VIGNETTE OF GAY MALE CLIENT*

Michael is a Mexican-American man who was adopted as an infant by a White family. He was never exposed to Mexican culture, was often teased and bullied because of his ethnicity, and learned to hate his physical appearance and his ethnic status. As a child he was subjected to daily physical abuse and psychological torture as well as incidents of sexual abuse. After high school he entered the military where he was raped twice. Around that time his drug and alcohol use escalated and by the time he presented to the clinic in his early 40s he had tried nearly every drug available. His most recent drug of choice was crack cocaine. After discharge from the military, he experienced two additional sexual assaults. He is one of the 22,000 male veterans identified by the Department of Veterans Affairs as comprising an "epidemic" of Military Sexual Trauma (MST) during service. It is believed that MST has an even higher prevalence for female veterans.

At his initial session for his most recent period of treatment, he presented with a written list of more than 30 treatment goals. Many of these goals related to fixing some "defective," "disgusting," or "sinful" part of himself, but he also included goals addressing an interest in sobriety, his hatred of his ethnicity, his desire to have God take away his homosexual attraction, a desire to treat his erectile dysfunction (ED), and an interest in addressing the effects of his personal traumas.

Before Michael's ED could be treated, the diagnosis and treatment plan needed to be considered within a much broader framework. His history as a trauma survivor caused him to have strong beliefs that he was defective, that it was acceptable for people to use him sexually, and that his sexual desires were secondary to his partner's desires. Additionally, the trauma led him to question his sexual orientation. He wondered whether he was gay or whether his sexual victimization caused him to pursue homosexual sexual experiences. Finally, his ethnicity presented another important issue. His Latino heritage has never been affirmed by his White adoptive parents. Therefore, he is disgusted by those physical attributes that remind him of his ethnicity. He also stated that he believed gay men focus on outward physical appearance and are not attracted to him because of his ethnicity. For example, at times he agreed to engage in sexual activities that he did not enjoy and that he often found degrading. Because his relationships typically begin this way, he finds it difficult to establish reciprocity and mutual respect.

Improving Michael's sexual health was about much more than treating his ED. After exploring his goals, it became evident that he wanted to find a relationship in which there was mutual respect, warmth, trust, and caring. Interfering with attaining this goal were his view of

---

* Names and identifying characteristics in all vignettes have been changed to protect privacy.

himself as a sexual object, his struggle with whether or not homosexuality is morally wrong, his beliefs about the motives of other gay men, and his hatred of his ethnicity. In short, Michael suffered from the chronic effects of internalized homophobia and racism.

Michael's first need was to address whether he wanted to continue to live as a gay man or acquiesce to his religious training and abstain from homosexual fantasies and activities. He often stated that he was condemned to hell for being gay, and he occasionally admitted that he was terrified of this prospect. A pivotal moment for him came when he answered the question, "What do you believe it takes for someone to go to heaven?" (in his terminology, "to be saved"). His answer addressed how badly he wanted to be reunited with his deceased family members, but did not list heterosexuality as a requirement. After that session he was able to settle this issue by believing that he could at least go to heaven. Michael stated, "Even if God wasn't entirely pleased with me being gay, I wonder why God would make me gay and then require me to be straight!" Treatment built on this shift and continued to encourage his development of a positive and affirming identity as a gay man.

The next phase of treatment helped Michael establish healthy boundaries so that he could protect himself and make healthy choices about the type of person with whom he wanted to be a partner. It is likely that he will continue to have fantasies involving "risky" people (i.e., those who are likely to be exploitive or abusive). However, he learned the requisite skills to enable himself to examine his sexual attractions while, at the same time, not act impulsively on them. Rather, he can ask himself whether acting on this attraction will put him closer to his ultimate goal of having a warm, caring relationship.

Along with the work he was doing in individual therapy, Michael was able to make significant progress in a men's sexual health group. In the context of this group he was able to form emotionally intimate but nonsexual relationships with other men, something he had never done before. Bonding emotionally with other men without using sex allowed Michael to realize that he possessed the skills to form healthy relationships, to appreciate the benefits of healthy relationships, and to create a template for a healthy relationship which he can apply when he decides to pursue a romantic relationship. Individual and group sessions were often scheduled on the same day, which allowed the momentum from one session to carry over into the next.

At the time of this writing, Michael remains single and has been able to avoid exploitive sexual relationships. He was accepted into a transitional residential community and has begun a 2-year vocational rehabilitation program. He has remained abstinent from drugs and alcohol for 1 year. He is employed in a supervisory position, has a sense of direction, and reports being happy and productive in his life.

DEFINITIONS AND PRINCIPLES RELEVANT TO TRANSGENDERED INDIVIDUALS

A commonly misunderstood and improperly used group of terms falls under the broad category of *transgender*, which refers to those who "transgress" (some prefer "transcend") gender and includes transgenderists, transsexuals, androgynes, transvestites, and intersex people. A *transgenderist* is one who lives and works as the opposite gender (Gainor, 2000) or somewhere between the two extremes of male and female (Pfafflin, 2003). *Transsexuals* also establish a gender identity other than the one assigned at birth, but they express a strong incongruence between their biological sex and their gender identity, to the point that they often report feeling that they are in the wrong body (Zandvliet, 2000). Transsexuals are usually interested in permanently establishing a cross-gender identity, which often includes an interest in sex hormones, plastic surgery, and gender reassignment surgery (GRS). For the *transvestite*, cross-dressing is motivated by emotional satisfaction or erotic pleasure (Pfafflin, 2003) and should be differentiated from those who cross-dress as entertainers, such as drag queens or drag kings (Gainor, 2000). *Androgynes* may identify as both male and female or neither male nor female. They may present a gender neutral appearance and establish this identity in order to be congruent with their personal sexual identity or to challenge societal expectations (Gainor, 2000). Finally, an *intersex* person (which used to be referred to as *hermaphrodite*) is born with both male and female biological characteristics (i.e., hormones, genitals). These people are often born with ambiguous genitalia (especially both ovarian and testicular tissue) and assigned a gender at birth that may or may not match their own gender identity. There are an infinite number of ways in which one may choose to "transgress" (or transcend) gender; the preceding is not intended to be an exhaustive list, but rather meant to provide a description of some common forms of gender expression.

Another key definition is offered by Ms. Dee Rockwood, one of the most effective educators in the country on the topic of the transgendered and transsexual experience. She defines transsexualism as a "surgically correctable birth defect," referring to her own perspective as a male to female transsexual individual. Her story is instructive in that her journey involves a journey into "hypermasculinity," a term referring to some men's efforts to secure a strong masculine identity through engaging in extreme risk-taking behaviors associated with the most masculine of men. Some, but certainly far from all, transgendered men experiment with flights into hypermasculinity as a means to cope with their transgender experience (the second clinical vignette in this contribution also offers insight into this phenomenon).

Ms. Rockwood's experience brought her to an early awareness of identifying with girls as preferred playmates and having hostile feelings toward boys because of their bullying when she was a young boy. This led her to martial arts and eventually winning international competitions, becoming a Hollywood stuntman, performing at Caesar's Palace, and having one of the most successful martial arts dojos in the Midwest. Adding to her masculine façade were adventures as a rodeo cowboy, race car driver, getting an engineering degree, and being married with two children. With all the exterior signs of success and happiness, she eventually found herself desperate living as a man.

Taking all risks (including the fear of losing her family) and giving up all the trappings of the "successful" life she lived, Ms. Rockwood found herself one day in front of a judge saying, "I am here to change my sex from male to female. If you do not allow me to change to a woman, I will walk outside this building and step in front of the first bus coming toward me."

One aspect of Ms. Rockwood's teaching that makes her so effective as an educator is her ability to supportively challenge her audience's stereotypes of transgendered people. Said differently, she leads the audience through some "gender bender reconceptualizations" that are instructive for this contribution. For instance, transgendered individuals are burdened not only by the changes their gender status makes in their personal lives, but the status changes put into effect for their significant others and family. Transsexual persons may engage in changing not only their gender (most frequently male to female) but their sexual orientation as well (heterosexual to homosexual typically) because the object of their attraction remains constant. A heterosexual partner or spouse of a transsexual person (whether or not the latter completes GRS) then has to wrestle with his or her perceived status change from heterosexual to homosexual. Some partners are accepting of this change and some are not. An increasing number of marriages do survive this transition, especially when support is provided to both parties in the relationship during counseling, not just to the transgendered individual.

What about the children? Again, without any personal changes being made by them as individuals, children go through changes that range from having the "norm" of a father and mother to the "exception" of having two mothers or two fathers. This issue is similar (although less complex) to that of children who have a parent engaged in the "coming-out" process and that parent is coupled with a same-sex partner. Generally, while experiencing prejudice and discrimination, lesbian and gay parents are more familiar, more understood, and more accepted by children, as well as the community, than are transgendered parents. Additionally, any "coming-out" process for the individual is accompanied by a "coming-out" process for parents, partners, and children. Obviously, there are often significant differences among people in their degree of comfort in "being out."

Any assessment and treatment of transgendered individuals needs to be conducted by therapists familiar with the *Standards of Care and Ethical Guidelines* published by The Harry Benjamin International Gender Dysphoria Association (HBIGDA), a professional organization devoted to the understanding and treatment of those with gender identity disorders. These guidelines delineate the consensus opinion in medicine (including endocrinology, psychiatry, and surgery) and psychology about the optimal care of those with identity disorders. Therapists engaged with this population are obligated to become both comfortable and competent with the standards of care, or they should refer transgendered clients to providers who specialize in this area of practice.

TRANSGENDER CASE VIGNETTE

Developmental History and Evaluation

The client in this vignette is referred to as Bill. Bill was referred by his psychiatrist for a psychological evaluation and psychotherapy. At intake, he said that he wanted treatment because he was told that in order to have a sex change operation he had to see a psychiatrist and a psychologist to "make sure he wasn't crazy." Bill had already contacted three facilities that provide the gender reassignment surgery (GRS) and knew what was going to be expected of him. He was married and his wife knew about his desire to be a woman. He reported that she was supportive of his doing so. He said his wife was a girl he started dating in high school and was the only girl he had ever dated. Surprisingly, they had never had sex. When asked why, Bill stated that neither one had interest in sex. However, they were very affectionate toward one another.

Bill reported that his mother was also aware of his intentions of GRS and that she was supportive. He had not told his father and had asked his mother not to tell him yet because he was sure that his father would be angry and be verbally abusive if he knew. His father had been verbally and physically abusive toward him in the past, but not toward his five siblings. His father ridiculed his "sissy" behavior and tried to "make a man" out of him by severely beating him for even small transgressions. His mother appeared helpless to protect him. His greatest solace during his childhood was to withdraw into music which he loved to listen to and to play.

During treatment, Bill revealed that from a very young age, probably as early as 3 or 4, he had felt that he was more like his sisters than his brother. He wanted to play with his sisters and receive the same kinds of toys for holiday gifts, and he desperately wanted to wear dresses. His first memory of a severe beating from his father was at about age 4 when his father found him wearing his sister's clothes. Bill recalled daydreaming many times during preadolescence about being a girl and drawing pictures of himself in girls' clothing. He was terrified of his father's anger about his desire to wear girl's clothes, so he contented himself by making drawings and hiding them.

By adolescence, Bill had endured so much pain and humiliation about his "girly" behaviors that he determined to make himself into the strong male that his father, siblings, and friends seemed to need him to be. So he joined the military as soon as he was old enough because he kept hearing how the military could "make you a man." At age 17, he enlisted in the Navy and trained as a Navy SEAL. He said that he became a "skilled warrior" and served his country well. He received many honors for his valor. After the military, Bill married and got a job as a police officer in a small town. He stated that he was a good "peace officer" but realized that his efforts to make everyone believe that he had finally become a man were making him increasingly depressed and withdrawn. He quit his job and opened a small business making and selling musical instruments in a large city. He decided that he needed to be in a community where he might find support for, and more acceptance of, his desire to be a female.

Bill confided his concerns to his physician, who was understanding and empathic. He was amazed that someone understood him. His physician referred him to a psychiatrist. The psychiatrist was willing and able to treat his depression but was not knowledgeable about the treatment of his gender issues. She referred him for the psychological evaluation and treatment. Bill's description of his history indicated a diagnosis of Gender Identity Disorder, attracted to females. In fact, he stated that he thought that he was probably a lesbian and that would "work well for me and my wife, if she is a lesbian, too." He thought that she might have those tendencies but had never "had the nerve to ask her."

Psychological testing indicated that Bill had no serious pathology (such as a thought disorder) but that he was depressed and anxious. In addition, he had a mild to moderate level of Posttraumatic Stress Disorder (PTSD). Bill had many preferences that were typically viewed as feminine. He agreed to work in the therapy to resolve his childhood abuse issues and the traumatic aftermath of his Navy SEAL experiences, which included having to kill people, including a woman, during a clandestine attack to rescue some prisoners.

Treatment

After consultation with his psychiatrist and his physician, during which a collaborative treatment plan was developed, treatment began. The first focus of the treatment was on resolving the childhood abuse issues. He was very motivated. He was willing to have two treatment sessions per week. Eye Movement Desensitization Reprocessing (EMDR) was the primary mode of treatment. He eventually was not only able to talk about his childhood without crying or feeling a lot of anger, but was eager to go to his childhood home and tell his father his plans to become a woman. The confrontation with his father went much better than he expected. He also reported that his siblings were somewhat okay with it too because his mother had talked with each one and asked them to support him.

After resolving those family concerns, he was ready to work on the Navy SEAL traumas. That work was more difficult for him to deal with than the childhood traumas because he felt much grief and sorrow that his attempts to be a "man" led him to vocational choices that involved killing people.

Bill's wife began to attend the therapy sessions. She was a very quiet, withdrawn woman who rarely made eye contact with others. She was very attached to her spouse and was supportive and encouraging toward him. She stated that she was eager to help him have the surgery he wanted because she knew he would be happier as a woman. She admitted that she had fears about the changes he was making, but she felt confident that the relationship could accommodate and survive any changes. The only issues that she had with her spouse were that Bill did not do as much around the house as she wanted him to do and that she would like to work part-time. He did not make enough money since he started his new business because much of what he made was being saved to pay for his GRS. They both felt that the money issue would improve as soon as they had saved enough for the surgery.

At this point in the treatment, his psychologist wrote a letter to his physician recommending him to begin hormone treatment. He was started on estrogen and an antiandrogenic medication. He also sought out and underwent electrolysis to remove facial hair and cosmetic surgeries to enhance his breasts and remove fatty tissue. As soon as the breast enhancement surgery was completed, he began to dress as a woman and assume a female identity. Bill passed as a rather attractive middle-aged woman. Her (switching pronouns) spouse (the wife) was complimentary of Bill and stated that she was a little jealous of her good looks. They used most of their therapy time talking about and figuring out how to deal with the reactions of their friends, families, and neighbors to the gender change.

After about 8 months living as a woman, Bill selected a surgical facility and made plans to have the surgery. Her psychiatrist, her physician, and her psychologist all wrote letters of recommendation to the surgeon and mental health professional at the surgery facility. Five months after first applying for the surgery, she was admitted to the facility and the surgery was performed. The surgery and the recovery period went well. Bill and her spouse remained in treatment for 6 months postsurgery. The general theme of the therapy during those final months was to help the couple adjust to their new relationship. Bill's wife expressed that she was finding herself to be more and more sexually attracted to her partner. At the final session, they were experimenting with sexual touching. They were both enjoying their shared touch and feeling that the surgery had helped both of them learn to express their lesbian feelings.

Case Discussion

This case is not typical of how many transgender cases unfold. Bill's story was selected because it is a case that illustrates a motivated, relatively mentally healthy individual who was willing to accept and follow a treatment plan that conforms to the *Standards of Care* as outlined by The Harry Benjamin International Gender Dysphoria Association. Another element that made this case atypical was that Bill had a partner who was not only supportive, but who also believed that there would be benefits for her from the gender change. A third element about this couple that is very atypical is the three-decade history of celibacy, raising questions related to the previous discussions about the asexual orientation.

The authors' experiences repeatedly demonstrate that many people who present with a desire to change their gender have been so frustrated by the lack of knowledge, understanding, and acceptance of their issues that they do not want to follow a treatment plan, which they often perceive as just another obstacle to getting what they so desperately need. Many others are very ambivalent about what they want to do because of their fears (real and imagined) of what will happen to them in their marriages, their jobs, their extended families, and their communities when people find out about their "secret."

What is typical of this case is an often repeated, but not universal, pattern of incredible endeavoring to meet the approval of parental figures and others in terms of "fitting into" society's demand for a strict and highly polarized gender code for behavior. This endeavor to find approval typically leads to one of two trajectories. One trajectory is that the individual experiences repeated failure and alienation so he or she lives a life of quiet desperation, severe depression, or possibly suicide. Once children leave the home, marriages fall apart, or a spouse is deceased, then the person may consider making changes in life that lead to happiness and authenticity.

The second trajectory involves the individual building an appearance of success via a flight into the "world of hypermasculinity," realizing that he or she is incredibly unhappy "faking it," and finally deciding (out of desperation as well) to "live as LOLA" (Living Out, Living Authentic). Bill's story and Ms. Rockwood's story demonstrate the hypermasculinity route to LOLA.

With transgendered individuals, the first task of therapy is to confront and deal with these issues. The person who is eager to "get it done" has to be able to see the value in taking the time necessary to ensure long-term emotional, psychological health before pursuing GRS. The person who is ambivalent because of the perceived repercussions the gender change could have needs to resolve those fears by considering all of the options and the consequences of those options, including finding satisfaction without GRS.

CONCLUSION

Hopefully, this contribution has helped the reader to understand how important it is to the successful treatment of people presenting with LGBT issues that clinicians be well informed about the special interests of sexual minority clients. Treatment is more successfully accomplished when clinicians possess a number of clinical skills and a depth of knowledge related to the APA guidelines, the HBIGDA *Standards of Care* when treating transgendered individuals, cross-cultural/ethnic issues, and training in sex therapy.

Some of these cases demand so much of the therapist that it is often advisable that even the most experienced therapist seek the consultation of another experienced therapist. Consultation may include an examination of the therapist's own biases, prejudices, myths, or misunderstanding of some aspect of the client's presenting complaints and/or sexual history. It is the rare clinician who has enough education, clinical experience, and life experience to fully understand and effectively treat all of the complexities presented by some of these clients.

Because our sexual heritage includes ignorance and prejudice toward this population, the mental health professions have made countless and damaging mistakes in their treatment of LGBT clients in the past. We have no excuse if maltreatment of these clients persists into the future. There are many guidelines, ethical standards, training programs, and much professional literature available to ensure that all mental health professionals can acquire the requisite skills and knowledge to provide the best care possible to this population.

CONTRIBUTORS

Benjamin Haffey, PsyD, recently graduated from Wright State University's School of Professional Psychology. He completed his predoctoral internship at the Dayton VA Medical Center where he trained in the medical center's Sexual Health Clinic. He is currently employed by Meridian Behavioral Health Services in Sylva, North Carolina. Dr. Haffey may be contacted at 154 Medical Park Loop, Sylva, NC 28779. E-mail: haffey.2@wright.edu

Frederick L. Peterson, Jr., PsyD, is a health psychologist at the Veterans Healthcare System of Ohio, Dayton Campus, where he coordinates a Sexual Health Clinic and the Smoking Cessation Programs. Dr. Peterson is the Co-Director of the Psychology Internship Program. He completed postdoctorate training as a Clinical Fellow at the Masters and Johnson Institute. Research interests include sex therapy, tobacco use treatment, and the effects of masculinity-related personality factors on health. He holds three academic appointments at Wright State University, including the School of Medicine (Department of Psychiatry), the School of Professional Psychology, and the College of Education and Human Services. Dr. Peterson can be reached at the Sexual Health Clinic, VA Medical Center, Dayton, OH 45428. E-mail: Docpete100@aol.com

Jill W. Bley, PhD, is a clinical psychologist. She is certified by the American Association of Sexuality Educators, Counselors, and Therapists as both a sex therapist and a supervisor. She taught sex therapy to graduate students in clinical psychology at the University of Cincinnati. During that time she trained and supervised many students. Dr. Bley wrote a syndicated column, "Speaking of Sex," which appeared in some downtown newspapers. Her columns addressed the diverse issues related to human sexuality. She is a founder of Women Helping Women/Rape Crisis Center and a Sex Therapy Clinic, both in Cincinnati. She has lectured extensively on topics of sexuality. Dr. Bley is a Volunteer Associate Professor in the Department of Psychiatry University of Cincinnati Medical Center. Dr. Bley may be contacted at 750 Red Bud Avenue, Cincinnati, OH 45229. E-mail: drjillbley@cinci.rr.com

Kathleen D. Glaus, PhD, PsyD, is Professor and Associate Dean for Academic Affairs in the School of Professional Psychology at Wright State University. She is trained in clinical psychology with special interests in clinical health psychology. Dr. Glaus can be reached at the School of Professional Psychology, 117 Health Science Building, Wright State University, Dayton, OH 45435. E-mail: Kathleen.glaus@wright.edu

RESOURCES

American Psychiatric Association. (1972). *Diagnostic and Statistical Manual of Mental Disorders* (*DSM*; 1st ed.). Washington, DC: Author.

American Psychiatric Association. (2000). *Diagnostic and Statistical Manual of Mental Disorders* (*DSM-IV-TR*; 4th ed. text rev.). Washington, DC: Author.

American Psychological Association. (2000). *Guidelines for Psychotherapy With Lesbian, Gay, and Bisexual Clients*. Retrieved January 25, 2006, from http://www.apa.org/pi/lgbc/guidelines.html

Carballo-Dieguez, A., & Remien, R. H. (2001). Sex therapy with male couples of mixed- (serodiscordant-) HIV status. In P. J. Kleinplatz (Ed.), *New Directions in Sex Therapy: Innovations and Alternatives* (pp. 302-321). Philadelphia: Brunner-Routledge.

Gainor, K. A. (2000). Including transgender issues in lesbian, gay, and bisexual psychology: Implications for clinical practice and training. In B. Greene & G. L. Croom (Eds.), *Education, Research, and Practice in Lesbian, Gay, Bisexual, and Transgendered Psychology: A Resource Manual* (pp. 131-160). Thousand Oaks, CA: Sage.

Hall, M. (2001). Beyond forever after: Narrative therapy with lesbian couples. In P. J. Kleinplatz (Ed.), *New Directions in Sex Therapy: Innovations and Alternatives* (pp. 279-301). Philadelphia: Brunner-Routledge.

Kinsey, A., Pomeroy, W., & Martin, C. (1948). *Sexuality in the Human Male*. Philadelphia: W. B. Saunders.

McNally, I., & Adams, N. (2000). Psychosexual issues. In C. Neal & D. Davies (Eds.), *Issues in Therapy With Lesbian, Gay, Bisexual and Transgender Clients* (pp. 83-101). Buckingham, United Kingdom: Open University Press.

Melby, T. (2005). Asexuality gets more attention, but is it a sexual orientation? *Contemporary Sexuality, 39*(11), 1-5.

Money, J. (1986). *Venuses Penuses: Sexology, Sexosophy and Exigency Theory*. Buffalo, NY: Prometheus Books.

Nichols, M. (2000). Therapy with sexual minorities. In S. R. Leiblum & R. C. Rosen (Eds.), *Principles and Practice for Sex Therapy* (pp. 335-367). New York: Guilford.

Pfafflin, F. (2003). Understanding transgendered phenomena. In S. B. Levine, C. B. Risen, & S. E. Althof (Eds.), *Handbook of Clinical Sexuality for Mental Health Professionals* (pp. 291-310). New York: Brunner-Routledge.

Ritter, K. Y., & Terndrup, A. I. (2002). *Handbook of Affirmative Psychotherapy With Lesbians and Gay Men*. New York: Guilford.

Zandvliet, T. (2000).Transgender issues in therapy. In C. Neal & D. Davies (Eds.), *Issues in Therapy With Lesbian, Gay, Bisexual and Transgender Clients* (pp. 176-189). Buckingham, United Kingdom: Open University Press.

Sexual Health of People With Chronic Illness and Disability

Kathleen M. Gill and Sigmund Hough

Human beings are adaptable. If we were not, then any change in sexual functioning across the life span (such as a new partner, or getting older) would be catastrophic. The fact that we can change means that we have a continually evolving sexuality. Instead of only one way to be a sexual person, there are many options that grow and change over time that are affected by our level of maturity, our values and beliefs, our emotional equilibrium, and our physical capacities. This contribution will present an overview of the process of adjustment from the consumer's perspective, provide information to providers on a stance to take that facilitates sexual adjustment, identify a number of diversity issues to consider in providing sexual counseling, and point out some specific issues that are faced by people with various types of illness or injury.

Major illness or injury can have profound effects on sexual functioning. After the initial response to medical crisis or emergency, adaptation begins, and choices are presented that can result in restoring – or improving – one's sexual life. We will present the psychological adjustment process in a way that can bring people to a new appreciation of their sexuality and sexual behavior. We emphasize resilience. Although there will be some individuals who will develop posttraumatic stress disorder (PTSD) as a result of the medical crisis or emergency and need specific treatment for this condition, the majority of our clientele is better viewed as having an adjustment process to manage. We focus on cultivating attitudes and language that give consumers the encouragement, information, and skills to accomplish this. Despite limitations in sexual functioning and altered repertoires of sexual behavior, which may initially decrease desire, everyone can function sexually in some satisfying ways – even though one may be required to differentiate from cultural norms about sexuality in order to embrace this viewpoint.

As sex educators and therapists, we are part of a mainstream culture that can discredit consumers with disabilities in an overt and covert manner. The authors recommend that readers take the opportunity to evaluate their own biases, define their own values, and reject concepts that disenfranchise, which is a prerequisite to working with individuals with disabilities. Similarly, we need to take care of ourselves to remain positive and effective and avoid burnout. There is a need to establish safety and boundaries for ourselves and our clients in order to deal directly with the topics of sex and intimacy. We must strive not to assume that clients have the same sexual values that we have and instead ask questions about their unique relationship to sex. We will practice nonjudgmental ways to ask about the gender of the partner, the number of partners, and the sexual behavior mutually enjoyed by the partners – or without partners. A rule of thumb that clients have found useful is to define sex as whatever is mutual (or individually acceptable), pleasurable, and practical, rather than as heterosexual intercourse in the "male-superior" position culminating in simultaneous multiple orgasms! Finally, we recommend that individuals with chronic illness and disability adopt an empirical approach to discover how to best express themselves sexually, to find out what works for them now, in contrast to approaching sexual rehabilitation as a struggle to fit in or as a goal-oriented mission to live up to particular performance criteria.

TASKS OF ADJUSTMENT: TO GRIEVE AND TO EMBRACE CURRENT OPTIONS

Illness or injury is a crisis that can catapult a person into the "sexual crucible" (Schnarch, 1997). Most of us have probably heard the saying that the Chinese character for "crisis" is a combination of the symbols for "danger" and "opportunity." The essence of the task-at-hand for people with disabilities is to change from results-oriented sex to self-validated-intimacy-oriented sex. Many authors, and the clients themselves, emphasize an understanding of sex beyond frequency and techniques to sex that encompasses the depth and breadth of one's relationship to self and other. Although this is, in fact, the task-at hand for all of us as we mature, the adjustment process that people face with chronic illnesses and disabilities certainly involves dealing with loss as well. However, we don't want to assume that it is sufficient to "get back or near to where you were before the injury," when we can instead suggest a more optimistic response: to use the crisis as an opportunity to grow beyond one's previous level of functioning. Hopeful, determined people won't let illness or disability stop them. Having a strong, flexible goal orientation predicts the best adjustment to disability (Elliott et al., 2000). This research confirmed that a strong set of goals that were flexible reduced the incidence of depression and anxiety during rehabilitation. A "Positive Psychology" approach empowers. According to a series of articles in the March 2001 *American Psychologist* (Fredrickson, 2001; Lyubomirsky, 2001; Masten, 2001; Sheldon & King, 2001), happy people do not compare themselves to others. They appreciate what they have without dwelling on what they do not have. They also recognize their own progress. Dwelling on positive emotions broadens cognition, undoes negative emotions, stimulates psychological resiliency, and triggers further emotional well-being. This is an ideal model for disability adjustment. Yet, over and over, people with disabilities report they were told by "experts" that they should not expect to reach their goals, especially with regard to sex. They hear that sex will never again be as satisfying, and that future relationships will involve only a "special partner" who also has a disability. Such limited viewpoints only contribute to frustration, demoralization, and potential loss of opportunity. In the rehabilitation setting, people with good potential for adjustment are said to have "healthy denial." However, the key element for optimal adjustment may be the ability to appreciate and embrace the work and the enjoyment, the crisis and celebration, and the hurt and the pleasure inherent in human existence. Returning to the perspective of resilience and listening to the voices of successful consumers, the theme is more hopeful:

- Out of 1,000 things I used to do, I can no longer do 900, but I focus on the 100 I can still do.
- When life deals you lemons, make lemonade.
- I have today and I had yesterday, today is a good day.
- Every morning when I hear myself breathe, I am not alone.
- Christopher Reeve promoting "cure research" at a time when it was considered an unrealistic fantasy.
- The young person with paraplegia in a readjustment group who took the advice to experiment with what works literally by seeing if he could get an erection and reporting the results at the next group meeting.

Few people who are newly injured or diagnosed embrace this focus on their remaining options in the beginning. Sex does change for a person with illness or injury, often dramatically, and sudden change is not easily absorbed. Immediately after the onset, the person is still defined by his or her previous identity. Finding a new sexual identity is part of the larger process of finding one's identity as a person with a disability. This takes time. Some clients ask about the sexual future immediately. Others put sex as a low priority as they struggle with physically surviving, planning a future that they did not ask for, and grieving the losses, which is not always a straight line within a predictable time frame (S. A. Jackson & Hough, 2004). When disability demands so much effort on a daily basis, the person may need to integrate issues of adaptation into his or her life first, work through the feelings, transform grief into challenge, and only begin moving on to sex when the time is right.

Another option is abstinence. Rather than thinking of abstinence as a pity, it can be seen as a choice that works well for a mature individual who has other sources of intimacy, affection, love, fun, or affirmation. Genital sexuality is not the only activity that supplies those benefits; not everyone needs to be sexually active all the time in order to be whole.

When a person with illness or disability becomes ready to move into sexual activity, the way he or she thinks can facilitate the process. We have been telling our clients and students for years that the brain is the biggest sex organ. Although this is meant to be humorous, it is also meaningful. If you believe in yourself, you can be sexually available to another, which is one of the prerequisites to intimacy. What counts is how the person feels about himself or herself, not what the dominant culture narrowly defines as sexy at a given time. Schnarch (1997, p. 101) says, "Until we evolved a neocortex, humans were not capable of intimacy." Intimacy is not an instinct but a function of higher mental processes. Parenthetically, that is what makes adjustment to cognitive impairments so difficult, and why sex and intimacy are not synonymous. Having a healthy sense of self is the basis for erotic desire and passionate sex. Although desire does decrease after disability for most people, at least temporarily, there are approaches that can make it worse, or better.

Consumers themselves (see the Life on Wheels website listed in "Selected Resources" on p. 235) say that staying stuck in what you want to happen or what used to happen reinforces the association of tragedy with your disability and costs you the pleasures that remain available. It also distances you from your partner. Sex may become more precious precisely because of the existence of limitations: what remains becomes more valued. Schnarch (1997) reminds us that we have to put the beauty into sex; it is not there without the creative process that individuals bring to it, and consumers who succeed at sexual adjustment lead with creative solutions. Intercourse may no longer be possible, and changes in sexual repertoire may initially feel like compromise and loss. However, it is possible to delight in discovering what previous and new pleasures are now available. Masturbation (such a generally negative-connoted word that we refer to it as "self-stimulation") is a great way to learn about one's own sexual response, so it is often prescribed therapeutically as an early step in a sexual growth program. If the illness or injury precedes the first intercourse, the loss is of potential, of the fantasy of what able-bodied sex might have been like. And there may be the added hurdle of finding partners. People with disabilities have found they need to recognize their own negative feelings about themselves, as they are raised in the same sex-negative culture as everyone else, and stop projecting the destructive attitudes into the heads of potential friends and lovers, who also need to reject these toxic messages. Becoming passionately involved with life increases one's attractiveness. Cultivating the confidence to speak up and reach out vividly demonstrates that a person with an illness or disability is not the stereotype that many people may have. Being assertive enough with a potential sex partner to discuss what is possible given the illness or injury is a direct and desirable way to approach connection that is sadly underrepresented in a culture of game-playing romance novels and manipulative "how-to" books. Not everyone is willing or able to break tradition to do this; not everyone can succeed in adjusting. People in committed relationships may find that partners, who also face the crisis caused by the illness or injury, cannot cope, and leave. Or the person who is sick or disabled may withdraw from the relationship. Yet, over and over, people with disabilities prove that they can deepen their relationships by coming to terms with their feelings, making adaptations, compromising, and somehow getting over it. Bob Mauro, a polio survivor, says sex with a disability involves the four T's: time, trust, trying, and talk. (See "Selected Resources," p. 236).

Certain factors that accompany disability such as stress, fatigue, depression, fear, loss of sensation, impaired self-esteem, chronic pain, and medications can reduce desire and interfere with sexual functioning. The task of adjustment is to address and remove, get around, or accommodate to these barriers. Although a type-A, "full speed ahead" kind of approach to sexual adjustment seems to be implied by all this, the opposite is the case. Dr. Mitch Tepper, a sexuality educator and a person who has a disability, recommends a focus on process, not outcome. (See "Selected Resources," p. 236). Goal-directed sex causes the mind to wander away from the erotic, while orgasmic sex is about being in the moment. If physical orgasm is prevented by illness or injury, a spiritual, whole-being orgasm is still possible (unfortunately called para-orgasm, which has a negative connotation). Numerous authors describe riding the wave of the partner's orgasm as a valuable experience of connection and pleasure. This conscious approach to being fully present in lovemaking enhances relationships, possibly to a level superior to what is frighteningly referred to as the "premorbid" level of sexual and relationship functioning.

All of us have abilities and disabilities. These principles are universal and do not apply only to those who have experienced illnesses or injuries. At times in this contribution, we specifically address "you," because it applies to all of us. Most of the content and resource material comes from people with disabilities speaking for themselves. The true experts in sexual adjustment to disability are those who have lived it and have identified their new conditions for good sex.

In summary, the process of restoring sexual functioning after the onset of illness or injury involves grieving, building an identity with positive self-esteem and body image, solving practical issues of adaptation, embracing the choices remaining, and expressing oneself as a social, assertive, and sexual person participating in life.

THE ROLE OF THE PROVIDER

The first task that health or mental health professionals need to master before becoming a resource to assist people with disabilities to adjust sexually is to recognize their own sexual values. It is acceptable to acknowledge discomfort or lack of information that you would be willing to research for the client. It is not recommended that you tell the person you understand what they are going through, unless you are trying to make them very angry or very suspicious of your naiveté, or unless you are a person with the same disability (and even then, be careful, because the person may not share your experience). You also do not know what will happen in the future, so instead of making a rigid prognostic statement ("I'm afraid your sex life is over"), give the consumer information on sexual adjustment guidelines based on the experiences of others in the same boat. You will have this information if you ask the consumers themselves what they are experiencing and if you take the opportunity to read about what they say has helped. Although these cautions may seem absurd, each is based on comments consumers have made to the authors about experiences they had with staff in hospital and rehabilitation settings. To summarize, the first rule is *don't "be an expert."* Instead, be "askable" about the things you are expert in: psychological adjustment as a process and treatment options that have been shown to help.

Not everyone recovering from illness or injury is expected to be clinically depressed, but as a clinician sensitive to the major change the consumer is going through, allow the person to grieve. It may be difficult to witness their emotional pain as they mourn their losses, but the clinician should have access to support so he or she can provide support to consumers. It is also helpful to recognize that consumers may already have access to their own healing resources, to resilience, and to support people, so that much as there is no "right way" to do sex, there is also no "right way" to do adjustment to disability.

The supportive clinician will send a message that satisfying sexual activity is still possible, while acknowledging that the rescripting of old models of one's sexual norms will be necessary. The "spin" that succeeds is to emphasize the positive; to look for remaining or newfound strengths. Stress a habilitative as opposed to a rehabilitative approach, a going-ahead rather than a going-back.

If there is a partner present, include that person in the discussion (with the client's permission, of course). It can be argued that both members of the couple are the interested parties, because the sexual changes are certainly going to affect both. Whereas only the person with the illness or injury had been defined as the client in the past, there is thankfully a continuing trend on including the significant others. For individuals without partners, the task may be one of reassurance that it will still be possible to form a relationship.

Watch your language. It is not "disabled or handicapped people," or even the more distinguished but pejorative "medically compromised populations." This phrasing implies a put-down, a disqualification of the person's wholeness. It *is* "people with disabilities" or "person recovering from or coping with (name of condition)." Behavioral descriptions are a better way to discuss the situation than medical terminology or colloquialisms when it comes to sexual terms, as well. Compare "difficulty with erections" to "erectile dysfunction" or, even worse, "impotence." Yes, a person who has difficulty with erections may feel powerless, but it is not helpful to label him with a term that means that very thing. The connotative meaning of the words the provider uses needs to be kept in mind in order to convey the most supportive and accurate message to the consumer.

Give information that clients can use. There is a selection of resources included in this volume that should help equip the clinician for this (see "Selected Resources," pp. 235-237).

To help clinicians and clients feel empowered with the skills they already have, we might consider that sexual growth after illness or injury uses the same principles as sexual enhancement for the able-bodied:

- Relax, be *in* your body, and reduce goal-orientation.
- Get information both from knowledgeable others and from your own experimentation with what works for and pleases you now.
- Communicate with your partner and with supportive others.

DIVERSITY ISSUES TO CONSIDER: PRACTICAL APPLICATION OF FAMILIAR THEMES

As is evident by now, the model of healthy sexuality we have focused on implies a committed heterosexual or GLBTI (gay, lesbian, bisexual, transgendered, intersex) relationship where the goal is the integration of sex and intimacy. This is not meant to exclude those whose sexual lifestyles do not correspond to the norm. Multiple relationships, group sex, swapping, BDSM (bondage and dominance, sadism and masochism), sex with animals, and other forms of "atypical" sex, which represent the extremes of sexual diversity to some and abnormality to others, remain controversial. The diversity of sexuality is the range of human existence tempered by the attitudes of the sociopolitical climate and cultural values. Individual tastes, desires, needs, drives, and enjoyment follow the rainbow of life possibilities. Also, GLBTI people do not necessarily share the same sexual values or experiences as the heterosexual community (Ducharme & Gill, 1995). An example is the increased rate of victimization in the gay and lesbian community with disabilities. Individuals go through the stigma and shame associated with intersexuality and are subject to genital surgeries for people born with an anatomy that someone decided is not standard for male or female. Hospitals may deny access by the life partner of people who are GLBTI if they lack an awareness of diversity in family composition.

The developmental stages required in the mastery inherent in the social learning of sexuality may be thwarted in the experience of some children with disabilities due to access and competing life-functioning factors. Similarly, acquiring a disability in late life may present new developmental tasks of redefining "a sense of self" long after that task had been established and now reexploring one's sexuality as well. Parenting with a disability is still fraught with society's discouragement and interference (Crawford, 2003). Aging with a disability also requires resourcefulness to retain sexual functioning in the face of competing priorities (Gill & Ducharme, 1992).

One's ethnicity, race, culture, and religious views and expression are very much the fabric of one's individuality and identity. These considerations can have a significant impact on perceived stress and life satisfaction after a medical injury (Rahman, Albright, & Yaroslavsky, 2005). Individuals who have lived through the stigma of prejudice and racism may try to avoid confrontation or acknowledgment during professional contact. Such a dilemma may require the healthcare environment to be proactive in trying to establish a safe environment for various beliefs and lifestyles. A safe, respectful, and appropriate evaluation procedure is needed in conducting an assessment of clinical need (Suzuki, Ponterotto, & Meller, 2000).

BRIEF CONSIDERATION OF SPECIFIC ISSUES

Before considering the impacts of specific disabilities and chronic illness on sexual functioning, an overview is in order. The onset of an illness or injury may influence sexual adjustment in many ways:

- It may interfere with the sexual response cycle either physically or psychologically. The emotional crisis of the disability and treatment may decrease desire. The usual timing and positioning may be changed, requiring planning or communication beyond the couple's behavioral repertoire. Medical treatment may make intercourse impossible or interrupt the normal frequency of sexual interactions, through confinement of the patient to a hospital or long-term care facility, fatigue, or side effects. Sexual fantasies may be experienced by the patient or the partner as depressing or guilt-engendering. Changes in sensation or function may lead to "spectatoring;" that is, not participating but standing outside oneself, observing the action from a detached or judgmental perspective. Pleasure may be outweighed by pain or by focusing on disappointing comparisons with the previous sexual repertoire. A new sexual repertoire has to be developed, often through trial and error, so that new efforts may be unsatisfactory and unfamiliar. Future sexual encounters may be avoided and feared, producing a pattern of further disappointment and avoidance. Partners may feel constrained because of changes in the patient and because of their own need to adjust to the medical crisis.
- It may interfere with social interactions prerequisite to developing intimate relationships. The stigma of the disability may limit the availability of partners. People

with disabilities experience discrimination in meeting potential partners because of the misunderstandings and misconceptions that are widely held in this culture. The effect of the disability may also reduce skills needed to communicate or conduct a relationship or tolerate intimacy.
- It may interfere with sexual self-image (e.g., facial disfigurement). Patients may feel unattractive or undesirable and subsequently develop sexual dysfunctions despite intact physical sexual capacity.

For each of the disabilities we survey, we will also mention potential solutions which can assist people in achieving a positive sexual adjustment. Management of sexual rehabilitation would ideally include a comprehensive physical, psychological, and social assessment followed by individually tailored psychoeducation regarding what might be expected and how to cope with it, removing any barriers to communication, building skills, suggesting alternative positions or techniques, and much more. As we have mentioned, sexual adjustment is a complex process and is undertaken in stages. For a more comprehensive treatment of this vast topic, the reader is referred to Sipski and Alexander (1997).

Arthritis/Chronic Pain

Pain problems can decrease desire by causing fatigue and distress over activity limitation; people in pain feel awful, which is not anyone's idea of conditions for good sex. It may or may not help to know that sex itself is an analgesic. To increase the probability of willingness to engage in sex while in chronic pain, pain management methods are recommended, which include regular practice of cognitive coping statements, relaxation or meditation, and physical therapy. Pain that is exacerbated by physical exertion will require activity pacing. To establish readiness for sex, plan sex for after rest, a warm bath, your regular dose of pain medications, and possibly after massage or gentle exercise, and take advantage of positions that support comfort (Schover, 2000).

Cancer

The adjustment issues that accompany cancer diagnosis and treatment include body image disturbance, psychological reactions (grief, depression, anxiety) to disability, and mortality concerns. Treatments also have side effects that have a direct effect on sexual function. Prostate cancer is treated with surgery which, despite modern nerve-sparing methods, may not protect sexual response. Testicular cancer treatment generally leaves desire, erection, and orgasm intact, but commonly chemotherapy decreases desire due to side effects such as nausea, diarrhea, fever, weakness, and fatigue. Breast and vulvar cancer may have a profound effect on sexual identity. Sexual frequency may decrease, and vulvar surgery may impair orgasm. Ovarian and endometrial cancers affect physical and psychological aspects of sexuality due to abrupt menopause, hormonal changes, and the impact on fertility. Cervical cancer is treated with radiation, which can result in decreased lubrication, stenosis, and pain (Waldman & Eliasof, 1997). Solutions are not simple but involve cultivating hope, receiving support, and turning toward thankfulness for life in the here and now while cultivating sexual alternatives.

Cardiopulmonary Illnesses

Coronary Artery Disease (CAD) may not directly affect the functioning of genital organs, but sexual frequency diminishes initially after a heart attack, with most people resuming sexual interest between 8 weeks and 1 year post myocardial infarction. The primary causes of this decreased desire are thought to be psychological: fear of re-infarct, the partner's fears of putting too much stress on the heart through intercourse or orgasm, or depression. Erectile dysfunction and CAD also share similar risk factors that can interfere with sexual functioning (Hood & Robertson, 2004). Angina may decrease sexual interest, and nitroglycerine to treat the angina is incompatible with Viagra. The actual risk of cardiac death during sexual activity is small and has been associated with risky behavior that increases stress (such as having a clandestine affair after a big meal and lots to drink). Solutions include a comprehensive cardiac rehabilitation program, which not only provides information on when it is safe to resume sexual activity, but also focuses on gradually increasing exercise tolerance. The "two flights of stairs" rule is well known, and implies that when the physician clears the person for regular exercise, it is safe to resume sexual activity. The more modern rule of thumb is to categorize people by their level of cardiovascular risk (Nusbaum, Hamilton, & Lenahan, 2003). In any event, congestive heart failure must be stabilized before it is wise to resume sexual activity, and at least 6 to 8 weeks of recovery is recommended after a heart attack. After coronary artery bypass, at least 4 weeks is recommended.

Chronic Obstructive Pulmonary Disease (COPD) does not seem to physically alter sexual function, but the fatigue, weakness, and shortness of breath can certainly interfere with sex by decreasing activity tolerance and decreasing desire. Solutions include planning sex for when rested, having a calm atmosphere to reduce the risk of hyperventilation, using an inhaler prior to sex and perhaps oxygen supplementation during, having supplies on hand for cough secretions, using a comfortable position, and arranging for the partner without the COPD to take the active role (see the Survey website in "Selected Resources," p. 236).

Cerebral Palsy

As a result of the muscle spasticity that affects mobility, sexual technique and positioning can be affected. Resulting from damage to the brain at or around birth, cerebral palsy (CP) affects muscular control. Typically it does not affect intelligence or cognition, but, because speech can be slurred, people with CP can suffer social rejection and isolation. Specific sexual problems result from muscle spasticity around the vagina, hips, and pelvis, which may cause penile insertion and missionary-style intercourse to be painful; changing positions and gentle or alternative-to-intercourse techniques are encouraged (Renshaw, 1987). The assistance of personal care attendants or assistive devices (vibrators) may be helpful.

Diabetes

The consensus is that level of desire (also called libido) is physiologically unaffected, but peripheral neuropathy and reduced circulation affect sensation and arousal in people with diabetes. Erection problems in men and decreased lubrication in women are frequently reported. Ejaculation may be retrograde but is present; orgasm is relatively unaffected. Amputation and blindness may result in advanced cases. However, positive, hopeful clients in good relationships can supercede expectations about their level of sexual functioning based on the level of severity of their illness. Good medical management with diet and medication can slow the progression of the disability. Men can be treated with erection aids, and women with vaginal lubricants. (See the Survey website on p. 236.)

Epilepsy

Sexual dysfunction may be related to adjustment issues as well as physiological problems in epilepsy. If the onset is in childhood, there may be limitations on the person's social and sexual development from managing a chronic illness. There can be anxiety about sexual activity precipitating a seizure. Temporal lobe lesions, which are often involved in seizure disorder, can cause hormone changes that decrease desire in men and women and could cause precocious puberty in girls (Kalayjian & Morrell, 2000). There can be other endocrine imbalances that result from the seizure aftermath and from antiepilepsy drugs. The solutions, then, are to solve the seizure control first, followed by an endocrinology work-up and hormone supplementation as needed.

HIV/AIDS

It is not surprising that sexual desire decreases when a person is found to be HIV positive, well before the physical disability (wasting, pain, muscle aches, malaise) that can accompany full-blown AIDS. Fear of infecting partners, the association of sex with death that accompanies sexual transmission of the disease, managing the illness and the fatigue, and other main and side effects of treatment all contribute. Low testosterone levels in men with HIV/AIDS also impair sexual performance. Women with the disease also report sexual dysfunction (Nusbaum et al., 2003). Suggestions for management include always using safer sex practices (condoms with water-based lubricants, dental dams, and not exchanging body fluids), as well as all the other suggestions for managing psychological adjustment, fatigue, and pain.

Multiple Sclerosis

The onset of Multiple Sclerosis (MS), a neurological disease, is in the prime of life, age 20-40, and produces fluctuating symptoms as the covering of the nerve fibers of the brain and spinal cord is damaged, affecting mobility, sensation, vision, and sexual response. It affects more women than men. Decreased desire is reported in one-third to one-half of clients. Sensation, arousal, and orgasm are impaired. Clients with MS also experience fatigue, spasticity, muscle weakness (including bladder and bowel incontinence), cognitive changes, and depression. In addition, the medications that are frequently used to manage symptoms interfere with sexual response. The uniquely difficult task of adjustment to MS is in managing expectations, because the symptoms in several forms of this disorder unpredictably wax and wane (Foley & Werner, 2000).

The management of sexuality is similar to that of spinal cord injury/dysfunction, where timing, positioning, increasing the stimulation, using what works and pleases as stimulation, and planning sex for the most opportune time are all recommended. The National MS Society is a national support organization that provides information on treatment, including treatment of sexual problems (see p. 236).

Neuromuscular Disease

The impact of these diseases on sexual function is again not because of interference with genital organs but from movement problems, weakness, and impaired breathing. Included here are muscular dystrophy, amyotrophic lateral sclerosis (ALS), polio, and Guillain-Barre syndrome (Bach & Bardach, 1997). Access to partners for those who are in restrictive care settings is a problem, with some facilities providing privacy rooms for patient use (even including portable ventilators for those who are ventilator-dependent), but, once again, people who acquire these illnesses young have the social isolation which limits them from developing skills or having opportunities to meet partners. As an example of resilience, a client of one of the authors could move only enough to use a mouth-stick to communicate online, but managed to arrange a sexual encounter in his residential care setting.

Psychiatric Problems

The major psychiatric diagnoses of anxiety disorders (including posttraumatic stress disorder or PTSD), depression, psychosis, and alcohol and substance abuse obviously affect sexual functioning. Over many years, we have made it a policy to recommend to clients that the stabilization of symptoms and ongoing treatment of these problems is prerequisite to systematically working on sexual enhancement. In part this is because anxiety, depression, and alcohol/drug abuse themselves impact physiology in ways that interfere with sexual functioning, and all the categories of diagnosis affect relationships. Unfortunately, a number of the medications that are vital to living fully with psychological problems also interfere with sex, but the cost-benefit ratio leads us to recommend continuing the medicines if an alternative that manages the psychological problem without sexual side effects cannot be found. (See "Sexual History and Referral Guidelines," pp. 238-239.) From a clinical perspective, a large percentage of people presenting for treatment of sexual dysfunction are survivors of childhood sexual abuse or sexual assault and have symptoms consistent with PTSD, requiring intensive, multistage therapy (Maltz, 2001). As both authors work with combat veterans, it is also interesting to note that recent research documents higher rates of erection problems in combat veterans with PTSD than those without PTSD and much higher than the nonveteran population (Cosgrove et al., 2002). Also, female veterans of the Gulf War who have chronic fatigue syndrome (one of the most common conditions in Gulf War veterans) have much higher rates of sexual desire disorder and arousal problems than nonfatigued controls (Gilhooly et al., 2001).

Spinal Cord Injury/Disorder/Dysfunction

The sexual changes that result from spinal cord injury/disorder/dysfunction (SCI/D) involve a very individualized response. There can be catastrophic changes to physical sexual response depending on the level and completeness of the injury. Erection, ejaculation, lubrication, and arousal can be affected. There are also changes to bladder and bowel functioning, temperature regulation, and obviously to sensation and mobility. A rule of thumb in rehabilitation settings is that it may take as long as 3 to 15 years, not necessarily linear in progression, to adjust to having a spinal cord injury. Demographically, more men than women have SCI/D. In men, the higher the level of injury, the more likely are reflex erections but the less likely is ejaculation. The lower the injury level, the more likely are psychogenic erections and ejaculation (but not reflex erections). Reflex erections result from physical stimulation to genital organs and are mediated by a reflex loop at the same level of the cord, unlike psychogenic erections which are mediated by the brain. That is to say, being kissed on the lips or having a sexual fantasy or thought cannot communicate down through the part of the cord that is interrupted, so unless the injury is below the level of cord that controls genital response (or is incomplete), psychogenic erections cannot occur. However, the majority of men with SCI/D can have erections, while ejaculation is less likely. Orgasm is somewhat independent of physical functioning, and level of injury does not predict whether one will be orgasmic, because orgasm is psychological and spiritual as well as physical. With modern fertility techniques, parenthood is still a possibility for men with SCI/D. With the development of sophisticated trauma care, most spinal cord injuries are incomplete, and research on curing SCI/D, once thought impossible, is progressing. Women with SCI/D have a certain advantage in that there is some neurological redundancy in women which preserves sexual functioning when compared to men with the same level and completeness of injury. Women retain much of their sexual response; they are able to be aroused and lubricate (Ducharme & Gill, 1997). About half who were orgasmic before the injury still are afterward (A. B. Jackson & Wadley, 1999). They continue to menstruate, and fertility is unaffected. They are able to complete normal pregnancy and delivery.

Desire can decrease after injury. The degree of desire is closely correlated with the ability to get an erection in men, so Viagra and its cousins have an important place in supporting sexual desire in men with SCI/D (S. Ducharme, personal communication, January 22, 2001; Lindsey & Brown, 2000). Despite the fact that Viagra has no direct effect on sexual desire (Goldstein et al., 1998), it provides nearly universal improvement of erection and intercourse satisfaction. It has not, however, proven effective for women in this same way. Research finds no difference in level of desire between women with and without disability (Nosek et al., 1996). Feeling attractive and desirable is cited as more important concerns to women than whether they can function genitally. Women who work through these psychological concerns succeed at reestablishing desire and an active sex life. Clearly Viagra (which may facilitate physical arousal and lubrication in women) does not contribute to these intrapsychic and interpersonal factors.

In addition to medications and medical procedures for erection (implant surgery, alprostadil injections, prostaglandin E1 inserted through the urethra, vacuum devices), and electroejaculation and sperm-banking for fertility, responding to the changes in sexual response in SCI/D includes modifying the sexual repertoire to emphasize what one still can do that one enjoys (kissing, touching the sensate areas, including the enhanced sensation at the cut-off sensory areas) and training oneself to become erotically sensitive in new ways (by sight, in different parts of the body than before, by using more intense stimulation, new positions). Spontaneity is probably less available, but much of sexual adjustment to SCI/D is a function of changing perceptions. Instead of thinking of spontaneity as the gold standard, have sex at times when the logistics are favorable given the reality of the current circumstances: when one is not fatigued and after the bladder and bowel are emptied. Couples who can be creative and flexible express much satisfaction with sex after SCI/D (see *Sexuality Reborn* videotape on p. 237). Clearly, sex education regarding how the impairment can impact mind and body, along with preventing or managing potential problems, can impact positively on the enjoyment and expression of sexuality (Klebine, Lindsey, & Rivera, 2005).

Stroke

Decreased desire in individuals after stroke is commonly reported. There is no general agreement as to whether the location of the cerebrovascular event makes a difference in the reduction of desire. Concomitant medical conditions may also be affecting sexual functioning; diabetes and cardiovascular disease certainly can. Medications in the form of beta-blockers and selective serotonin reuptake inhibitors also interfere with sexual response. However, again the psychological adjustment issues may be the biggest factor in altered sexual interest. These include depression, fear of having another stroke during sex (which is a small risk, more likely when the first stroke was hemorrhagic rather than ischemic), fear of rejection by the partner, decreased self-image, changes in role and status, the partner's reaction, altered communication, and cognitive and emotional changes (emotional lability, the denial and impulsivity that accompanies right hemisphere stroke, or the cautiousness and decreased initiation that goes with a left hemisphere stroke). Overall, as in traumatic brain injury, hyposexuality is more common than hypersexuality (Monga & Kerrigan, 1997).

Specific suggestions for managing these changes include extended foreplay, which actually reduces cardiac stress during orgasm (and certainly follows the classic sex therapy prescription to decrease performance pressure), using verbal or nonverbal communication signals to initiate sex, and adopting pillow-assisted sidelying positions that leave the unaffected side of the body to touch and be touched.

Traumatic Brain Injury

The etiology of sexual disorders after Traumatic Brain Injury (TBI) is unclear; organic factors are probably not the primary cause of the frequently reported loss of desire, and it is not known whether the site of the lesion or the severity directly affects sexual functioning in mild to moderate head injury. Hypogonadism (decreased testosterone) is associated with severe head injuries affecting the hypothalamic-pituitary axis, which explains the loss of desire in severe injury. Probably the major impact on sexual functioning in TBI is the change in intellectual, cognitive, and personality variables. These changes in interpersonal awareness, judgment, and emotional regulation necessitate an overhaul of the existing relationship. The changes are persistent, and the partners may lose desire if they are unable to learn to behaviorally manage the changes and come to terms with the fact that the person to whom they were initially attracted is no longer the person they are with. Impaired interpersonal skills and severe behavioral dyscontrol make it difficult for some survivors with TBI to meet and develop relationships with new partners, and they may benefit from more behavioral approaches (Zasler, 1995; Zencius et al., 1990).

Here the suggested solutions have to do with comprehensive brain injury rehabilitation, including cognitive training, building interpersonal skills through relationship counseling and social skills training, affect management training, support groups, staff training, and strategic programming such as the Sexual Intervention Program (Aloni & Katz, 2003).

EDUCATION AND INTERVENTION WITH THE SIGNIFICANT OTHER

Ideally the process of sexual history taking (see "Sample Interview Format" on pp. 240-241) and psychoeducation about sexuality should begin in the hospital or rehabilitation setting and continue with the client and concerned others into the outpatient setting. The sexuality provider not only evaluates and intervenes with the person who has been ill or injured, but will engage the significant others: the partner or spouse if there is one, the parents of minor children, and the friend or caregiver who will be in close communication with the person recovering. Consistently favorable feedback has been provided to the authors over the years for the acknowledgment of their existence and inviting the support system people to participate.

In conclusion, we hope that you have found useful this overview of difficulties that consumers with disabilities or illnesses may encounter and our suggestions for helping them manage the process of developing their sexual health. In our clinical experience it is both possible and desirable to help clients find the illness-and-disability-free-zone where they can cultivate a present-time awareness which enhances sexual experiencing. We encourage clients to communicate with their partners and with their providers, so our major focus has been on equipping you with concepts and strategies that support that. We certainly don't know the answers, and in fact believe in creative, flexible, and process-oriented solutions rather than rigid answers.

Selected Resources

This is not an all-inclusive list; it has been prepared to acknowledge the potential wealth of information and to motivate the reader to continue the search for personalized information.

Websites*

Aging and Sexuality Resource Guide, edited by Dr. Antoinette Zeiss, an annotated bibliography of journal articles, books, and videos, as well as organizations and information for elders.
www.apa.org/pi/aging/sexuality.html

American Academy of Pain Management
www.aapainmanage.org

American Association of Sexuality Educators, Counselors, and Therapists
www.aasect.org

American Association of Spinal Cord Injury Nurses
www.aascin.org

American Association of Spinal Cord Injury Psychologists and Social Workers
www.aascipsw.org

American Heart Association
www.americanheart.org

American Pain Society
www.ampainsoc.org

Brain Injury Association of America
www.biausa.org

Christopher and Dana Reeve Paralysis Resource Center, with a searchable database for disability adjustment topics.
www.paralysis.org

Disability Resources
www.disabilityresources.org/SEX.html

International Society for the Study of Vulvovaginal Disease *and* **The National Vulvodynia Association**
www.issvd.org / www.nva.org

Let's Face It (for people with facial differences)
www.faceit.org

Life on Wheels. Disability resources from Gary Karp, a person living well with a T12 spinal cord injury. He is a speaker and author who trains rehabilitation professionals and employers about living with a disability.
www.lifeonwheels.net

---

* Although all websites cited in this contribution were correct at the time of publication, they are subject to change at any time.

Lovebyrd. Virtual community for disabled adults seeking love, friendship, and support.
www.lovebyrd.com

Mauro, Bob. Introduction/dating services or information services for people with and without physical disabilities. Mr. Mauro had polio as a child, writes on disability, sexuality, and relationships, and welcomes input on his interactive site, which includes the PeopleNet Disability DateNet home page.
www.hometown.aol.com/bobezwriter

National Association of the Deaf
www.nad.org

National Dissemination Center for Children With Disabilities
www.nichcy.org

National Federation of the Blind
www.nfb.org

National Multiple Sclerosis Society
www.nmss.org

The National Spinal Cord Injury Association
www.spinalcord.org

National Stroke Association
www.stroke.org

Planned Parenthood Federation of America
www.plannedparenthood.org

The Sexual Health Network, hosted by Mitch Tepper, PhD, MPH. The Sexual Health Network's website provides easy access to sexuality information, education, counseling, therapy, medical attention, and other sexuality resources for people with disability, illness, or other health-related problems. The Sexual Health Network also provides continuing education and training for health professionals and facilitates educational groups for people with disability or illness.
www.sexualhealth.com

Sexuality and Disability: History and Practice
www.mypleasure.com

Sexuality Information and Education Council of the United States publishes a wonderful annotated bibliography on sexuality and disability.
www.siecus.org/pubs/biblio

The Society for the Scientific Study of Sexuality
www.sexscience.org

Survey of practical information about managing sexuality after illnesses and injuries.
www.cvillewellness.com

Journals

Journal of GLBT Family Studies, Harrington Park Press, Binghamton, New York (an Imprint of the Hawthorne Press, Inc.). This peer-reviewed journal addresses issues related to being gay, lesbian, bisexual, and transgender and their families. Focus includes parent-child relationships, child development, sibling relationships, family structure, intimate relationships, stepfamilies, alternate family structures, and extended family relationships.

Sexuality and Disability, Springer Publishing, New York. This peer-reviewed journal is the most relevant source for scientific articles in this field.

Videos

Sexuality and Spinal Cord Injury. From BC Rehabilitation in Vancouver. (604) 737-6225. The video is designed for staff members and for training of staff. There may be parts of the video that would be useful for group discussion.

Sexuality Reborn, C. J. Alexander & M. L. Sipski, 1993. Explicit videotape highlighting interviews and footage of people with spinal cord trauma who have succeeded in adjusting to their injuries. Produced by Kessler Institute for Rehabilitation, 1199 Pleasant Valley Way, West Orange, NJ 07052 and available at www.kmrrec.org/KM/nnjscis/sexuality_reborn.php3 or call (973) 243-6812.

Sexual History and Referral Guidelines

General

The purpose of these guidelines is to provide the health/mental health practitioner with a model for gathering information on sexual functioning from clients. Surveys have repeatedly documented the widespread incidence of sexual concerns and verify that clients are reluctant to bring up the topic unless practitioners show a willingness and sensitivity to discuss it. The importance of providing the opportunity to discuss sexual issues is that sexual health is intimately related to physical health and to psychological well-being. In this light, sexuality (including self-esteem, body image, sexual identity, gender roles, sexual orientation, affection, desire, genitally focused behavior, and interpersonal relationships) is an integral component of successful treatment.

Establishing the Atmosphere of the Interview

1. Conduct the discussion sometime during the assessment phase. To ensure the client's privacy, hold the interview in a private, quiet setting.
2. Assure the client of the confidentiality of the information to be discussed, and limit the amount of detail that is placed in medical records that can be accessed by insurers, clerical workers, and others.
3. Approach the person in a relaxed, respectful manner that encourages openness.
4. Be sensitive to his/her/their feelings. Be aware of and acknowledge discomfort or embarrassment in yourself and the client.
5. Avoid making shaming or judgmental statements, or forcing your own values on the client.
6. Provide information on sexual health and the effects of stress, mood, and illness on sexual functioning. Feel free to say, "I don't know, but I will get that information for you." The important aspect is to be "askable."
7. Use language that is simple and direct. Avoid overly technical jargon and street language. Descriptive terms that are neither evaluative nor provocative are preferred.
8. Cultivate ways to ask questions in an open-ended fashion. For example, "What are your sexual values and what is your sexual repertoire?" is much better than "Do you have intercourse? Just with your spouse or outside the marriage? Isn't that against your principles? What else do you do?" You will develop your own strategies for how to phrase questions about sex.
9. Remember that the more you practice including this information, the more comfortable you'll be.
10. Move from less threatening topics to more difficult ones as the interview proceeds, so that greater rapport can be established.
11. Set limits on any attempts to develop a personal relationship between the interviewer and the client.

Content of the Sexual History

1. Brief history of the client's relationship with significant others: family of origin, dating/marriage/commitments, divorce/separation, children, and friendships.
2. Current sexual adjustment, including the repertoire of sexual behavior they consider appropriate and their level of satisfaction. Include the question: "Do you talk with your partner about sexual needs and concerns?"
3. Partner's sexual adjustment.
4. Effects of illness/injury, medication, developmental stage, and psychological adjustment or trauma on their ability to function sexually.
5. Current difficulties and attempts at solving sexual problems.
6. "Is there anything I haven't asked you about that is important to understanding your sexual adjustment?"
7. Close by thanking the client and asking for feedback on how the interview was perceived by the client.

Referral Guidelines

Sex therapy is the treatment of choice when:

1. the primary problem is a sexual dysfunction, including the very prevalent sexual desire disorders.
2. higher priority problems have been resolved or are absent. Active depression, anxiety disorders, psychosis, posttraumatic stress disorder (including that which results from sexual abuse), and alcohol or substance abuse must be resolved or under good control prior to the initiation of sex therapy.
3. physical factors have been identified and treated. A recent physical exam, including referral to specialists as needed, is required to rule out medical problems (such as infection, medication side effects) or to diagnose medical conditions that serve as upper limits to sexual functioning (such as diabetic neuropathy, circulatory problems, hormone imbalances, etc.).
4. interfering situational events are not present. The timing of the therapy should avoid such events as a recent death in the family, moving, job change, pregnancy, and lack of privacy in the household. I do not offer treatment to couples involved in ongoing extramarital relationships.
5. the relationship is basically stable, or improving it becomes the first stage of the treatment. The relationship is a committed one, as opposed to one on the verge of dissolution. The couple has a basic repertoire of communication skills. No major secrets are being withheld. The couple's life and relationship goals are mutually compatible (such as whether to have children, that the relationship is monogamous vs. open, etc.). Individuals, either those without a partner or those whose partner declines involvement in the therapy, may be appropriate for sex therapy.
6. there are "therapy-positive" factors present. The individual or couple must believe that sex therapy is potentially helpful and be motivated to pursue treatment and to commit time and energy to it.

Sample Interview Format*

Introduction

I'd like to discuss with you your present sexual functioning. (Assurance of confidentiality)

Current Sexual Functioning (General)

Are you sexually active at present? Do you find yourself interested in sex?

Have you ever been sexually active?

Are you satisfied with your current sexual relationship(s) or with your current sexual adjustment?

Do you relate sexually to men, women, both, or neither?

How has your illness or injury affected your sexual enjoyment, level of desire, or ability to engage in sexual relations? (Frequency, quality, course of adjustment)

Do you have any concerns or questions about your sexual functioning? (Stop if no concerns or questions)

Current Sexual Functioning (Specific)

What is your sexual repertoire? Or what types of sexual and affectionate behavior do you engage in?

Is self-stimulation (or masturbation) one of the options that you choose?

Men — Are you able to have and maintain an erection sufficient for intercourse? Is this a problem to you or your partner? Under what circumstances do you have difficulty?

Are you able to delay ejaculation long enough to satisfy yourself and your partner? Is lasting too long ever a problem? Under what circumstances?

Women — Are you able to reach orgasm? From intercourse, or by other means of stimulation? In what situations do you have difficulty?

Are you able to have sexual relations without pain or discomfort? Is insertion of the penis difficult? Under what circumstances? Are you lubricating sufficiently?

---

* Adapted with permission from Table 3 in S. Ducharme, K. M. Gill, S. Biener-Bergman, and L. Fertitta, "Sexual Function: Medical and Psychological Aspects." From *Rehabilitation Medicine: Principles and Practice* (2nd ed., pp. 763-782), by J. DeLisa (Ed.), 1993, Philadelphia: J. P. Lippincott. Copyright © 1993 by J. P. Lippincott/Williams & Wilkins.

Partner Satisfaction/Relationship History

Are you able to stimulate and satisfy your partner? Does your partner know what pleases you?

Are you able to communicate effectively about sex? About other aspects of the relationship?

How long have you been in your present relationship? Have you been able to work out a compatible adjustment? What difficulties have you encountered, and how did you resolve them successfully?

How has having children/not having children affected your relationship?

Other Effects on the Relationship

How stable is your health at present? What is your expectation about your health in the future?

Do you take any prescription medications?

What method of contraception do you use? Are you satisfied with it?

What precautions do you take against sexually transmitted infections (STIs)? Have you been tested for HIV?

Do you use alcohol or other drugs? How often? How does this affect your relationship? Your sexual relationship?

Have you had any negative or traumatic sexual experiences?

Follow-Up

Would you be interested in speaking with a specialist in sexual functioning about the questions or problems you've raised in this interview?

CONTRIBUTORS

Kathleen M. Gill, PhD, is a Clinical Psychologist in the PTSD Program at the VA Outpatient Clinic in Rochester, New York. She has worked in psychiatric and rehabilitation settings specializing in sexuality and disability for 30 years. These include Brockton/West Roxbury VA Medical Center, Braintree Hospital, and Lahey Clinic's Center for Sexual Function. She trained graduate students in sex therapy at the VA and at McLean Hospital, and was on the adjunct faculty of Harvard Medical School. She is currently Clinical Assistant Professor of Psychiatry, University of Rochester Medical School. She is a Certified Sex Therapist and Clinical Supervisor with AASECT and coauthor of *Sexuality After Spinal Cord Injury*. Dr. Gill may be contacted at 465 Westfall Road, Rochester, NY 14620. E-mail: Kathleen.Gill@va.gov

Sigmund Hough, PhD, ABPP, is a Clinical Neuropsychologist in the Spinal Cord Injury Service, VA Boston Healthcare System, West Roxbury, Massachusetts. He is Editor-Elect for the journal *Sexuality and Disability*. He also serves as Director of Training for the Boston Consortium Postdoctoral Psychology Fellowship Program. Dr. Hough received ABPP board specialization in Rehabilitation Psychology. He holds faculty appointments at Boston University School of Medicine and Harvard Medical School, a medical staff appointment in Psychiatry at Melrose-Wakefield Hospital, and rank of Adjunct Associate Professor at Bridgewater State College. As a Surveyor for The Commission on Accreditation of Rehabilitation Facilities (CARF), he conducts accreditation surveys nationwide for the division of Medical Rehabilitation. Previously, he has served in the capacity of Clinical Director and Director of Psychological Services at private rehabilitation facilities, case reviewer for a nationwide managed care company, and as a clinical service provider in both the public and private sector. In 2004, Dr. Hough received the Clinical Performance Award from the American Association of Spinal Cord Injury Psychologists and Social Workers. Dr. Hough can be reached at Spinal Cord Injury Services (SCI #128), VA Boston Healthcare System, 1400 VFW Parkway, West Roxbury, MA 02132. E-mail: Sigmund_Hough@hms.harvard.edu

RESOURCES

Aloni, R., & Katz, S. (2003). *Sexual Difficulties After Traumatic Brain Injury and Ways to Deal With It*. Springfield, IL: Charles C. Thomas.

Bach, J. R., & Bardach, J. L. (1997). Neuromuscular diseases. In M. L. Sipski & C. J. Alexander (Eds.), *Sexual Function in People With Disability and Chronic Illness* (pp. 247-260). Gaithersburg, MD: Aspen.

Cosgrove, D. J., Gordon, Z., Bernie, J. E., Hami, S., Montoya, D., Stein, M. B., & Monga, M. (2002). Sexual dysfunction in combat veterans with post-traumatic stress disorder. *Urology, 60*(5), 881-884.

Crawford, N. (2003). Parenting with a disability: The last frontier. *Monitor on Psychology, May*, 68-70.

Ducharme, S., & Gill, K. M. (1995) Sexuality and disability. In L. Diamant & R. D. McAnulty (Eds.), *The Psychology of Sexual Orientation, Behavior and Identity: A Handbook* (pp. 398-408). Westport, CT: Greenwood.

Ducharme, S., & Gill, K. M. (1997), *Sexuality after Spinal Cord Injury: Answers to Your Questions*. Baltimore, MD: Paul H. Brookes.

Elliott, T. R., Uswatte, G., Lewis, L., & Palmatier, A. (2000). Goal instability and adjustment to physical disability. *Journal of Counseling Psychology, 47*, 251-265.

Foley, F. W., & Werner, M. A. (2000). Sexuality. In R. C. Kalb (Ed.), *Multiple Sclerosis: The Questions You Have, The Answers You Need* (pp. 281-310). New York: Demos.

Fredrickson, B. L. (2001). The role of positive emotions in positive psychology: The broaden-and-build theory of positive emotions. *American Psychologist, 56*, 218-226.

Gilhooly, P. E., Ottenweller, J. E., Lange, G., Tiersky, L., & Natelson, B. H. (2001). *Journal of Sex and Marital Therapy, 27*(5), 483-487.

Gill, K. M., & Ducharme, S. (1992). Sexual concerns of the elderly. In E. Calkins, A. B. Ford, & P. R. Katz (Eds.), *The Practice of Geriatrics* (2nd ed., pp. 276-281). Philadelphia: W. B. Saunders.

Goldstein, I., Lue, T. F., Padma-Nathan, H., Rosen, R. C., Steers, W. D., & Wicker, P. A. (1998). Oral sildenafil in the treatment of erectile dysfunction. *New England Journal of Medicine, 338*, 1397-1404.

Hood, S., & Robertson, I. (2004). Erectile dysfunction: A significant health need in patients with coronary heart disease. *Scottish Medical Journal, 49*(3), 90-92.

Jackson, A. B., & Wadley, V. (1999). A multicenter study of women's self-reported reproductive health after spinal cord injury. *Archives of Physical Medicine and Rehabilitation, 80*, 1420-1428.

Jackson, S. A., & Hough, S. (2004). Adjustment to the process of grief following spinal cord injury/dysfunction. *SCI Psychosocial Process, 17*(3), 145-155.

Kalayjian, L. A., & Morrell, M. J. (2000). Female sexuality and neurological disease. *Journal of Sex Education and Therapy, 25*(1), 89-95.

Klebine, P. L., Lindsey, L. L., & Rivera, P. A. (2005). Sexuality for women with spinal cord injury. *SCI Psychosocial Process, 18*(1), 27-31.

Lindsey, L. L., & Brown, J. F. (2000). Viagra (Sildenafil) and spinal cord injury: Review and update. *SCI Psychosocial Process, 13*(1), 13-16.

Lyubomirsky, S. (2001). Why are some people happier than others? The role of cognitive and motivational processes in well-being. *American Psychologist, 56*, 239-249.

Maltz, W. (2001). *The Sexual Healing Journey: A Guide for Survivors of Sexual Abuse*. New York: Quill.

Masten, A. (2001). Ordinary magic: Resilience processes in development. *American Psychologist, 56*, 227-238.

Monga, T. N., & Kerrigan, A. J. (1997). Cerebrovascular accidents. In M. L. Sipski & C. J. Alexander (Eds.), *Sexual Function in People With Disability and Chronic Illness* (pp. 189-219). Gaithersburg, MD: Aspen.

Nosek, M. A., Rintala, D. H., Young, M. E., Howland, C. A., Foley, C. C., Rossi, D., & Chanpong, G. (1996). Sexual functioning among women with disabilities. *Archives of Physical Medicine and Rehabilitation, 77*, 107-115.

Nusbaum, M. R. H., Hamilton, C., & Lenahan, P. (2003). Chronic illness and sexual functioning. *American Family Physician, 67*(2), 347-354, 357.

Rahman, R. O., Albright, K. J., & Yaroslavsky, I. (2005). Perceived stress and life satisfaction in women with a spinal cord injury: An exploratory look at racial differences. *SCI Psychosocial Process, 18*(1), 1-8.

Renshaw, D. (1987). Painful intercourse associated with cerebral palsy. *Journal of the American Medical Association, 257*, 2086.

Schnarch, D. (1997). *Passionate Marriage: Love, Sex and Intimacy in Emotionally Committed Relationships*. New York: W. W. Norton.

Schover, L. (2000). Sexual problems in chronic illness. In S. Leiblum & R. Rosen (Eds.), *Principles and Practice of Sex Therapy,* (pp. 398-422). New York: Guilford.

Sheldon, K. M., & King, L. (2001). Why positive psychology is necessary. *American Psychologist, 56*, 216-217.

Sipski, M. L., & Alexander, C. J. (Eds.). (1997). *Sexual Function in People With Disability and Chronic Illness*. Gaithersburg, MD: Aspen.

Suzuki, L. A., Ponterotto, J. G., & Meller, P. J. (Eds.). (2000). *Handbook of Multicultural Assessment: Clinical, Psychological, and Educational Applications* (2nd ed.). San Francisco: Jossey-Bass.

Waldman, T. L., & Eliasof, B. (1997). Cancer. In M. L. Sipski & C. J. Alexander (Eds.), *Sexual Function in People With Disability and Chronic Illness* (pp. 337-354). Gaithersburg, MD: Aspen.

Zasler, N. D. (1995). Traumatic brain injury and sexuality. *Physical Medicine and Rehabilitation: State-of-the-Arts Reviews, 9*, 361-375.

Zencius, A., Wesolowski, D. M., Burke, H. W., & Hough, S. (1990). Managing hypersexual disorders in brain-injured clients. *Brain Injury, 4*, 175-181.

Culturally Competent Sex Therapy

Frederick L. Peterson, Jr., James Dobbins,
Florence Coleman, and Jouhaina Razzouk

This contribution is designed to assist mental health professionals in achieving three goals. First, we want to stimulate clinicians to further develop their awareness of the key principles and concepts related to culturally competent care. Second, we want to guide them toward implementing their awareness and knowledge into behavioral skills and interventions that lead to effective treatment of culturally diverse clients. Finally, we want to assist them in building confidence and competence in applying their behavioral skills to culturally diverse clients with sexual health concerns. To achieve these goals, a new model for building cultural competence development will be shared. The new model, called "The Pyramid Metaphor," was developed by the first two authors, Drs. Peterson and Dobbins. Specific suggestions and guidelines for developing cultural competency as a mental health professional are shared through three stages of development: (a) cultural sensitivity, (b) cultural competency, and (c) cultural responsibility. Additionally, an example of clinical application of this material with clients is included.

PRINCIPLES OF MULTICULTURAL COMPETENCY

The mental health professions have become increasingly aware of the relevance of cultural issues, especially the topics of cultural sensitivity and cultural competency as related to research, organizational development, treatment, and training outcomes. Most professional associations (including those in medicine, psychiatry, and psychology) that govern training and practice in medicine and mental health have developed position papers or treatment guidelines on the importance of providing culturally sensitive care to clients. These guidelines can be accessed through their respective websites.

The weight of the current literature strongly suggests that traditional psychological interventions have proven to be less effective with minority clients than with Caucasian clients (Sartorius, Pedersen, & Marsella, 1984; D. W. Sue & D. Sue, 1990). It is no different for sex therapy. It is no less important to apply the principles of cultural competency and multicultural therapy when the counseling happens to address sexual health. For example, the American Psychological Association has established guidelines for the assessment and treatment of gay, lesbian, and bisexual clients (see the contribution on sexual minority clients, pp. 209-221).

Sexuality is defined within a cultural setting and depends greatly on socialization (Bullough, 1976; Reiss, 1986). It is well documented in the literature that sexual behavior is accountable to cultural and social influences (Kulhara & Avasthi, 1995) and that various cultural beliefs influence sexual functioning (Bhugra & de Silva, 1995). There is a need for a broader perspective that considers not only traditional elements of psychotherapy but also the impact of cultures and subcultures on the patient or the couple (Bhugra & Cordle, 1989). Despite the recognition that sexuality is embedded in a cultural context, and the numerous references to the importance of taking this context into account, there continues to be paucity in the literature relating multicultural therapy to sex therapy in particular.

In spite of these accounts and the concerted efforts of the health disciplines, confusion still exists as to how clinicians can advance from the point of simply recognizing differences to actually being (and feeling) proficient in service delivery to diverse groups. We assert that this confusion is understandable, because both cultural competency and sexual health are complex areas of human service delivery. They require awareness of a broad set of contextual realities, specific knowledge of diverse cultures and intervention, the integration of these areas with state-of-the-art clinical information (especially related to sexual health), and a personal and professional style that can tolerate a great deal of ambiguity and diplomacy. The confusion is also maintained because sometimes people do not have the mindset that cultural competency is a journey as opposed to a destination.

Indeed, we propose that the journey is long but the process need not be obscured. We propose that the journey can be made relatively less ambiguous if clinicians are provided access to principles by which the traveler might be able to find his or her way. At the same time we are advocating that understanding the nuances of culture cannot be reductionistic, meaning that we cannot just learn a list of facts about a given culture and apply these facts using traditional lenses and methods. Culturally competent care requires a relevant contextual analysis about the cultural function of communication.

We also assert that guidelines and principles of diversity are understandable if one is willing to suspend and challenge one's own assumptions about others. Such openness means becoming willing to affiliate with people different than oneself and learn how to deconstruct issues of privilege based on speciously constructed definitions of privilege (Schreier, 1998). Within sexual health, this challenge is even greater because the additional taboo of sexuality goes beyond the usual stigma of mental health issues.

A general review of the principles of cultural diversity presented in this contribution can help in the development of cultural competency and lead to an ability to practice the skills required in what Jackson (1995) and D. Sue, Ivey, and Pedersen (1996) have defined as multicultural therapy (MCT). They propose some of the very guidelines and principles that we have just discussed. When these principles are presented in sensitivity workshops, we find that people are still saying things such as, "This is interesting, but how exactly do I develop skills at multicultural interventions and achieve a satisfactory level of cultural competence?"

In answer to this question, the first two authors (Dobbins and Peterson) offer a pyramid metaphor as a foundation for skill development. The model was developed after a review of other models of MCT, the above-referenced guidelines from the various health professions, and the theory of MCT. The model is called a "Synthesis Pyramid Metaphor" (SPM) for reasons that will be further elaborated in this discussion.

The SPM rests on four assumptions:

1. Cultural sensitivity is a construct that can become a learning outcome via acknowledgment of the value of cultural factors and the need to master basic humanistic principles such as the unique importance of each person's experience, including the experience of the therapist.
2. Cultural competency is developed from an awareness and ability to use one's own journey in order to put MCT knowledge into practice for others.
3. Cultural competency cannot be fully achieved without a commitment to social responsibility that includes advanced proficiency skills, daily living that reflects advocacy, and recognition of the need to speak truth to power on behalf of the underserved.

4. The principles and practices of MCT can be applied to all forms of psychological intervention to improve treatment outcomes, from basic counseling of uncomplicated anxieties to neuropsychological assessment and sex therapy.

THE NATURE AND DEVELOPMENT OF MULTICULTURAL THERAPY

MCT has been described as therapy that occurs between or among individuals from different cultural backgrounds (Jackson, 1995). In one sense, all therapy relationships are multicultural experiences. However, in the sense that MCT is intended, therapy occurs between people of different ethnic and cultural backgrounds. It should logically follow that because MCT is an enterprise that requires adherence to the principles that have already been mentioned, not all therapy between therapist and client from different cultural paths can be called MCT. Again, we believe that it is the clinician's duty to be able to accurately and successfully deconstruct or activate relevant discussion and interventions aimed at the exploration of cultural variables, especially power and privilege, that constitute the essential multicultural ingredients of MCT.

MCT acknowledges that culture is a reality and cultural competency is an essential entity for competent care. MCT allows the concept of historical authority already expressed by the world's cultures to enter the therapeutic dialogue where cultural factors may be validated or invalidated as a process moving toward greater humanistic fulfillment (Rodis & Strehorn, 1997). This includes the historical suppression of women's sexual expression by most of the world's cultures. MCT opens the door for the clinician to understand the social origins and context of pain, especially pain related to cultural separation and cultural oppression. It also supports the need to tap into the client's strengths and wisdom in regard to his or her own culture. Rodis and Strehorn (1997) remind us that it may be these elements that have created some of the conflicts, but it is also these same environments that have sustained people for many generations. Additionally, MCT emphasizes cultural positives, because some of those positives may be devalued in Western ways of thinking and processing change.

We are asserting that there is much beauty to be embraced in diversity, such as the respect of differences and an emphasis on equality. However, we are also asserting that MCT is not the be-all and end-all for cultural competency. The extent to which MCT can embrace all that diversity entails is empirically undetermined, and so there is still room for more theory and experimentation. For example, is it possible for MCT to embrace controversial and sometimes fatal non-Western cultural practices, such as wife burning and honor crimes? Sexual health examples include polygamy, female genital mutilation, male and female circumcision, and all forms of coercive sex. Mental health professionals practicing in Western countries may not have to struggle as often with some of these issues as do practitioners in Africa, Asia, and the Middle East, who do not have the weight of law to help enforce what Western practitioners often consider basic human rights.

One relevant discussion on these contradictions was provided by Murphy (1955) as a precursor to our current MCT formulations. Murphy asks the quintessential question of whether counselors should impose their will and personal values on clients or instead limit themselves to techniques that allow clients to find their own internally derived values. Dobbins and Skillings (1991) make a similar observation as they question the therapist's motive in the functional outcome of therapy in multicultural transactions. They ask whether the therapist is a liberator or a reformer. For example, does he or she use therapy to get the client to conform to the counselor's own values, which are often embedded in traditional Western Descartian logic ("I think, therefore I am")? Or, does the counselor take the role of a learner and expert facilitator within a traditional non-Western philosophy of "We are, therefore I am"? MCT is not unaware of this position. Ponterotto and Pedersen (1993) concluded that MCT emphasizes the positive reception of other cultures. Murphy (1955) also suggested that it is more important for counselors to learn about their clients' values and cultures than it is to learn techniques and skills.

SPECIFIC GUIDELINES TO CULTURAL COMPETENCY

Several guides have been published to assist therapists in building their cultural competency. Generally, these are not comprehensive, tending to resemble the "rules of thumb" of their authors for interaction with clients. It is of special interest to note that none of these published "quick guidelines" are specific to sexual health, nor were they published in sexuality oriented publications.

Pope-Davis published a simple two-step formula for cultural competency (Pope-Davis & Coleman, 1997) in which clients are first asked for help by the therapist in understanding the clients' value system and the norms for their community. Second, therapists are instructed to ensure that clients feel that the cultural differences between them are not only respected but also appreciated.

A similar "three step guide" is presented by Peterson et al. (2002), which serves as a quick reminder to facilitate communication about cultural competency. This guide discusses three characteristics of client interaction:

1. Acknowledgment of cultural differences that exist between provider and clients in order to give permission to talk about them and to express respect for these differences.
2. Asking clients how their cultural experiences influence their concept of health, illness, definitions of acceptable interventions, and how they communicate about their health to providers.
3. Assisting clients in understanding the concept of cultural blind spots and that, while you share mental health expertise from your specialty as a provider, clients need to share their expertise of their cultural and individual worldview.

As one of the clear theoretical leaders of MCT, D. Sue described key characteristics of those who are competent to provide care to people of different cultures (D. Sue et al., 1996). He suggested that the three key characteristics are (a) scientific mindedness, or the ability to form and test hypotheses regarding cultural variables of a particular client, (b) focus on dynamic sizing, which is knowing when to generalize and when to individualize particular cultural attributes of clients, and (c) culture-specific expertise, developed through understanding cultural groups to which clients belong.

More elaborate guides using mnemonic acronyms are available as well. Noteworthy is the ASKED model. Campinha-Bacote (2002) developed a five-factor conceptualization of developing cultural competency: cultural awareness, cultural skill, cultural knowledge, cultural encounters, and cultural desire. She indicated that the last factor is defined as the motivation to want to engage in the process of becoming culturally competent (Camphina-Bacote, 2002). The ASKED acronym is designed to remind therapists to ask themselves five key questions prior to or during their interaction with clients:

A Awareness (Am I aware of my biases and prejudices toward other cultural groups as well as the effects of sexism and racism in healthcare?)
S Skills (Do I have the skills for conducting a culturally competent assessment?)
K Knowledge (Am I knowledgeable about the worldviews of different cultural/ethnic groups as well as knowledgeable about biocultural ecology?)

E Encounters (Do I seek out face-to-face interactions with individuals who are different from myself?)

D Desire (Do I really want to become culturally competent?)

THE PYRAMID METAPHOR FOR CULTURAL COMPETENCY

We now describe the metaphor to provide a conceptual foundation for a step-by-step guide to self-development of cultural competency among mental health professionals. The pyramid was selected as a metaphor for several reasons (see Figure 1 below).

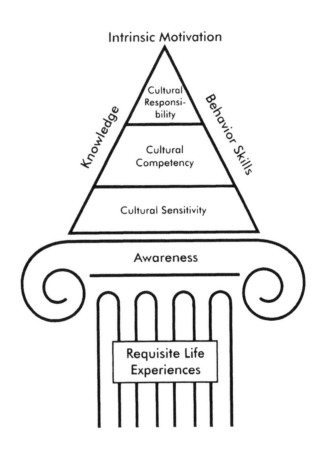

Tessa Kalman is the illustrator of the pyramid.

Figure 1. The Pyramid Metaphor.

First, pyramids are familiar and readily recognizable. They are easy to conceptualize in terms of outside appearance as well as having interior contents. Additionally, they represent the exotic nature of one of the "wonders of the world" and reflect the different backgrounds among people inherent in multicultural therapy. Finally, pyramids represent strength and endurance, which are to be associated with ideals of strengthening the efficacy of clinical practices and increasing positive treatment outcomes within MCT.

The pyramid metaphor builds upon the three most cited factors associated with cultural competency in the extant literature (awareness, knowledge, and behavior skills) and then adds two additional factors. The pyramid metaphor synthesizes these five factors to demonstrate key points of the authors' conceptualization of development of cultural competency for mental health professionals: (a) requisite life experiences, (b) awareness, (c) knowledge, (d) behavioral skills, and (e) intrinsic motivation. The use of the pyramid for the conceptualization of interior contents as well as an easily recognizable exterior is important here, because the pyramid metaphor represents a container and repository for what we know to be most helpful for developing cultural competency.

The first factor, requisite life experiences, serves as a solid foundation on which to sustain a pyramid over time. Requisite life experiences are similar to the role that humanistic psychology gives to the importance of experience as described by Rogers (1961). It is the cultural soil from which each of us is nurtured and developed. Requisite life experience as we mean it also involves having had experience with interpersonal relations sufficient to allow individuals to be predisposed to developing awareness of multicultural issues.

This basic level of interpersonal orientation would include a genuine curiosity about others, contact with others who are "different," and ultimately a capacity for communication that facilitates the breaking down of stereotypes (Allport, 1954) and the exchange of divergent worldviews. This requisite life experience is partially based on the research of Schultz and his classification of interpersonal needs (Schultz, 1966), in which he describes a fundamental interpersonal relations orientation (FIRO). If a person does not have sufficient interest and focus on other people, it is not likely that he or she will have, or be open to, requisite life experiences that can later serve as the basis of cultural sensitivity.

There are three cornerstones of the pyramid that rest upon the foundation of requisite life experiences in this metaphor. They are three components of cultural competency that have been discussed extensively in the literature: awareness, knowledge, and behavioral skills. The fourth factor is intrinsic motivation. It is the key factor that transforms the previously discussed three factors (representing a two-dimensional triangle) into a three-dimensional pyramid reflecting implementation. Motivation is at the apex of the pyramid and conceptually "activates" an individual to operationalize the knowledge, awareness/attitude, and behavioral skills. In other words, mental health professionals can know what to do and how to do it effectively but will not "activate" risk taking in the application of their knowledge and skills without the motivation to do so.

Having synthesized a five-factor metaphor of a three-dimensional pyramid, the pyramid directs one's journey through three stages of self-development. The three stages of self-development are cultural sensitivity, cultural competency, and cultural responsibility (the latter we see as advanced proficiency). Basic sensitivity, the first stage and lower third of the pyramid, involves increasing awareness by acknowledging the value of cultural factors and mastering basic principles of multiculturalism. This awareness serves as a foundation for further development of attitude change and skill implementation. Without this basic sensitivity, there is no incentive for further self-development.

Cultural competency, stage two and the midsection of the pyramid, involves continuing one's own personal journey of cultural competency by putting knowledge into practice. With this second stage, basic competency can be achieved through personal growth in all three dimensions; expanded awareness, a shift in attitudes, and practicing culturally relevant behavioral skills in service delivery.

The final stage of development, represented by the top third of the pyramid, is cultural responsibility. It involves daily living, reflecting an "integrated culturally relative identity," as well as the development of intrinsic motivation for implementing all the components of cultural competency in all mental health practice. Each stage is operationally defined below in terms of how MCT transforms cross-cultural relations. Special emphasis is given to developing cultural competency as a mental health therapist addressing sexual health concerns of clients.

STAGE I DEVELOPMENT: CULTURAL SENSITIVITY

This stage has two parts: (a) awareness of the importance of MCT and (b) developing a lexicon for conceptualizing the process and content of the multicultural relationship.

Understanding the Importance of MCT

MCT (a) helps the therapist to orient to the client, (b) helps to build rapport in the provider-client relationship, (c) helps clients feel they are being treated with respect, (d) promotes client responsiveness to care provided, (e) can increase provider job satisfaction, (f) can increase qualifications toward organizational requirements for accreditation, and (g) reflects America's movement toward social and cultural plurality (Van den Berghe, 1967).

Learning Basic Definitions and Key Principles of Multiculturalism:

Readers are referred to pages 257 to 258 for a review of basic definitions and key principles of MCT. This guide defines race, racial identity, racism, ethnicity, ethnic plurality, cultural diversity, cultural competency, minority or minority group, and prejudice. Key principles discussed include the process of pursuing cultural competency, "who owns the problem," the differences between racism and modern racism, and the consequences of racism. This guide does not include definitions and principles specific to sexual minority status; you are referred to the contribution on the assessment and treatment of sexual minorities for such essential information as the Kinsey scale for sexual orientation, what GLBTQA stands for (gay, lesbian, bisexual, transgendered, questioning, asexual), the multiple dimensions of gender, and the difference between transvestites, transsexuals, and transgenderists (see pp. 209-221).

STAGE II DEVELOPMENT: CULTURAL COMPETENCY

This stage implies that the required intrinsic motivation is there and that you have added to your requisite life experience. One of the elements of experience that is essential here is that you have tried to forge multicultural and cross-cultural relationships and been rejected. The tendency here would be to withdraw into privilege and abandon the effort to stay on the quest for deeper levels of knowledge and skill. If you get to this stage, you must consider ways to advance your knowledge and skill while also trying on new behaviors. A good self-assessment and coach or sponsor (Dobbins & Skillings, 2004) would be of great help here.

Advancing One's Own Cultural Competency Journey

1. Assess your own degree of cultural awareness and knowledge as a baseline via standardized measures such as one of the several measures of homophobia, heterosexism, or multicultural awareness.
2. Go to workshops and seminars regarding cultural populations that you serve as a professional.
3. Become familiar with the authors and theories of multiculturalism in the literature.
4. Participate in discussions or study groups that engage in dialogues on racial or ethnic themes.

5. Participate in culturally specific activities in the communities and populations that you serve.
6. Understand the differences, utilities, and influences of the "melting pot" versus the "quilt" or "salad" models of assimilation.
7. Explore and appreciate the transgenerational influences within your family system as they relate to your identities.

Putting Awareness and Knowledge into Implementing Competency Guidelines

Employing clinical practice guidelines as presented in the literature or using the pyramid metaphor as presented here, organizing a developmental sequence for your learning, and becoming proficient at cultural competency skills in therapy are ways to begin implementing cultural competency in your practice. A collegial peer group process will augment your mastery of the behavioral skill set involved in cultural competent psychotherapy. Alternatively, as already noted, working with a "cultural coach," a mentor, or others (e.g., participating in the "Dialogue on Race" series) is highly recommended for inspiration, insight, and accountability. For more information, contact your local Urban League or join one of the many online discussion groups, such as the Race Relations Online Discussion List (www.uky.edu/StudentOrgs/Aware/Dialog).

STAGE III DEVELOPMENT: CULTURAL RESPONSIBILITY (ADVANCED PROFICIENCY IN CULTURAL COMPETENCY)

In this stage of development, one moves beyond competency. This is a personal process that requires you to find a voice for change. It includes the awareness that a therapist is a powerful person and that he or she can either be a part of a sociopolitical solution or help to perpetuate problems. Sometimes this means confronting clients with what they are not advocating for themselves culturally; at other times it means taking issue with the slights, neglect, and discrimination that clients project onto others. In fact, cultural responsibility involves confronting and advocating not just with clients, but with whomever and wherever as necessary, including family and friends. This requires that you see diversity as a mission field where you choose to be an ally and an advocate for the underserved. At its core, you must be ready in a situation of discrimination to speak truth to power.

Stage III development of cultural responsibility includes the following points and guidelines:

1. In relation to your own ethnic/cultural heritage, understand the differences in developmental theories between majority and minority ethnic/racial identity (Ponterotto & Pedersen, 1993).
2. If you are a majority culture member in contemporary America (Caucasian heterosexual, able-bodied Christian male who is not living in poverty), to the extent you can, affiliate with those individuals and groups different from your background. Even better, spend time experiencing life as someone perceived to be a member of a minority population whom you serve as a professional (such as gay, lesbian, bisexual, and transgender [GLBT]; disabled; or other minority status).
3. If you are a member of one minority group, to the extent you can, spend time experiencing life as a member of another minority population whom you serve as a professional. For example, if you are an African-American able-bodied woman, spend a week living in a wheelchair at home and going to work. Or, if you are a Hispanic

heterosexual male, go to your next conference wearing a rainbow pride pin and allow some people to identify you as gay and respond to you accordingly.

4. Work toward realizing daily living that reflects the ideal descriptions of a fully integrated nonracist identity, such as cleansing oneself of internal prejudices and thoughts after freeing yourself from behavioral acts of discrimination based upon another's minority status.

5. Develop increasingly higher levels of intrinsic motivation to practice as a culturally competent therapist through values clarification and appreciation of your core values for social justice related to gender, ethnic, nationality, and other differences.

6. Develop a personal "balancing point" as a multicultural therapist between cultural relativism and cultural relativity, toward the goal of understanding universal human rights while respecting the needs represented in endogenous cultural practices (Razzouk, 2004).

7. Make multiculturalism part of your lifestyle by raising children in a school and home environment where they develop a consciousness in which the principles and practices of multiculturalism are the norm.

MULTICULTURAL THERAPY VIGNETTE: PATIENTS PRESENTING WITH SEXUAL HEALTH CONCERNS*

This clinical vignette involves not just the intersection of MCT and sex therapy, but also includes the cultural differences related to gender status, racial/ethnic minority status, and religious affiliation. A middle-aged Hispanic couple sought sex therapy because of their inability to have children, not because of biological abnormalities or lack of sexual intercourse, but because of lack of intravaginal ejaculation by the husband. The couple was well-to-do socioeconomically, were both working professionals, and came from upper-middle class families (high degrees of assimilation). They had been to marital counselors before and even a sex therapist. They reported their consultations with these professionals as helpful to their relationship but that they did not "correct the problem." The couple was affiliated with a conservative religious denomination that promotes having a "biblical marriage," by which the male was seen as the spiritual head of the family who made all decisions. The couple married in their late twenties, were now in their late thirties, and were running out of time to conceive. Based upon their religious beliefs, they were virgins when they married, and this was an important consideration in dating each other.

The case was referred from a fertility center where the couple consulted. They wished to attempt one last behavioral treatment to conceive naturally before going through expensive and invasive in vitro procedures. No physical reason was found for the lack of conception during their 10 years of having sexual intercourse except his report of not being able to ejaculate during intercourse. The man could ejaculate during masturbation, but both individuals had objections based upon their religious teachings. Beside a sense of the "biological clock" ticking, the couple was experiencing considerable pressure from both sets of parents to produce grandchildren. Values of family and having children are core to Hispanic culture. Additionally, women are not considered fully mature or accepted until they have children. Similarly, children are an overt sign of masculinity and heterosexual status for many Hispanic males.

Although most referrals involving couples are preferably seen by a male/female therapy team, the first author did not have a female cotherapist available at the time and, therefore, saw the couple as the sole therapist. The couple completed a sexual health assessment protocol

---

* Names and identifying characteristics have been changed to protect confidentiality.

involving an initial evaluation, psychological testing, a sexual development history, and a results-sharing conference (see a detailed description in the contribution on sexual minorities [pp. 209-221] or Peterson, 2000). To facilitate communication about the influence of cultural differences, the three-step guide referenced earlier (Peterson et al., 2002) was employed. It was noted that the couple sometimes spoke Spanish when addressing each other. Assessment tools were available in Spanish but, when asked, the couple said they preferred to complete the assessment using English. In the therapist's opinion, this reflected their high degree of cultural assimilation.

The wife was within normal range on measures of depression, anxiety, and sexual functioning. She experienced sexual desire, arousal via labia swelling and vaginal lubricating, and orgasm of frequent consistency and high satisfaction. She denied any problems with sexual pain. She reported high levels of satisfaction with both her sexual and overall relationship, with the exception of his lack of ejaculation and their lack of children. Behaviorally, she reported a complete pattern of sexual intercourse without other forms of sexual pleasuring, such as solo masturbation, manual stimulation, oral sex, or anal sex.

The husband was within normal functioning on measures of anxiety but was within the moderate range of depressive symptoms. He reported some decline in sexual interest but masturbated with some regularity. Frequency of intercourse (both reported being monogamous) was approximately twice per week, and he reported masturbation on a weekly basis. Even though he felt distressed and guilty by his masturbatory behavior, he reported feeling a strong need "for release" through ejaculation via masturbation.

In the results-sharing conference, what was learned about the couple through interview, testing, and previous treatment records was summarized. The confidentiality ensured to each person is a tradeoff for honest disclosures that the therapist would otherwise not hear. A draft treatment agreement was reviewed, answering all questions they had regarding the nature, frequency, duration, and cost of treatment. Although it was explained that their conceiving a child could not be assured, the couple was told that they had a good prognosis for correcting their presenting problem of lack of intravaginal ejaculation.

However, they would have to temporarily engage in sexual behavior outside of their comfort zone (masturbation) to reach their goal of regular intercourse resulting in male ejaculation inside the wife. Although this was acknowledged to be contrary to their religious belief, discussion pursued that emphasized three key points:

1. The biblical condemnation of masturbation by most Christian denominations is a general guideline that supports the primary directive of "go forth, be fruitful and multiply" (see section on sexual heritage, pp. 6-8). The prescription of masturbation in this specific treatment would greatly increase their likelihood of conceiving, supporting the primary directive as well as the cultural values of the clients. Hence, engaging in masturbation should be considered as permissible on a temporary basis to support their goals.

2. The biblical condemnation of masturbation is based on a misinterpretation of the act of Onan refusing to impregnate his deceased brother's wife, which was customary under the law of the time. While trying to make appearances of complying with the law, he did not want to complete the act (speculation was that he did not want to create new heirs), so he "spilled his seed upon the land," hence creating history's first record of coitus interruptus. This act of "spilling his seed," as a way to not dilute his inheritance to his children with his wife, has been confused with the act of masturbation. Hence, if the client wants to live with this interpretation of the Bible's prohibition against masturbation, it is logical that he would also want to follow the biblical instruction to impregnate his sister-in-law in the case of his brother's untimely demise.

3. Finally, the clients' ambivalence regarding this treatment approach was validated. They were encouraged to discuss this option, consult with their minister, and pray about it if they felt so moved.

To the therapist's surprise, the couple looked at each other and stated they wished to proceed immediately. He was given behavioral prescriptions of masturbatory training using a successive approximation approach leading to intravaginal ejaculations. Specifically, the husband was instructed to masturbate in every room of the lower level of the house over the course of the next week. He was to use any sexual fantasy he wanted but at the point of ejaculatory inevitability, switch to the sexual imagery of ejaculating during intercourse within his wife's vagina. While he was masturbating, the wife was to be in bed and fully aware of his activity.

The following week, the husband came back having completed his assignment. He was then told to move to the second floor of the house where the couple has their bedroom. In week two of treatment, he was to masturbate in every room of the second floor, moving progressively closer to the master bedroom but stopping before entering where his wife waited for him. The third week was when the finale occurred. He first masturbated in the master bath, with the door open. Two nights later, he masturbated while lying in the bed next to his wife with her observing. Two nights later, the couple enjoyed foreplay and she became aroused with vaginal lubrication. She was instructed in how to masturbate him with the use of hand guiding. When he felt himself approaching climax, the wife straddled him and inserted his penis into her vagina. He was able to ejaculate inside her for the first time ever.

The couple came to their next session reporting that they had made love together and experienced three intravaginal ejaculations since their last appointment. Their next session was scheduled 6 weeks later, and their last session was at 4 months after start of treatment. They reported having intercourse with ejaculation on a regularity of about two to three times per week. They were not using any contraception and were hoping to become pregnant. On a follow-up appointment 6 months later, the couple came into the office and took off their winter coats, revealing the wife's bulging belly. Several months later, the first author received a picture of the newborn inside a "thank you" card.

MAINTAINING MOTIVATION

There are many models of professional development relating to cultural competency, and several have been reviewed. In this discussion, we noted that commitment and motivation are critical variables in the development of effective and authentic cultural competency. Yet we are also working with issues of privilege where the clinician holds a great deal of influence and power due to his or her position in the therapeutic relationship; this may also be coupled with the power of gender and racial standing in the historical traditions of the U.S. Power and privilege will allow the therapist to default to these sources of comfort and security in times of conflict and ambiguity in relationship stress. The question might arise, "Why should I keep pursuing more cultural competency than I already have?"

Let's examine reasons why mental health professionals would want to maintain an active personal program of cultural competency development. The first point of motivation is in awareness and knowledge. Currently, ethnic/racial minority groups comprise approximately one-third of the American population. The U.S. Census Bureau (2000) estimates that minority groups will grow to be more than half of the U.S. population within 30 to 40 years. As a nation, the United States will be making the shift to a true ethnic plurality to which several regions have already evolved, such as New York, California, and Florida. This national shift to plurality will occur during the maturation of the next generation of new mental health professionals.

The changing demographic reality of American culture forces mental health professions to face the shifting characteristics not only of our clientele, but also those of the practitioners of the professions. Professional graduate programs are recruiting diverse student bodies as well as changing training curricula to help prepare students with necessary skills in MCT. Hence, another obvious reason to emphasize the development of cultural competency is the need to meet the standards related to cultural diversity that accreditation bodies mandate on curriculum, faculty, and student body levels.

Personal reasons may be the most compelling motivators to continually develop cultural competency. The sense of personal growth is often reported as a motivating factor, which for many professionals is described as a way of making work more interesting. To some, the journey of developing cultural competency is like a continually unfolding story that demonstrates the old adage, "The more you know, the more you know you don't know." There is always suspense, in that there is always more to learn and, therefore, "more to the story." These personal reasons are at the core of the "intrinsic motivation" component of the pyramid metaphor. They are why people practice cultural responsibility: not because they have to but because they want to.

DISCUSSION

Plurality means that no one ethnic group represents a majority in a society. This has overwhelming implications for the notion of privilege and who can and cannot afford to work on the issues of cross-cultural and multicultural relations. Most essentially, the traditional patterns of power and dominance will not be tenable. New knowledge and skills are required. Although MCT is part of the new knowledge and skill sets, we also have acknowledged that MCT is not the be-all and end-all of effective therapies. More ideas, different perspectives, and innovations will be needed to meet future challenges.

We live in an information age within a world that is shrinking due to the explosion of technology, the building of world economies, and easier access to once-remote parts of the world. Those professionals who have sufficient multicultural skills will be able to sustain themselves and their respective professions in the new pluralistic era.

The most compelling reason to stay on the journey is that multicultural realities are also pointing out the need for new knowledge and skill in ethics (Caldwell & Tarver, 2004). Treating people right or professionally cannot be taken for granted as if our current professional guidelines and principles will be adequate to maintain rapport with people who are poor, underserved, and without power to compete in the new plurality.

This is a prospective ethical stance in which one sees the need and activates professional and personal resources to meet the need. It is an awareness of the fact that the personal is political, and that what happens to one of us can happen to all of us. A second awareness is that although we cannot always act globally, there is always opportunity to act locally. Small actions have larger systemic meaning and consequences. It was Margaret Mead who said, "A small group of thoughtful people could change the world. Indeed, it's the only thing that ever has."

Our increasing plurality in society emphasizes the need for more sophisticated levels of cultural competency for current mental health therapists and demands it as a necessity for the next generation of sexual health and sex therapy practitioners. The pyramid metaphor and the preceding stages of development are offered as tools to help achieve these goals.

Basic Definitions and Key Principles of Multiculturalism

(Note: This guide does not include definitions and principles specific to sexual minority status; you are referred to the contribution on the assessment and treatment of sexual minorities for this information [see pp. 209-221]).

1. **Basic Definitions:**

    a. *Race or Racial Identity.* A sense of group or collective identity based on one's perception that one shares a common racial heritage with a particular racial group (Helms, 1990).

    b. *Racism.* Any behavior or pattern of behavior that systematically tends to deny access to opportunities or privilege to one social group while perpetuating privilege to members of another group (Ridley, 1989; compare to Skillings & Dobbins, 1991).

    c. *Ethnicity.* Part of a segment of society whose members are thought, by themselves and/or others, to have a common origin, share important aspects of a common culture, and participate in shared activities in which the common origin and culture are significant ingredients (Yinger, 1976).

    d. *Ethnic Plurality.* The state of no one racial/ethnic group maintaining a statistical majority within a population.

    e. *Cultural Diversity.* Variations among people across disability status, ethnic and racial groups, country of origin, gender, language, religious and spiritual traditions, sexual orientation, socioeconomic class, and other dimensions.

    f. *Cultural Competency.* A set of professional skills involving awareness, knowledge, and skills of the provider related to cultural factors of a client and which lead to more effective interventions with that client (Peterson et al., 2002).

    g. *Minority or Minority Group.* A group of people who, because of physical or cultural characteristics, are singled out from others in the society in which they live for differential and unequal treatment and who therefore regard themselves as objects of collective discrimination. Minority status carries with it the exclusion from full participation in the life of the society (Wirth, 1945).

    h. *Prejudice.* An antipathy (or belief) based upon a faulty and inflexible generalization that is directed toward a group as a whole or toward an individual because he or she is a member of that group (Ponterotto & Pedersen, 1993).

2. **Key Principles:**

    a. *Cultural Competency.* A continuum from cultural destructiveness and incapacity on one end to cultural competency and proficiency on the other (Cross, 1991).

    b. *Who Owns the Problem.* No single racial/ethnic group has a monopoly on prejudice and racism, because prejudice and racism transcend all ethnic/racial groups in the world. For this reason, combating prejudice (and developing cultural competency) is everyone's responsibility (Ponterotto & Pedersen, 1993). For example, White people are wrong when they say cultural diversity issues belong to minorities (disowning the problem), and minority members are wrong when they say they have cultural competency by virtue of possessing minority status.

    c. *Racism.* Discriminatory acts are reflected in behavior, while prejudice reflects an internal belief or attitude. Racism can be performed by nonprejudiced as well as prejudiced people and is determined by the consequences (not the intent) of the behavior.

    d. *Modern Racism.* A continuing Eurocentric philosophy that values mainstream (dominant culture) beliefs and attitudes more highly than culturally diverse belief systems. The modern racist believes discrimination is a thing of the past and that minority groups are violating cherished "American" values as well as making unfair demands to change the status quo (Sabnani & Ponterotto, 1992).

    e. *Consequences of Racism.* The effects of discriminatory acts and policies (institutionalized discrimination) that hurt members of the dominant culture as well as the minority member upon which they are perpetrated.

    f. *Race.* A biological determinant of physical characteristics which has little utility as a concept applied to differentiating people. It is important to note that there are as many, if not more, variations between members of the same "race" as there are between members of different races.

g. *Practicing Cultural Competency.* This does not mean you have to know everything about all cultures of clients with whom you are working, nor everything about any single cultural group. Practicing cultural competency means that you have made a commitment to develop your awareness, knowledge, and skills related to the cultural factors of your clients, toward the goal of increased effectiveness in providing services to diverse populations.

CONTRIBUTORS

Frederick L. Peterson, Jr., PsyD, is a health psychologist at the Veterans Healthcare System of Ohio, Dayton Campus, where he coordinates a Sexual Health Clinic and the Smoking Cessation Programs. Dr. Peterson is the Co-Director of the Psychology Internship Program. He completed postdoctorate training as a Clinical Fellow at the Masters and Johnson Institute. Research interests include sex therapy, tobacco use treatment, and the effects of masculinity-related personality factors on health. He holds three academic appointments at Wright State University, including the School of Medicine (Department of Psychiatry), the School of Professional Psychology, and the College of Education and Human Services. Dr. Peterson may be contacted at the Sexual Health Clinic, VA Medical Center, Dayton, OH 45428. E-mail: Docpete100@aol.com

James Dobbins, PhD, is currently Professor and Director of Postdoctoral Training for the School of Professional Psychology at Wright State University and holds a Diplomate in Family Psychology. His professional experience includes work with health attitudes and beliefs among underserved groups, systems of health intervention for stress management, multicultural organizational and school consultation, and child, adult, and family therapy. He is an active member in the National Council of Schools of Professional Psychology, the Association of Black Psychologists, and served a 2-year term as the Secretary of the American Board of Professional Psychology for Family Psychology. Dr. Dobbins can be reached at Wright State University SOPP, Ellis Human Development Institute, 9 N. Edwin C. Moses Boulevard, Dayton, OH 45407. E-mail: james.dobbins@wright.edu

Florence Coleman, MD, is the Acting Chief of Special Programs, the Coordinator of Psychiatry Residency Training, and the Coordinator of Continuing Education at the VA Medical Center, Dayton, Ohio. Academically, Dr. Coleman is Assistant Professor with the Department of Psychiatry, School of Medicine, Wright State University. She is also Assistant Clinical Professor, College of Medicine, Department of Psychiatry at the University of Cincinnati Medical Center. Among professional organizations, Dr. Coleman is affiliated with the American Psychiatric Association, the American Academy of Addiction Psychiatry, and the American Medical Association. Dr. Coleman may be contacted at VA Medical Center (116), Dayton, OH 45428. E-mail: Florence.Coleman@med.va.gov

Jouhaina Razzouk, PsyD, has lived and studied in Africa, the Middle East, and the United States. She is a staff therapist at the Adult Diagnostic and Treatment Center, a state facility for the treatment of repetitive and compulsive male sex offenders in Avenel, New Jersey. Dr. Razzouk's research and clinical experiences include multicultural therapy, gender issues, trauma, dissociation, and sex offender treatment. She earned her doctorate degree in clinical psychology from Wright State University. Dr. Razzouk can be contacted through the first author. E-mail: j_razzouk@yahoo.com

RESOURCES

Allport, G. (1954). *The Nature of Prejudice*. New York: Addison-Wesley.

Bhugra, A. D., & Cordle, C. (1989). Sexual dysfunction in Asian couples. *British Medical Journal, 292*, 111-112.

Bhugra, A. D., & de Silva, P. (1995). Sexual dysfunction and sex therapy. An historical perspective. *International Review of Psychiatry, 7*(2), 159-167.

Bullough, V. (1976). *Sexual Variance in Society and History*. Chicago: University of Chicago Press.

Caldwell, L. D., & Tarver, D. D. (2004). An ethical code for racial-cultural practice: Filling gaps and confronting contradictions in existing ethical guidelines. In A. Carter (Ed.), *Handbook of Racial-Cultural Psychology and Counseling: Training and Practice* (pp. 37-49). Hoboken, NJ: John Wiley.

Campinha-Bacote, A. (2002). *The Process of Cultural Competence in the Delivery of Healthcare Services: A Culturally Competent Model of Care*. New York: Transcultural C.A.R.E. Associates.

Cross, W. E. (1991). *Shades of Black: Diversity in African-American Identity*. Philadelphia: Temple University Press.

Dobbins, J. E., & Skillings, J. H. (1991). Race labeling: A conceptual tool for the social science practitioner. *Journal of Counseling and Development, 70*, 11-16.

Dobbins, J. E., & Skillings, J. H. (2004). White racism and mental health: Treating the individual racist. In A. Carter (Ed.), *Handbook of Racial-Cultural Psychology and Counseling: Training and Practice*. Hoboken, NJ: John Wiley.

Helms, J. E. (Ed.). (1990). *Black and White Racial Identity: Theory, Research and Practice*. New York: Greenwood Press.

Jackson, M. L. (1995). Multicultural counseling: Historical perspectives. In J. G. Ponterotto, J. M. Casa, L. A. Suzuki, & C. M. Alexander (Eds.), *Handbook of Multicultural Counseling* (pp. 387-414). Thousand Oaks, CA: Sage.

Kulhara, P., & Avasthi, A. (1995). Sexual dysfunction on the Indian subcontinent. *International Review of Psychiatry, 7*(2), 231-240.

Murphy, G. (1955). The cultural context of guidance. *Personnel and Guidance Journal, 34,* 4-9.

Peterson, F. L., Jr. (2000). The assessment and treatment of erection dysfunction. In L. VandeCreek & T. L. Jackson (Eds.), *Innovations in Clinical Practice: A Source Book* (Vol. 18, pp. 57-71). Sarasota, FL: Professional Resource Press.

Peterson, F. L., Jr., Coleman, F., Dobbins, J., & Boyce, J. (2002). Understanding the importance of cultural competency in psychotherapy, supervision, and consultation. In L. VandeCreek & T. L. Jackson (Eds.), *Innovations in Clinical Practice: A Source Book* (Vol. 20, pp. 343-354). Sarasota, FL: Professional Resource Press.

Ponterotto, J., & Pedersen, P. (1993). *Preventing Prejudice: A Guide for Counselors and Educators.* London: Sage.

Pope-Davis, D., & Coleman, H. (1997). *Multicultural Counseling Competencies.* London: Sage.

Razzouk, J. (2004). *Respect or Neglect? An Examination of Multicultural Therapy in Light of Human Rights Issues.* Unpublished manuscript, Wright State University, Dayton, Ohio.

Reiss, I. L. (1986). A sociological journey into sexuality. *Journal of Marriage and Family, 48*(2), 233-243.

Ridley, C. (1989). Racism in counseling as an adverse behavioral process. In P. B. Pederson, J. G. Draguns, W. J. Lonner, & J. E. Trimle (Eds.), *Counseling Across Cultures* (pp. 227-239). Honolulu: University of Hawaii Press.

Rodis, P. T., & Strehorn, K. C. (1997). Ethical issues for psychology in the postmodernist era: Feminist psychology and multicultural therapy (MCT). *Journal of Theoretical and Philosophical Psychology, 17,* 13-31.

Rogers, C. (1961). *Becoming a Person.* Boston: Houghton-Mifflin.

Sabnani, H., & Ponterotto, J. (1992). Racial/ethnic minority instrumentation in counseling research: A review, critique, and recommendations. *Measurement and Evaluation in Counseling and Development, 24,* 161.

Sartorius, N., Pedersen, P. B., & Marsella, A. J. (1984). *Mental Health Services: The Cross-Cultural Context.* Newbury Park, CA: Sage.

Schreier, B. (1998). Of shoes, and ships, and sealing wax: The faulty and specious assumptions of sexual reorientation therapies. *Journal of Mental Health Counseling, 20,* 305-314.

Schultz, W. C. (1966). *FIRO: A Three-Dimensional Theory of Interpersonal Behavior.* New York: Holt, Rinehart and Winston.

Skillings, J., & Dobbins, J. (1991). Racism as a disease: Etiology and treatment implications. *Journal of Counseling and Development, 70,* 206-212.

Sue, D., Ivey, A., & Pedersen, P. (1996). *A Theory of Multicultural Counseling and Therapy.* Pacific Grove, CA: Brooks Cole.

Sue, D. W., & Sue, D. (1990). *Counseling the Culturally Different: Theory and Practice.* New York: John Wiley.

U.S. Census Bureau. (2000). *Overview of Race and Hispanic Origin: Census 2000 Brief.* Washington, DC: Economics and Statistics Administration.

Van den Berghe, P. (1967). *Race and Racism: A Comparative Perspective.* New York: John Wiley.

Wirth, L. (1945). The problem of minority groups. In R. Linton (Ed.), *The Science of Man in World Crisis* (pp. 347-372). New York: Columbia University Press.

Yinger, J. (1976). Ethnicity in complex societies. In L. Coser & O. Larsen (Eds.), *The Uses of Controversy in Sociology* (pp. 86-98). New York: Free Press.

Golden Sexuality:
Sex Therapy for Seniors

Larry M. Davis

PHILOSOPHY

Sexuality in America is full of contradictions. We have become ever more eroticized as a culture, with sexual stimuli coming at us from multiple areas. Our Judeo-Christian tradition presents a strong, patriarchal, religious criticism of sexuality. Ownership of our individual Eros is at least discouraged as children and adolescents and often seen as shameful throughout our years. Our leadership reacts with outrage to Janet Jackson's nipple getting broad TV exposure, while graphic presentations of sex on the Internet reach into homes and offices as part of the $10 billion-a-year sexuality business in America. We are youth focused: Millions of teen females want to follow Britney Spears' sexually charged behavior as suggested by her ads for Pepsi. Our culture expects older men and women to be physically weak and sexually retarded.

For the first time in America, over half of our population is over 50. Many of us challenge the "grandfather in a rocking chair" concept of a few decades ago, pursuing intense sports like skiing, hiking, and mountain climbing. Activities such as gardening, cooking, construction, fishing, golf, and other active sports further illustrate a new zest for living by 50-, 60-, 70-year-olds and beyond. The ancient Chinese in 2000 B.C.E. believed that golden sexuality rested in the old ones, who were assigned the task of keeping sexual secrets and teaching sexual ecstatic function to adolescents, young adults, and others (including royalty and their courts). The great ancient teacher, Lao Tzu, wrote on full sexual ownership and high sexual spirits and practice as a worshipful activity desired by all. He wrote, "an individual's approach to sexuality is an indication of his level of evolution" (Ni, 1979, p. 192).

Today, in America, I would like every health care provider to ask patients, "Do you have a sexual concern that you would like to share with me?" I believe half will tell their health professional that they do. Over the years of my sex therapy practice, I have seen an increasing number of couples in their 50s and beyond seeking a new personal awareness and sexual connectedness as a couple. The number of couples who have taken their sexuality to an entirely new and deeply satisfying level at 50 years old or beyond is increasing. The therapeutic process of guiding them is one purpose of this contribution.

To appreciate and to understand the helpful or healing aspects of sex therapy, I have needed 36 years of experience as a sex therapist/physician as well as the experiences that only growing older can provide. I have worked with patients and couples in a wide range of ages, genders, preferences, and experiences. In this contribution I share my observations, beliefs, and techniques that have made my work with the sexuality of those over 50 especially rewarding. I have three wishes for your experience herein. The first is to inspire you to adopt an attitude of excitement and affirmation while working with the sexuality of older individuals and couples. Second, I hope to guide you to some new skills and tools useful for this work. As a sex therapist of older people, you can guide your clients/patients to new behaviors with a goal of achieving a higher level of sexuality than they have previously experienced. Third, I want you to take away something useful for your own sexual life, now and in the future.

Sexuality is arguably the most complex of human endeavors. Sex therapy, therefore, requires an expansion of skills and knowledge for every discipline involved in the sex therapy field. I have been blessed as a physician and sex therapist by the experiences of great change that allow me to blend decades of many health care approaches with current technology. As a high school boy, I was privileged to make over 2,000 house calls with my general practice father, Marvin Davis, MD, and directly experienced the care, time, and focus with which my father connected with his patients. I know the value that a healing attitude brings to the work of any health care therapy. Sex therapy is one of the few remaining areas of medical care where such care and adequate time remain. In 1970, a young psychologist, Rose Chapman, PhD, and I worked together as a sex therapy team in the Masters and Johnson model, in conjunction with a faculty cotherapy sexual team, to represent the Indiana University School of Medicine. These were the early acknowledged days of sex therapy. Over the last 36 years I have added my physician orientation to sex hormone rebalancing, general physical health care, and sexual enhancing pharmacology, with newly available laboratory tests and technical procedures for improved sexual function. Effective approaches in sexual therapy today add sexual technology to talk therapy, individual assessment, a balanced treatment program, and a positive expectation of good sexual and quality of life outcomes. Health literacy is very important to a new paradigm of medical care, that being to teach patients to take responsibility for their own health. Sexual literacy is critical to successful functional sexuality and connectedness in a couple.

GOLDEN SEXUALITY

I gladly share my belief that 21st-century sexuality should occur as an active human experience between the ages of at least 15 (obviously younger for many) and 85 or more, assuming good health and maintenance of sexual physiology. Fifty-year-old men or women are at the midpoint of their sexual life! I have learned through clinical experience with my over-50-year-old patients that a beautiful sexual life can and should occur at 50 and beyond. Golden sexuality, the sense of luminous, fulfilling sexuality in our older years, is accessible to many of us reading these words.

There are at least four areas of our sexuality that reveal why many years of preparation are necessary to achieve golden sexuality. The first is sexual knowledge, not easy to acquire in this culture. Although we have lots of erotic stimulation (70% of prime time TV in November of 2005 had overt sexual content), we teach our children, adolescents, young adults, and older adults essentially nothing about sexual function, only sexual hazards. There are very few sex positive curriculums culturally endorsed in America. Therefore, knowledge about sexual function must be sought individually. Individuals can and should explore and develop their unique erotic life. I believe that therapists must incorporate education throughout their work with an individual or couple. Do not assume that your patients already know sexual information that you consider bedrock. Conversely, respect and honor the sexual knowledge your older patients often bring to you.

Secondly, many years are required to overcome, at the least, sexual functional ignorance, and at the most, sexually traumatic experiences of childhood, adolescence, or young adulthood. Unfortunately, many religions in this culture discourage full ownership of our individual sexuality, labeling many of our sexual behaviors as sinful, or at least a misdemeanor against the Divine. In other words, years or even decades seem necessary for many to endorse and appreciate their unique sexuality, and many need guidance to do so.

Third, about the time that sexual knowledge, sexual experience, and self-understanding have matured to the level of potential sexual excellence, overall health and hormonal physiology may begin to decline. Libido, sensual responsiveness, arousal, and ability to reach climax or orgasm will all decrease when hormones fall below a functional level. Therapy today cannot be limited to talking therapy when symptoms of hormonal inadequacy are identified and confirmed in the laboratory. Restoration of hormonal balance at a level usually found in the 40s is a critical base on which a new level of sexual functioning can be developed. Other medical causes such as the presence of drugs like chronic opiates or selective serotonin reuptake inhibitor (SSRI) antidepressants must be addressed and often skillfully removed. Other blocks to quality of life, such as conflict, anger, depression, or performance anxiety require identification and improvement if sex therapy is to be effective. Exercise, nutrition, stress management, and best possible general health practices are the support structure for golden sexuality.

Fourth, the interchange of sexual energy at a deep, even spiritual level requires the context of respect, love, and appreciation for the beauty and uniqueness of the sexual partner. Especially in a long-established relationship, focusing on appreciating the partner, rather than depreciating aspects (or behaviors) of the other, requires maturity, capacity for intimacy, and communication skill.

In Pursuit of Golden Sexuality

I define golden sexuality as joyful mind, body, and spirit connectedness in a committed couple. Each must have achieved sexual knowledge, personal sexual awareness, physiological sexual health, and a capacity for intimacy and integrity. Both individuals must bring a conscious desire to further expand their sexuality, experiencing themselves sexually in the context of the other. A clear goal and real work shared by both can achieve glorious sexuality at 50 and beyond. Real work often includes sex therapy with a knowledgeable and skilled sex therapist. For many of us, our sexuality to about age 50 is about learning and growing. Sexuality for many couples after 50 should be filled with ongoing curiosity, exploration, pleasure, appreciation of the partner, and joy.

When a couple near or over 50 years old approaches you for therapy, spend some time with them together helping them to see the opportunity of the new beginnings available to them. Experience teaches that many older couples are more enthusiastic about trying new sexuality with each other than the same couple was in their 30s. Help them appreciate that years of work on self and partner understanding has created an opportunity to seek golden sexuality together. If time allows, explore how they have balanced their sexual desires, managed their power conflicts, communicated to solve conflicts, and how they have come to appreciate or depreciate each other. Be prepared to spend one or more sessions establishing their past viewpoints and encouraging their new sexual beliefs and sexual techniques. See them separately and examine guilt that they have applied to their sexual experiences. Encourage them to release their guilt and convert their shame to sexual self-learning. The more you are able to change their sexual attitude to fearlessness and exploring together old myths and prohibitions, the greater will be their movement toward golden sexuality and the joy of their sexual connectedness.

I am experiencing a growing number of patients in therapy with me who are well past 50. As we proceed, they tell me that they have begun experiencing the sexuality together that in all their early years they held out as a frustrated possibility. As you begin working with older couples, you will soon change pessimism (and therefore reduced effort) into optimism and increased treatment effort for older couples. You will learn that 35 to 40 years of age for a woman, and 45 to 50 years of age or older for a man, are the times, for most, when intimacy, commitment, and interconnectedness come together with the integrity and spirit that define maturity. After 50, a larger part of sexual pleasure can become partner directed. Before 50, integrity, trust, personal accountability, reduced blaming, negotiation, and mentally and verbally blessing the other are vague concepts or only partially developed.

Talking sex therapy has several common areas that usually must be addressed. Undoing sexual blocks and distortions, sexual learning from autoeroticism (masturbation), communication errors, and nonsynchronous sexual goals are common areas of focus.

PERSONAL SEXUAL BLOCKS AND DISTORTIONS

Sexual blocks or distortions are either learned from direct positive or negative sexual experiences or taught by others, either adults or peers. Most of us begin our sexual interactions with others by adolescence. However, for young men and women talking with peers, there is little willingness to share fears, unpleasant experiences, or sexual failures. The data about the sexual experience is usually not as important as the judgments about the data, or the feelings about the judgments about the data. Negative feedback from one or more sources has often caused men and women to develop doubts about the attractiveness of their physical bodies. Some are taught in childhood that their sexual body parts are ugly or unclean. Distortions and self-criticisms include women saying their breasts are too big, too little, too soft, too hard, and so forth, or a man convinced that his penis is too small.

Some avoid most social contacts in the mistaken belief that they are physically ugly in body and face. Even sexual fantasies, normal and helpful to the sexual response cycle, can become sources of guilt and shame. Many experiences and attitudes will block sexual openness and exploration. Therapeutic gain may be stopped until a skilled sex therapist helps pull the sexual psychological block into full awareness and hopefully release it. The therapeutic work of convincing an older couple that they are capable of golden sexuality is critical to their growth.

If these factors come together (sexual knowledge, personal sexual awareness, physiological health and balance, and intimacy and connection), a couple with a conscious desire by each individual to expand their sexuality and experience of themselves and the other can achieve glorious sexuality at 50 or beyond. Well-managed sexual health should result in years of curiosity, exploration, pleasure, and appreciation, leading many into a sexually fulfilling life until 85 years old and older. For many, the first half of our sexual lives, up to age 50, is about learning the complexity of our individual and connected sexuality. The second half, from 50 on, is to reap the benefits of intrapersonal and interpersonal sexual pleasure and the joy of connectedness and intimacy.

A surprising observation from my work in sex therapy over these many years is that a couple at 55 years of age, with a positive seeking attitude of sexual newness, is easier to work with and more enthusiastic about trying new sexuality with each other than a couple in their 30s. Although my gay patients in sex therapy often have a very youthful orientation to their preferred sexual partners, the same rules of maturity for connectedness and intimacy apply. Older couples, either recently married or long married, still have much to teach us as therapists about balancing sexual desires, power conflicts between them and conflict management, passive versus aggressive negotiations, keeping score and withholding, appreciating, and honoring. I hope you will work with your patients to help them shift depreciation to appreciation for the other.

CHANGING DEPRECIATION TO APPRECIATION

I would like you to consider for patients, clients, friends, and especially yourself, the elements necessary for great couple connectedness and therefore critical to creating life-changing Eros. The task of changing negative scorekeeping to positive attention and praise is difficult for most well-established couples, but easier after 50. Twelve "bedrock" foundation elements for a great sexuality for a couple are trustworthiness, commitment, understanding, communication, observation, affection, support, personal accountability, playfulness, passion, creativity, and spirituality. There may be others, but the important point is to choose certain categories to keep a score card of ourselves (see pp. 274-275 for such score cards).

For many, once the newness and excitement of early connecting wears off, we begin keeping score of the failures or important contradictions of these elements by our partner. Usually to ourselves, but sometimes out loud to our partner or others, we depreciate the other. To ourselves we often keep a running score as to which person has lost the most points. Often we score these errors more than the successes and moments of joyful cooperation and caring. As conflict develops between a couple who have kept the depreciation list for a while, each person may begin the very poor practice of quietly thinking, "My wife/husband/partner is behind, especially by that screw-up last week or last month. I'm not going to approach him/her positively or give first. He/she owes me one (or more)." These thoughts usually come on strong when the other is seeking notice, recognition, praise, or at least seeking positive connection. Most of us never outgrow our neediness or sense of rejection from the withholding other, and the conflict builds.

In couple conflict, males, or the male role in a gay relationship, may choose to *go into* sex to relieve conflict and associated stress. Usually the feminine energy, when stressed by conflict, *goes away from* sex. This ever-so-common practice of the masculine energy is to do sex to feel good. The feminine will retreat from physical sex into "above the neck" loving to feel better. Increased fighting occurs with accent comments like, "You no longer love or want me (you bitch)," or "All you ever want me for is sex (you bastard)." These angry/painful/shameful feelings quickly magnify the original conflict.

It is often helpful to teach the couple about masculine and feminie energy. Carl Jung, in his writings identified the conscious masculine energy thought processes and responses to be *animus* and felt that all of us acting from the conscious masculine energy have an unconscious feminine energy, which he labeled, *anima*. Conversely, a person predominately consciously feminine (*anima*) has an unconscious masculine energy (*animus*). Both men and women 50 and older, in my clinical experience, can come to understand the role of their unconscious energy more readily than they did in their 20s, 30s, and even 40s. Helping each individual to greater self-understanding could be of great help in their shift towards appreciating their partner.

Vigorous description of this process by the therapist of the couple and vigorous practice by the couple with each other must occur if the connectedness is to improve. I have attached an addendum to this contribution (see pp. 274-275) so that readers can quickly score their feelings about both their behavior and their partner's behavior in the preceding 2 weeks. This form is designed to be shared with each other and the therapist. These practices are meant to focus on the positives. The effort is intended to reverse the scorekeeping focus from depreciation to points of appreciation. This and other exercises are designed to increase the likelihood of an upward spiral of mutual appreciation.

Furthermore, on a daily basis, both in therapy and long after, a couple should sit together in a loving, 1-minute ritual that has been called a "candle ceremony." They should light a candle between them, if one is available, and simply say, "(Loving name), I appreciate you today for your _____ (integrity, commitment, etc.)." The recipient can say nothing or can respond by saying "Thank you, I'm glad you noticed my _____ (integrity, commitment, etc.)." The other person reciprocates. A hug is a good conclusion. I recommend that this very brief exchange occur while sitting comfortably in chairs or on the floor. Finally, an agreement should be sought between the couple that if either one feels that their connectedness has gone astray, they may ask the other for a candle ceremony at the earliest convenience, marking their awareness that mutual appreciation is due and needed.

FOCUS ON COUPLE CONNECTEDNESS

I am excited to share the effectiveness of my therapeutic interventions with older patients. I am delighted by their enormous capacity for exploring sexual beliefs, redefining their sexual philosophies, trying a variety of new sexual techniques, examining shame and guilt as powerful feelings they have applied to their sexual experiences, becoming increasingly aware of the little boy or little girl within, enjoying the awareness about the conflict between their internal "highchair tyrant" and their sexually mature adult, and on and on. In the details that follow, I hope to inspire a number of therapists to be more affirming of themselves and their older patients.

Sexual learning from autoeroticism is an important zone in understanding our unique physiological response patterns and how they shift and change. Masturbation and associated fantasy is an indicator of what we find erotically appealing as well as disagreeable. Negative attitudes about masturbation often inhibit women from masturbation for decades. Encouraging increased learning from masturbation is often important in sex therapy for a woman over 50. Males, at least in the past, have masturbated earlier and much more frequently than females, perhaps due to their strong physiological genital drive. However, shame and guilt associated with masturbation is often strong in both sexes.

Exploring masturbation attitudes and activities needs to be done individually by the therapist. If the couple is ready, encouraging and guiding them to masturbate together as a gift to the other I have found to be a very powerful intervention in developing intimacy in a couple. One partner can assist the other by holding hands, touching breasts or nipples, cupping testicles, inserting a finger into the vagina, and kissing or snuggling during a partner's masturbation. Most of us are capable of masturbating to a highly intense orgasm under these circumstances. Many of us will be reluctant to do so. Experiencing anxiety, avoidance, or observing unique style are all material for discussing with the therapist and the partner and will almost always result in growth for the couple.

Often sexual addictive behaviors practiced over the years block the couple's connectedness. One definition of sexual addiction is targeting for sex an object or a human as an object, or seeking self-centered sexual release, and then regretting placing so much effort into superficial, genital-focused sex. In my experience, sexual addictive behaviors are best treated indirectly by developing the capacity for sexual connectedness with an appropriate beloved other.

SEXUAL HEALTH LITERACY

Today's health care often falls short of teaching the individual patient or couple the professional's assessment of their diagnosis, important aspects of their condition, appropriate treatment plans, other risk assessments for that dysfunction, and so forth. Health literacy includes taking time to actively teach patients what they need to know; in this case, their own sexuality. Health literacy includes informing patients so that they can make good choices about how to approach and treat their problems. In sex therapy, health literacy is teaching patients knowledge about their own sexuality and, in the process, demystifying and decreasing their shame. Sexual knowledge, sexual self-awareness, and capacity for intimacy all require lots of time.

Most couples should read, separately or together, an open and accurate sexuality guidebook like *Guide to Getting It On!* by Paul Joannides (2004). An increase in sexual knowledge is useful in almost all sex therapy; I rarely see a couple who have had any instruction on their sexual function.

Let me start by refreshing everyone's memory about the four phases of the sexual cycle. Identifying which phase of the sexual cycle is involved in an individual's sexual dysfunction is critical to later care.

The first is the desire phase: libido or sexual hunger. This is the mental process where once in a while we start thinking, feeling, and desiring sex. Much of our sexuality occurs here.

The second phase is arousal, a physiological response to sexual stimuli usually requiring physical stimulation. In most 50-year-old males, physical stimulation is necessary to start the sexual cycle. In an 18-year-old male, little if any physical stimulation is necessary. Vaginal lubrication in females is physiologically and neurologically similar to erection in males. The arousal phase should show steady progression to a high level of physiological excitement with the entire body activated. The parasympathetic nervous system is involved in arousal, and the sympathetic nervous system is involved in climax.

The third phase, sexual climax, is the sudden shift into massive, sympathetic or adrenergic neuronal discharge in the body. This almost instantaneous shift is marked by uterine contractions in women and ejaculatory contractions in males. Orgasm, on the other hand, seems to be a learned behavior in humans, especially in men. Younger men often ejaculate. Hopefully an older man has learned that an orgasm is a full letting go into an egoless, timeless, and natural state. It is not ejaculation and is often separate from ejaculation by a moment in time. When the Tantric masters talk about connectedness with the Divine, it has to do with the profoundly altered state of consciousness that is the orgasmic experience, once it has been learned. Intensified orgasms are one of the benefits that very often occur in working with the sexuality of an older individual or couple.

The fourth phase is the resolution or calming down of the system. There is a physiological reality that males drop off climactic peak very quickly into resolution and then have a refractory period. During the refractory period, no amount of sexual stimulation will cause a restart of the sexual cycle. The refractory period gets longer with age. At 60 it may be 2 or 3 days, by 70 perhaps 5 days, and by 80 a week or longer. Women do not have the same experience with resolution and, with ongoing effective stimulation, can have multiple orgasms routinely. Males clearly have multiple orgasms, but it is an uncommon male who does so. After a satisfying orgasm that is a fully emotionally and physically fulfilling experience, many women will go for days in a version of the refractory period, even though, if effectively stimulated, they could resume the sexual cycle.

Sexual dysfunctions occur in one or more of the phases of the sexual cycle just described. As an example, an orgasm dysfunction, often secondary to certain antidepressants such as Prozac or Paxil, may not interfere with libido or arousal for some time. When libido is down, arousal is often compromised as well, but not always.

All elements of the sexual cycle (libido, arousal, pleasure with sensation, and ability to reach climax) will decrease when testosterone in males or females falls below a certain functional level. Estrogen levels are important for females and quite probably male sexual function as well, influencing sexual lubrication, arousal, and vaginal tissue health and other areas of the general physiology in women and probably men. The psychology of desire is primarily influenced by testosterone. The psychological states of nurture, warmth, and affection are very much influenced by estrogens.

Adequate thyroid hormones are important for general function and energy. With today's knowledge of hormone restoration, it is inappropriate to undertake sexual dysfunction therapy without assessing hormone levels and being prepared by either personal prescription or referral to a physician colleague to see to the restoration of hormones to good functional levels. If restoration of hormone levels to those normally found in a person's 30s can be achieved, and if hormone balancing and restoration of sexual function can at least be closely paralleled with the partner, talking sex therapy can move forward nicely. In my experience, if either partner is significantly low, especially in energy and testosterone levels, sex therapy is, for the most part, just well-intentioned talking.

HORMONE ASSESSMENT AND REPLACEMENT THERAPY

In males, testosterone is the primary hormone to evaluate for replacement. In high-dose testosterone replacement therapy, and especially in high-BMI (obese) males, some testosterone changes to estradiol. Testing should include testosterone (total and free), estradiol, prostate specific antigen (PSA), a free T3 or at least thyroid stimulating hormone (TSH), and prolactin (for men under 40 and on other medicines, especially major tranquilizers). Lab normals vary for total testosterone but frequently are in the 270 to 820 ng/dl range. Levels of total testosterone under 350 ng/dl usually correlate with some decrease in one or more areas of the man's sexual cycle. Such men will often report general fatigue. Retesting after replacement should show total testosterone levels in the 600 to 1,200 ng/dl range depending on the dosage and form. Free testosterone normal male values will be in the range of 7 to 22 pg/ml. In the same way, free testosterone (direct) available for use by the body should be increased to a target of approximately 25 to 40 pg/ml. Sex hormone binding globulin (SHBG) in males will have normal values in most labs of 30 to 135. Supplemental testosterone will usually create adequate free testosterone for improved function. Estrogen (estradiol) male levels should be < 55 pg/ml. Elevated estrone (E1) may be an important factor for prostatic cancer in males and might at least increase the risk for benign prostatic hypertrophy. Prostate specific antigen (serum) should be < 4 ng/ml as an indication of prostatic health. Drugs to lower estrogen levels are rarely used in males, but Femara and Arimidex have been used for that purpose. Be aware that each lab will have its own range of normal values and units measured. Always review the normal range for that lab.

In females, the balance between testosterone, the three natural estrogen components, and bio-identical progesterone, should be monitored. Adult women of all ages respond similarly regarding their sexual cycle in relationship to their total and free testosterone levels. In young women, elevated estrogen levels as found in oral birth control may greatly increase SHBG binding with total testosterone and leaving inadequate free testosterone. It is often necessary to discontinue oral birth control to effect a recovery of sexual energy. Idiopathic low testosterone levels certainly seem to be the case in many younger women whose menstrual cycling is normal but libido and arousal are low. Such women will usually respond well to testosterone replacement, laboratory monitoring, and limited sex therapy.

In naturally or surgically postmenopausal women, free and total testosterone levels are generally dramatically lower than an adequate functional level. When handicapped with low estrone, estradiol, and progesterone, your female menopausal patient's physiology often needs assistance. Although each lab establishes their own hormone reference range, a general guideline is free testosterone 0.9 to 7.3 pg/ml, total testosterone 20 to 70 ng/dl, SHBG 13 to 100, and total estradiol 12 to 100 pg/ml.

In women, generally good clinical function is correlated with total testosterones of 50 to 150 ng/dl and free testosterones of 10 to 20 pg/ml.

Estrone (E1) and estradiol (E2) are generally the stronger components of estrogens; estriol (E3) is the third component of a woman's estrogen production. Signs of estrogen deficiency are poor concentration, depression, some anxiety, mood swings, hot flashes, and fatigue. Sexual frequency and self-image and desire for nurturing are usually lower. Dry eyes, skin, and vagina are commonly experienced. Low estrogen may contribute to weight gain and osteoporosis over time. Estrogens require twice daily dosing due to their short half-life. Expect subjective patient reporting, and evaluate the balance point between gains and adverse events (side effects) to adjust dosing.

Bio-identical progesterone is important in balance and is helpful for commonly experienced breast tenderness and water retention. It also increases high density lipoprotein (HDL; good cholesterol). Progesterone, dosed generally in the range of 20 to 50 mg/day of bio-identical progesterone, seems optimal to obtain levels in the 15 to 20 ng/ml range. Progesterone cream can be applied to sore breasts or upper arms. Menstruating women should use it during the last 10 days before their menses.

It is important to note that SHBG levels are significantly increased with estrogen-only therapy and decreased with the addition of testosterone. SHBG binds some of the total testosterone leaving a reduced amount of free testosterone, the active molecule. In younger patients on oral birth control pills, I have seen SHBG levels as high as 236 with the result of almost no free testosterone and almost no sexual desire.

ASSESSMENT OF THE
OLDER INDIVIDUAL OR COUPLE

When seeing an individual or couple for an initial appointment, at least 40 minutes, and preferably an hour, is essential to establish initial contact and comfort, gather enough data to form an overall opinion of the nature of the sexual problem, and communicate caring and competence to your new patient or client. Regardless of the referral source, the discipline of the practitioner, or the nature of the complaint, a detailed assessment is critical. If your time is severely limited during regular hours, schedule the individual or couple as the last appointment of the day and allow yourself a fulfilling experience with a satisfying and meaningful assessment.

It is often helpful to start by recognizing the anxiety and discomfort many older individuals will carry with them into this initial appointment — or even the first few. You might ask them to share with you the feelings they have been having in anticipation of their appointment. Ask them about their attitude toward the sex therapy process and their belief about the attitude of their partner. Tell them that you intend to listen carefully to their experiences and sexual hopes. If both individuals are present, ask each one in turn to describe what they believe are the important sexual questions or problems that they bring with them to therapy. Usually in the first hour the couple is present, and after 10 to 15 minutes of working with the couple, I separate them for at least brief interviews so each can express themselves more openly.

All experienced sex therapists have had patients/clients who are "turned off" toward their primary partner but have strong sexual love toward another. They often present themselves as having a sexual dysfunction such as low libido or low arousal. Explore sexual traumas from the past and the "high water mark" of sexuality for more important data. Often questions about each person's quality of life can be asked when they are together or separate. If one individual comes in wanting help with a sexual relationship with his or her partner, encourage as much as possible a separate and second visit with the identified sexual partner.

Remember that successful therapy, enhancing the sexuality of one individual in a couple, may further unbalance the relationship. As a general rule, don't improve the libido or arousal of one partner without warning and without trying to improve the libido and arousal of the other.

Late in the first interview, or into a second or third session, assess each individual's areas of sexual comfort and discomfort such as nakedness, touch, talking during sex, giving and receiving oral sex, preferred sexual positions, the stimulation necessary for successful climax, and so on.

Usually in the second or third interview, the experienced sex therapist should review the phases of the sexual cycle with the couple and help them to understand in which phases they are having difficulties.

Assessment should include a physical exam and medical history. Nonphysician sex therapists should insist that their patient either provide a current physical exam (less than 6 months old) or acquire one as part of the sexuality work-up. Medical diseases and low overall energy, as well as many medications, are critical to sexual dysfunction. Laboratory assessment is indicated in all but those sexual dysfunctions that are actually related to high sexual function. Rapid ejaculation is an especially good example of overall excellent sexual function, which unfortunately results in a very rapid sexual cycle.

Always inquire if the patients have been sufficiently concerned about their sexual function or problems to have sought therapy previously. Ask about hormone replacement therapy and attempt to get documentation, especially dosage and form of testosterone or other hormones administered by whom and when. If therapy as a couple, including sex therapy, has been attempted, inquire of both partners about their experiences. Always ask an individual or couple if they have information that they think would be important and that the therapist has not explored or asked about.

Teaching and reviewing basic sexual information for both the male and female and the couple is critical in that one or both may be operating from major distorted information from sexual myths.

THERAPY

As I have indicated, many older males will have functionally low testosterone levels. If so, testosterone replacement therapy will be both effective and very beneficial to the quality of life of the man. A sense of emotional and physical well-being, improved overall energy, increased physical strength and durability, and distinctly increased sexual interest and function will usually occur within a few weeks. Injectable testosterone cypionate or enanthate is increasingly used. In my clinical practice, I have noticed that many men prefer the intramuscular route. After a period of adjustment and laboratory retesting, we often teach men to self-administer injectable testosterone. Using an oil base to slowly absorb injectable testosterone at 200 mg per cc and at a dose of 1.7 to 2.2 cc (340 to 440 mg) intramuscular every 2 weeks usually correlates with effective function and high normal laboratory values. Some men will prefer fewer peaks and valleys and use half the injectable amount on a weekly basis. Testosterone gels or creams are available in formularies such as Androgel or from compounding pharmacies. They usually provide effective maintenance but are a little less consistent on blood level maintenance. Troches containing 5 to 10 mg, and absorbed sublingually, are gaining in popularity. Long-acting testosterone undecanoate, which allows an injection every 3 months and is currently available in Europe, may be available in the United States in the future.

Please note that males over 50 often have testosterone levels too low for good sexual function, even though they may fall within the normal laboratory blood levels. (Refer to hormone assessment section for guidelines.) As an example, a male with total testosterone under 350 ng/dl may function poorly with notably low sexual interest, difficulty obtaining and maintaining erections, difficulty with arousal sequenced with difficulty reaching climaxes, and long refractory periods. Also, I have seen individuals with adequate total testosterone determinations and inadequate free testosterone, the active form.

Human chorionic growth hormone and human growth hormone are beyond the scope of this contribution but may contribute to good sexual function in males when administered.

Women often have testosterone levels inadequate to support good sexual function in their 20s and 30s. The ovaries produce approximately 60% of a woman's testosterone, which can decrease for several reasons in a younger woman and very often after menopause with inactivation of ovarian production. In these women, testing should occur to determine their total and free testosterone and certainly their SHBG. I recommend replacement with testosterone available in several forms. As in men, an advantage of initially using injectable testosterone is that it provides a rapid and clear clinical response, which may be important in conjunction with sex therapy. Testosterone cypionate at 60 to 100 mg intramuscularly every 2 weeks can be initiated with retesting a week after the third injection. Masculinization is a slow process and will not be difficult with that regimen. Early symptoms of excessive testosterone include hoarseness or irritability and acne. I have always seen it as reversible with dose reduction. Testosterone cream or testosterone troches (sublingual) in the range of 1.0 mg to as much as 4 mg per daily dose usually will provide high normal female testosterone levels. Some have found clitoral administration of testosterone cream to be beneficial for sexual arousal and genital sensation. Others will apply the cream to forearms or other nonsexual areas. Additionally, in the postmenopausal female, I recommend replacement with bio-identical estrogens such as triest or biest. A dose level of 0.125 to .625 mg twice daily should be effective. Again there are several routes of application such as vaginal creams, troches, and so forth. The estrogens have a short half-life and therefore should be given at least twice daily. Progesterone in the 20 to 50 mg per day range (usually at bedtime because of a tendency toward sedation) again works well in bio-identical form.

Most health practitioners are aware that women have been frightened of hormone replacement therapy because of data suggesting that synthetic estrogens and progesterone may be associated with increased female sex organ cancers. Synthetic hormones may increase the incidence in a few cases per million, but it still constitutes a low risk against an important gain for many women. Please be aware that testosterone, now rarely used, is still beneficial in the suppression of female sex-related cancers such as ovarian, uterine, or breast.

For readers who are nonmedical sex therapists, it is important to find and be comfortable with a doctor (MD, DO, or ND) who is comfortable managing both hormone replacement in general and bio-identical hormones in particular.

Males with erectile dysfunction with difficulty achieving or maintaining erections will usually benefit from one of the three phosphodiesterase inhibitor drugs (Viagra, Cialis, or Levitra). Caverject (or other) alprostadil (injected into the penis) may be needed. It is important to understand that these drugs only affect erections, not libido, and are *not* therefore in and of themselves sufficient if libido is low. Penile prosthesis placement surgery is less needed or used today.

Without exception, in my experience, when hormone levels have become low and/or sexual function is decreased, patterns have been established of avoidance of sexual situations. The sexual lifestyle of patients must be addressed in therapy if they are to dependably change. I suggest to couples that they work on reconnecting. Advise them to start by talking, appreciating, loving "above the neck," walking together hand in hand, and so on. Advise the couple in body caressing. Give each individual advice on sensuous appreciation of the body, such as bathing, slow self-stroking, and so forth.

In either case start with nonsexual body parts, slowness, lubricating lotion in a warm room, and progress only after several exercises to breast and genital touching. Advance the couple to one-way pleasuring, the conscious effort by one to focus their attention on activating and pleasuring the sexuality of the other. Encourage mutual masturbation side by side and mutually supportive as a very effective barrier-dropping procedure for most couples. Many of my patients have not done so previously. Often there will be some resistance that will open communication for the couple. If the couple is still actively coming in for therapy, introduce them to coital bridging, intercourse accompanied by self-stimulation in the receiving partner to "bridge" their orgasmic response with coital activity. Encourage the couple to follow up with you with several monthly appointments (assuming you've achieved great results) to help them integrate their new sexuality into their lifestyle.

NEW TRICKS FOR OLD PRACTITIONERS

Some older couples have never figured out that our biological clocks are winding down after 9:00 or 10:00 o'clock each evening. They also have never been told that the high energy system of our bodies – hormonally, cardiovascularly, and in thoughts and feelings – peaks for most of us between about 10:00 a.m. and 4:00 p.m. Basic rules should be reviewed:

1. Heavy food and drink pulls blood to the stomach and intestines and often away from the genitalia, where it is needed for great sex. Do not eat and drink heavily and expect to perform well sexually. Do enjoy the sensuality of great taste very lightly as a heart-spirit-"foreplay" event, followed by sex, then heavier food, and finally rest or sleep.
2. Avoid distracting environments, such as a television or computers running in the area, high noise levels, or the room being too hot or cold, and so on. Arrange for coverage, and then shut off the (rude) cellphones. Create an environment that is comfortable and pleasing to the senses. Attention to time and place often will greatly enhance the sexual experience. Bathe more than you think necessary and always before sexual possibilities.
3. Check cologne with your partner as to intensity, pleasantness, and location.
4. Most bodies benefit from clothing, and I recommend spending some time at it. Wear clothing, at least in private with your partner, more outrageous than you would wear around others. Encourage yourself to strut, reveal, and tease as much as possible, and laugh together if either feels foolish.
5. Play music that pleases you and turns you on but then, at the first opportunity, see if the same music pleases and turns on your partner. If it does, keep it; if it doesn't, look further.
6. Consider reading passages from very sexual books such as Anne Rice's, *The Beauty Trilogy* (1999) or very soft erotic books like *Rumi: The Book of Love: Poems of Ecstasy and Longing* (Barks, 2003).
7. Carefully select erotic videos and DVDs. Preferably select them on an evening devoted to that purpose in a playful attitude with several examples; talk about and even make notes about sections that one or both of you find sexy. Clearly identify such vignettes that you both agree are stimulating, and only play those. Remember, after your years of experience, that erotic films and other materials are only as good as their ability to shift you from the busy day world of your left brain to the wonderful passionate right brain endlessness.
8. You also should agree to enter a sexual time and concentrate as fully as possible on it. Both of you should set aside at least an hour, preferably longer, for the slow sexual dance between you. Frequency, every day or two, is not as important as quality, which may be every week or two. Dependable and beautiful Eros on a weekly or biweekly basis allows both of you several days of anticipation and time for active appreciation of your partner.

Much has been written, and source books are available, about detailed plans for enhancing the presexuality. Most guidebooks focus on touch, slow touch, with lubricated hands in a warm environment delivered with a deep attitude of appreciation so that both can appreciate that rhythm and touch is a wonderful communication of love and blessing. Thirty to 45 minutes may be necessary for a good massage and should always be reciprocated by an equally long massage by the other, either on the same occasion or on another day. Professional massages can be quite good, and several practitioners, including my wife at the Yellow Rose Inn in Indianapolis, will arrange two massage therapists and two tables side by side. Although they are limited in not doing direct sexual touch, side by side massage can be a great experience for the couple.

An excellent practice is to challenge a couple to speak together, preferably not during sex, of experiences they have had or desired, first asking the permission of their partner to do so. The focus should be on fantasy and desire, but may include any particular caress or procedure that they had previously experienced or might enjoy. The person receiving the information needs to have an attitude of gratitude and acceptance and to take in the positive suggestions warmly as a gift.

OUR CHALLENGE

Now is the first time that over half of our American population is more than 50 years old. Now is the best time in human history for the management of sexual physiology for those over 50 years old. Now is the time that pursuit of golden sexuality is accepted by many and pursued by a rapidly increasing number. I challenge us as individuals and health and sexuality professionals to take this time to expand our own personal sexual horizons and to provide time and guidance to our patients/clients for their growth. Please join me in a clear opportunity to make a difference.

Davis Appreciation/Depreciation Scale
(How I Experience My Partner)

Bedrock elements for great connectedness for couples rating ourselves and our important other. Purposeful attention to **changing depreciation to appreciation**.

Directions: In the past 2 weeks I believe <u>my partner, toward me, has been</u> (*circle the most appropriate response*):

1. Trustworthy	Bad	Poor	Adequate	Good	Excellent
2. Committed	Bad	Poor	Adequate	Good	Excellent
3. Understanding	Bad	Poor	Adequate	Good	Excellent
4. Communicative	Bad	Poor	Adequate	Good	Excellent
5. Observant	Bad	Poor	Adequate	Good	Excellent
6. Affectionate	Bad	Poor	Adequate	Good	Excellent
7. Supportive	Bad	Poor	Adequate	Good	Excellent
8. Accountable	Bad	Poor	Adequate	Good	Excellent
9. Playful	Bad	Poor	Adequate	Good	Excellent
10. Passionate	Bad	Poor	Adequate	Good	Excellent
11. Creative	Bad	Poor	Adequate	Good	Excellent
12. Spiritual	Bad	Poor	Adequate	Good	Excellent

Comments:

Signature _____ Date ____ / ____ / ____

Davis Appreciation/Depreciation Scale
(What I Give to My Partner)

Directions: In the past 2 weeks I believe that <u>toward my partner I have been</u> (*circle the most appropriate response*):

1.	Trustworthy	Bad	Poor	Adequate	Good	Excellent
2.	Committed	Bad	Poor	Adequate	Good	Excellent
3.	Understanding	Bad	Poor	Adequate	Good	Excellent
4.	Communicative	Bad	Poor	Adequate	Good	Excellent
5.	Observant	Bad	Poor	Adequate	Good	Excellent
6.	Affectionate	Bad	Poor	Adequate	Good	Excellent
7.	Supportive	Bad	Poor	Adequate	Good	Excellent
8.	Accountable	Bad	Poor	Adequate	Good	Excellent
9.	Playful	Bad	Poor	Adequate	Good	Excellent
10.	Passionate	Bad	Poor	Adequate	Good	Excellent
11.	Creative	Bad	Poor	Adequate	Good	Excellent
12.	Spiritual	Bad	Poor	Adequate	Good	Excellent

Comments:

Signature _____ Date ____ / ____ / ____

CONTRIBUTOR

Larry M. Davis, MD, is in private practice as psychiatrist, sex therapist, forensic psychiatrist, and clinical researcher. Dr. Davis not only does psychotherapy and psychopharmacology, but also innovative professional consultation on his website, www.sexual-medicine.com. He is active as elder in the international men's organization, the ManKind Project. Dr. Davis may be contacted at Davis Clinic PC, 1431 N. Delaware Street, Indianapolis, IN 46202. E-mail: Larry@DavisClinic.com

RESOURCES

Cited Resources

Barks, C. (2003). *Rumi: The Book of Love: Poems of Ecstasy and Longing.* New York: HarperCollins.

Joannides, P. (2004). *Guide to Getting It On!* Waldport, OR: Goofy Foot Press.

Ni, H-C. (1979). *The Complete Works of Lao Tzu: Tao Teh Ching & Hua Hu Ching* (Laozi & H-C Ni, Trans.). Los Angeles, CA: Seven Star Communications.

Rice, A. (1999). *The Sleeping Beauty Novels: The Claiming of Sleeping Beauty/Beauty's Punishment/Beauty's Release* (Boxed Set). New York: Penguin Putman.

Additional Resource

Center for Sexual Medicine – http://www.sexual-medicine.com

Section IV:
Therapist Guides and
Patient Handouts

This section of *Innovations* includes therapist guides and handouts that practitioners can use to collect and organize information. Although some of the items included here have been formally developed and normed, others were designed for informal application and should not be used as formal instruments or for making specific diagnoses.

The value of forms and instruments depends upon their appropriate application by the clinicians who use them. It is important to emphasize that these forms are not necessarily designed to generate the types of inferences often associated with more formalized tests that have a long history of use. Readers should recognize the potential as well as the stated limitations of these materials and use them in accordance with accepted ethical principles and practice standards. It is assumed that anyone who uses these instruments will have a general clinical knowledge of the areas being evaluated.

Given the limitations noted previously, we have attempted to ensure that the materials that follow include sufficient information to allow readers to evaluate their appropriate application. Certain basic information and instructions have been included with each contribution, and the Resources sections contain references to more detailed materials and studies. Readers who wish to use these materials are advised to obtain the additional resources. If there is a desire to use the material for research purposes, most authors would appreciate being contacted so that data may be shared.

Six therapist guides are included in this section. The first one, "Code of Ethics – ASSECT," is a copy of the Code of Ethics from the American Association of Sexuality Educators, Counselors, and Therapists. It is a companion piece to the chapter by Catherine Dailey Ravella in Section I entitled "Ethics in Sex Therapy." Sex educators, counselors, and therapists can consult their primary professional code of ethics as a guide to their professional practice. The ASSECT code can be used as an adjunct to the other professional codes, with special applications for work with clients with concerns about sexual health.

The next two instruments, the "International Index of Erectile Function (IIEF)" and the "Female Sexual Function Index (FSFI)," provide quick and easy ways for clinicians to assess the sexual health and areas of dysfunction for men and women. Both measures have been used for several years and have been extensively studied and are found to be reliable and valid.

The fourth therapist guide is entitled, "The Complexity of Sexual Diversity: Sexual Identity Cube and Self-Awareness Exercise," by Frederick L. Peterson, Jr. It is a good companion piece for the contributions in the earlier section, SEX THERAPY WITH SPECIAL POPULATIONS. The exercise provides a self-awareness exercise that helps readers expand their understanding of the many forms of sexual identity.

In most instances of sex therapy, the therapist and client work collaboratively on identifying problem areas and potential solutions. The next therapist guide, provided by Frederick L. Peterson, Jr., is an example of a treatment plan for sex therapy that he prepared for one of his clients. It is entitled, "Sharing the Treatment Plan for Sex Therapy." The treatment plan is prepared with the intention of discussion with the client as a proposal and the client is informed that he or she is encouraged to have input into the final version and to make modifications as needed.

Several contributions in this volume of *Innovations,* especially the second contribution, have noted that a careful assessment of the client's history of sexual experience and attitudes and beliefs about sexuality are essential to understanding sexual health issues. In the next therapist guide, Jill W. Bley has shared a "Sex History Questionnaire" that clinicians can use to ensure that all pertinent information is gathered.

Three patient handouts are also provided in this volume of *Innovations*. The first two are exercises that may help clients address their dissatisfactions with their sexual health. The first one, presented by Jill W. Bley, "Sexual Pleasuring (Sensate Focus Exercises)," provides step-by-step suggestions for clients who are having sexual problems to regain their previous level of functioning and for couples who cannot have sexual intercourse to learn how to have a loving sexual relationship through touch.

The second handout, "Kegel Exercises (Pelvic Floor Exercises)," presented by Jill W. Bley, will assist clients in strengthening the muscles of their "pelvic floor" as a means to gain more muscle control over sexual responding. These exercises are appropriate for many sexual problems but especially for clients with problems with low sexual arousal and orgasm.

The final patient handout, by Frederick L. Peterson, Jr. and Christina C. Peterson, entitled, "A Health Care Professional's Guide to Contemporary Sexual Myths," identifies several sexual myths that may interfere with clients' understanding of sexuality. Christina C. Peterson has her bachelor's degree in psychology from Wright State University and works with her husband Fred in the field of psychology and sexual health, providing therapeutic services as well as professional writing.

In addition to the instruments and handouts presented here, several contributions in other sections include useful office forms, brief screening and assessment devices, handouts, and guides.

Code of Ethics - American Association of Sexuality Educators, Counselors, and Therapists

Most mental/physical health disciplines have a national society, such as the American Psychological Association or the American Medical Association, that establishes their own codes of ethical conduct. Likewise, most mental/physical health disciplines have governing boards which are mandated by the various states to guide and control the practice of each discipline within that state. In recent years organizations that certify practitioners to practice in a specialized area of treatment have also set up guidelines for ethical/professional conduct that must be followed within the subspecialty.

These subspecialty codes of ethical conduct are very specific guidelines. The Board of the American Association of Sexuality Educators, Counselors, and Therapists (AASECT) has been especially cognizant of the need to guide and control the practice of sex therapy. This subspecialty, more than any other, requires that the therapist be held accountable to practice at the highest possible standards of care and professionalism. Sexuality educators, counselors, and therapists not only have the burden of helping their clients and patients experience a healthy sexual life, they must also do everything in their power to overcome many sex negative attitudes and many misrepresentations of how sexuality educators, counselors, and therapists perform their work as seen in the popular media.

AASECT has kindly granted permission to reprint their Code of Ethics here for the benefit of our readers. The Code of Ethics can also be seen on the AASECT website at www.aasect.org.

Code of Ethics

American Association of Sexuality Educators, Counselors, and Therapists

P.O. Box 1960, Ashland, Virginia, 23005-1960

Prepared by the AASECT Code of Ethics Committee:
Jack S. Annon, PhD (Chair): Douglas Liebert, PhD;
Catherine Ravella, RN, MA; Craig Robinson, PhD
Board approved May 2004

Recognizing its responsibilities to society and given its own national objectives, AASECT has adopted the following Code of Ethics. The Code: **(1)** is a condition for membership; **(2)** applies to all AASECT members, regardless of their certification or member status: and **(3)** embraces *any* activity that directly or indirectly relates to professional identity or training. The Code does not replace or modify the requirements for or purposes of certification as a sex educator, counselor, therapist or Supervisor.

Public Policy: By public policy, AASECT has a duty to promote (and enforce) quality services from and proper conduct/professionalism by its members. Professionalism is a product of society. Professional status is a privilege, not a right earned by holding a degree, certification, or membership. While professional ethics are not law, they are permissive and they establish both aspirational standards and guidelines for professional practice. AASECT accepts that a professional association has a public duty to advocate standards for the services offered by its membership, so as to (ensure) promote both the protection of and benefits to the consumer. Therefore, AASECT promulgates ethical standards that must be honored by its members.

Goals and Objectives: (Objectives:) The Code of Ethics is intended to advance the status of sex education counseling, therapy, supervision and research. The Code of Ethics should not be viewed (solely) as disciplinary in intent. The purpose is to provide guidance to AASECT practitioners and to provide an observable code from which society and consumers may derive expected behavior. (The benefits are primarily for the consumer and society, and only secondarily for the practitioner and AASECT.)

Self-Regulation: Integrity, competence, confidentiality, responsibility and other applicable standards are not always subject to finite definitions, descriptions, prescriptions or proscriptions. Virtually every professional situation requires that the practitioner make judgments as to propriety. Through setting forth suggested standards (rules) of ethical conduct for practice-related conditions, qualities, skills and services, the Code of Ethics is intended to assist AASECT members with such judgments. Each member must exercise self-regulation and satisfy governmental regulatory and legal requirements.

Accountability to AASECT: While ethics do not have the same authority as law, membership in AASECT is predicated upon adherence to the Code of Ethics. That is, members of AASECT, in the conduct of all aspects of their life that relates to their professional work and identity, are expected to honor the Code of Ethics, and to act according to general principles of professional ethical practice that may not be directly dealt with in this Code of Ethics.

The Code of Ethics creates accountability for the member to AASECT. It should be underscored that the Code of Ethics is relevant to justifying membership in AASECT, and is not intended to serve as a standard of care for professional practice in legal proceedings.

Membership in AASECT may be terminated for sufficient cause as outlined in the Bylaws, the Membership Application, and the formal Application for Membership and/or Certification. A prerequisite for initial membership and a requisite for continued membership in AASECT is that each potential member or current member must notify the AASECT Board of Directors in writing of any previous or current legal (civil or criminal), ethical or regulatory (licensing) complaints or judgments, relevant to their practice, and provide any documentation or information pertaining thereto that is requested on behalf of the AASECT Board of Directors. The member shall inform AASECT in writing of any adjudicatory outcome relevant to their practice. Such notification must be done within thirty (30) days of the members' knowledge of the complaint and any request from AASECT for information or documentation must be fulfilled within thirty (30) days. Decisions on all applications for AASECT certification or recertification will be suspended until the adjudicatory outcome of complaints have been determined. Termination shall be by two-thirds vote of the entire Board of Directors in accordance with the policies and procedures established by the Bylaws, and the Letter of Application, and the Formal Application for Membership and Certification.

Disciplinary Action: The Board of Directors shall determine the appropriateness of continued or terminated membership in AASECT for any AASECT member who is: (1) adjudged to have violated a civil law that is material and relevant to professional practice; (2) convicted of a criminal misdemeanor or felony, (3) disciplined by a professional ethics committee of the State to which the member belongs, (4) disciplined by a State Licensing or Certification Board, (5) disciplined, or expelled by an Institutional Grievance Boards of the University, College, governmental agency, or organization to which the member belongs; and (6) for religious counselors, disciplined by the State Leader of the Religious Denomination or other appropriate leadership group to which the member belongs. The information available to and the deliberations of the Board of Directors shall be deemed confidential by all AASECT sources. The action regarding continued or terminated membership, with concomitant conditions made by the Board of Directors is final. (No appeal right exists). The member will be notified by the Board in writing of any membership or certification termination. There is no appeal to this process.

ETHICS PROCEDURE

Inquiries From AASECT Members: The AASECT Ethics Committee-AEC has a duty to respond to inquiries from AASECT members only. Members who contact the AASECT office in need of ethics consultation will be referred to the AEC Chairperson. The AEC Chairperson will assess the inquirer's needs, provide some immediate feedback, and arrange for follow-up consultation if appropriate. Before the follow-up consultation, the Chairperson will collaborate with other AEC members on the issues at hand. Some or all of these meetings may occur by telephone, or through e-mail or other electronic means, with identities concealed. The identity of all inquirers will be held in confidence within the AEC.

The Chairperson will keep a written record using the AEC Inquiry Consultation Form of all inquiries and make special note of the ethical principles and standards relevant to each inquiry. The Chairperson will collaborate with at least one AEC member on each inquiry. Each inquiry will be discussed at the next scheduled AEC meeting. Further contact will then be made with the inquirer, if indicated by committee consensus.

CODE OF CONDUCT

Principle One: Competence and Integrity

The AASECT member shall accept responsibility for the consequences of his/her acts, by omission or commission, and make reasonable efforts to ensure that all professional services are appropriate and adequate for the consumer.

The member shall bear a heavy social responsibility because society deems the services as representing specialized expertise and because the consumers using the services are vulnerable. The member shall, therefore, be committed to maintaining high standards of scholarship and practice and shall be accountable as an individual to the standards of the profession. At a minimum, the member shall perform any professional service in accord with the prevailing standards of performance in professional activities when measured against generally prevailing peer performance.

The member shall have training in sex education, counseling, therapy, and/or supervision that is in accord with the standards promulgated by AASECT and the laws relevant to the jurisdiction in which the member practices.

The member shall recognize his/her limits of competence and shall communicate them at the earliest possible time and at any time thereafter to the consumer. When the member's level of competence does not afford optimal benefits to the consumer, the member shall, in a timely and efficient manner, recommend referral to better-qualified sources.

The member shall not knowingly permit any consumer to misunderstand the member's competency and shall clarify credentials, training, affiliations, experiences and skills in an honest and accurate manner.

The member shall recognize the necessity and benefit of professional growth by participating in continuing education.

The member shall not enter into association for professional practice with or assist, aid, or promote in any manner the practice of an unqualified or incompetent person which shall include any person whom the member knows or has reason to believe, does not adhere to the standards of AASECT or is in violation of any law. This shall include, but is not limited to, making a referral to an unqualified or incompetent person. The member shall verify the competence and integrity of the person to whom a consumer is referred.

The member shall not willfully make or file any false report record, or information, or induce another person to make or file any false report, record or information.

The member shall not provide any remuneration, regardless of form, to any source for receiving the referral of a consumer for professional services unless the source of the referral maintains continued involvement in the care of the consumer. Conversely, the member shall not receive any remuneration regardless of form from any source for providing the referral of a consumer for professional services unless the member maintains continued involvement in the care of the consumer. Any such financial arrangement must be disclosed to and approved and acknowledged in writing by the consumer.

The member who becomes emotionally, physically or otherwise impaired or disabled to a degree that it impacts on the best interest of the consumer shall, in a timely and efficient manner, make a referral of the consumer to a qualified and appropriate professional source so as to avoid any undue abandonment of the consumer.

Principle Two: Moral, Ethical, and Legal Standards

The AASECT member shall accept that the quality of his/her professional services (are) is dependent upon both personal morality and professional ethics and on the ability to maintain legal standards.

The member shall be aware of and monitor the fact that his/her personal needs may influence judgments and actions in the therapeutic relationship and shall, regardless of experience or training, have a qualified review source such as a supervisor available to assist in safeguarding against unwise or inappropriate judgments and acts.

The member shall not enter into any dual relationship regardless of nature that jeopardizes the well-being of the consumer.

The member shall avoid any action that might violate or diminish the legal and civil rights of the consumer.

The member shall not engage in or condone practices by any source that are inhumane or that result in illegal or unjustifiable action relevant to race, handicap, age, gender, sexual orientation, religion or national origin.

The member shall make only factual, honest, and clearly stated (not misleading) public announcements, statements or communications such as (but not limited to) for advertising or promotional purposes.

The member shall not set forth identification with AASECT such as (but not limited to) membership or certification status in an announcement statement, or communication, whatever the form, that also includes a college or university degree, unless that degree is based on academic merit and is from an appropriately accredited higher education institution.

The member shall act in accord with AASECT ethics, standards and guidelines related to education, counseling, therapy, supervision and research.

The member shall act in accord with the standards and guidelines for the protection of consumers promulgated by other professional associations with which the member is affiliated and the laws of the jurisdiction(s) in which the member provides professional services.

The member shall report any ethical, regulatory, or legal complaint or judgment relevant to their practice filed against the member with this report being submitted in writing within thirty (30) days of knowledge to the Chair of the AASECT Ethics Committee.

Principle Three: Welfare of the Consumer

The AASECT member shall accept that the consumer is in a unique position of vulnerability in respect to services related to sex education, counseling, therapy, research, and supervision, and shall constantly be mindful of the responsibility for protection of the consumer's welfare, rights and best interests and for the rigorous maintenance of the trust implicit in the educational, counseling or therapeutic alliance.

(A) The member shall, from the onset of professional contact with a consumer or a potential consumer, clarify;

(1) Professional training, experiences and competencies;
(2) The nature of the professional services available to the consumer (with an explanation of mutual roles and duties);
(3) The limits of intervention effectiveness;
(4) Personal values or professional preferences that reflect biases rather than being responsive to the needs and well-being of the consumer;
(5) Any exceptions to confidentiality and privileged communications (e.g. duty to warn, mandatory reporting, etc.); and
(6) Any financial issues, especially the payment obligations of the consumers.

(B) The member shall treat all information received about a consumer as confidential, even if some portions of the information appear trivial, irrelevant or not to require confidentiality; even the existence of an educational counseling or therapeutic relationship with the consumer is confidential. Where required by law, the AASECT provider will design a HIPPA policy and follow all legal requirements protecting consumer privacy.

(C) The member shall advocate the consumer's privileged communication, *as* granted by the laws of the jurisdiction applicable to the consumer and/or the member in the event that there is uncertainty about the effectiveness or validity of the consumer's consent to release information that is potentially confidential and/or privileged, the member shall obtain appropriate legal determination.

(D) The member shall divulge information received from a consumer or prospective consumer to the extent required only in the following circumstances

(1) When the consumer provides written and informed consent, which indicates:

(a) The type and nature of information to be released;
(b) Knowledge of the purpose for which the information will be used;
(c) Designation of the source that will receive the information;
(d) That the consent is given voluntarily and with competency; and
(e) The consumer's name and the date on which the consent is given.

(2) When there is clear and imminent danger of bodily harm or to the life or safety of the consumer or another person disclosure shall be made in accord with the laws of the jurisdiction in which the member practices.
(3) When applicable law declares that such information may be released.

(E) The member shall obtain the consumers' written informed consent for using any identifiable information about the consumer for purposes of education, training, research or publication.

(F) The member shall reveal a consumer's confidential information to a professional source with a limited right to know, such as (but not limited to) a supervisor or consultant in an appropriate manner; it is the member's responsibility to take reasonable steps to assure that the other professional source will properly treat the information in a confidential manner.

(G) The member shall keep meaningful records relevant to the professional services provided to and contacts (of any nature) with the consumer and shall have a secure system for the preservation of records with the minimal contents and duration of retention being in accord with the laws that are applicable to the jurisdiction in which the member practices: at a minimum:

(1) A full record shall be retained intact for no less than three (3) years after completion of the last date of professional services or contact.

(2) A full record or meaningful summary of the record shall be maintained for no less than twelve (12) additional years.

(H) The member shall have a formal (written) arrangement for the preservation of consumer records upon his/her ceasing of practice, death or incapacity. This arrangement must be in accord with the laws of the jurisdiction in which the member practices.

(I) The member shall, when providing professional services in a group context or to a couple or family make a reasonable effort to promote safeguarding of confidentiality on the part of each consumer in the group, couple or family.

(J) The member shall orient the minor consumer to the limits of confidentiality pertaining to a parent's right to know as defined by the laws of the jurisdiction in which the member practices.

(K) The member shall, regardless of the reasons for which the consumer sought professional services and regardless of the theory or technique being used by the member, predicate every sex counseling or therapy intervention upon diagnosis and meaningful consumer(s) treatment plan, which shall be consistently documented in writing, justified academically, evaluated for effectiveness, monitored for strengths and weaknesses and modified accordingly.

(L) The member shall as needed to protect the best interest of the consumer, seek consultation and/or supervision with special reference to the treatment plan and to the personal elements of the therapeutic relationship.

(M) The member shall not engage in any dual relationship, regardless of nature or circumstances, with a consumer or with persons who have a primary relationship with a consumer served by the member if such dual relationship could potentially be detrimental to or jeopardize the well-being of a consumer. A dual relationship occurs when a member is in a professional role with a person and (1) at the same time is in another role with the same person, and/or (2) at the same time is in a relationship with a person closely associated with or related to the person with whom the member has the professional relationship, and/or (3) promises to enter into another relationship in the future with the person or a person closely associated with or related to the consumer.

(N) The member practicing counseling or therapy shall not engage, attempt to engage or offer to engage a consumer in sexual behavior whether the consumer consents to such behavior or not. Sexual misconduct includes kissing, sexual intercourse and/or the touching by either the member or the consumer of the other's breasts or genitals. Members do not engage in such sexual misconduct with current consumers. Members do not engage in sexual intimacies with individuals they know to be close relatives, guardians, or significant others of a current consumer. Sexual misconduct is also sexual solicitation, physical advances, or verbal or nonverbal conduct that is sexual in nature, that occurs in connection with the member's activities or roles as a counselor or therapist, and that either (1) is unwelcome, is offensive, or creates a hostile workplace or educational environment, and the member knows or is told this or (2) is sufficiently severe or intense to be abusive to a reasonable person in the context. Sexual misconduct can consist of a single intense or severe act, or of multiple persistent or pervasive acts. For purposes of determining the existence of sexual misconduct, the counseling or therapeutic relationship is deemed to continue in perpetuity.

(O) The member shall terminate professional services to the consumer when it is reasonably evident or should be evident that the consumer is not obtaining benefits sufficient to justify continued intervention. Upon termination the member shall make referral to another professional source and/or offer reasonable follow-up to further the best interests of the consumer.

Principle Four: Welfare of Students, Trainees and Others

The AASECT member shall respect the rights and dignity of students, trainees and others (such as employees), maintain high standards of scholarship and preserve academic freedom and responsibility.

(A) The member shall, from the onset of professional contact with students, trainees and others over whom the member has administrative, educational or supervisory authority clarify: the member's professional qualifications and competencies; the objectives, responsibilities and duties of all concerned and any financial issues, especially any payment obligations.

(B) The member shall accord confidentiality to information of a personal or intimate nature obtained in his/her professional role; the provision of confidentiality does not, however, preclude fulfilling a professional responsibility or duty to consumers, educational or training institutions or programs, professional associations or governmental-regulatory or legal sources.

(C) The member shall maintain high standards of scholarship and present information that is accurate and timely in all administrative, educational and supervisory activities.

(D) The member shall keep meaningful and systematic records of all administrative, educational and supervisory activities.

(E) The member shall not coerce or require a student, trainee or other to serve as a subject for a research project.

(F) The member shall not provide diagnosis, therapeutic counseling or therapy or any other clinical service to students or trainees or those over whom the member has administrative, educational or supervisory authority.

(G) The member shall not harass in any manner a student, trainee or other person over whom the member *has* administrative, educational or supervisory authority. Members do not engage in sexual relationships with students or supervisees who are in their department, agency, or training center, or over whom members have, or are likely to have, evaluative authority.

(H) The member shall not, during the administrative, educational or supervisory period enter into any dual relationship, regardless of nature, that jeopardizes the well-being of the student, trainee or others.

(I) The member shall not, during the administrative, educational or supervisory period, engage, attempt to engage or offer to engage the student, trainee or other in sexual behavior.

(J) The member shall be cognizant that a dual relationship subsequent to the administrative, educational or supervisory period may potentially jeopardize the well being of the student, trainee or other.

Principle Five: Welfare of Research Subjects

The AASECT member shall conduct his/her investigations with respect for the dignity, rights and welfare of the subjects. Research must be ethical and legal at its inception and not justified solely by its intended or achieved outcome.

(A) The member shall be involved only with sex research that is carried out by persons qualified to do such investigations or under the direct supervision of persons so qualified.

(B) The member shall be involved only with sex research that designates and identifies (in writing) to the potential subjects the names and professional qualifications of the person or persons with ethical scientific and legal responsibility for the conduct of the investigation.

(C) The member shall be involved only with sex research that provides adequate protection(s) to human subjects at risk. Any research project must:

    (1) Include the voluntary and informed consent of each subject; and

    (2) Be in accord with applicable legal prescriptions or proscriptions.

(D) The member shall be involved only with sex research that protects the confidentiality of research data including the identity of participants or others revealed during the investigation.

(E) The member shall be involved only with sex research that requires all investigators to be honest and accurate in their dealings with research subjects and all persons receiving information about the research.

(F) The member shall be involved only with sex research that offers to provide an explanation of the purpose of the investigation and of the individual and collective results to each person who serves as a research subject.

(G) The member shall be involved only with sex research that has been prefaced by the submission of a research proposal for peer review with special reference to ethical and legal safeguards for the potential research subjects. This peer review may occur in different forms, such as an institutional review board for evaluation for ethical propriety, and must be in accord with all relevant laws.

(H) The member will not engage in any type of sexual relationship or sexual misconduct with research subjects as defined above in Principle Three (N).

(Final revision June 7, 2004)

International Index of Erectile Function (IIEF)*

National Library of Medicine

The International Index of Erectile Function is a reliable, brief, self-administered assessment tool for clinicians and clients to assess problems with erectile function with men. The 15-item questionnaire contains five domains: (a) Erectile Function (6 items), (b) Orgasmic Function (2 items), (c) Sexual Desire (2 items), (d) Intercourse Satisfaction (3 items), and (e) Overall Sexual Satisfaction (2 items). Each domain captures a unique dimension of responses relating to male sexual or erectile function. The questions ask about the man's sex life over the last 4 weeks, with ratings on a five-point (1 to 5) Likert scale with lower values indicating relatively more erectile dysfunction or sexual dysfunction, depending on the item. The instrument was validated for use in 10 languages in 12 countries.

SCORING

Items load on the five scales as follows:

Erectile Function:	Items 1, 2, 3, 4, 5, and 15
Orgasmic Function:	Items 9 and 10
Sexual Desire:	Items 11 and 12
Intercourse Satisfaction:	Items 6, 7, and 8
Overall Sexual Satisfaction:	Items 13 and 14

A particular domain score is computed by summing the responses of its individual items, with lower values suggesting more dysfunction. No firm cut-off scores are used; however, some research has suggested using a cut-off score of 25 for the Erectile Function scale. That is, men who scored 25 or less would be likely classified as having erectile dysfunction, while men who score above 25 would be likely classified as not having erectile dysfunction. Other research has suggested that a cut-off score of 21 is preferred.

INTERNATIONAL INDEX OF ERECTILE FUNCTION (IIEF)

HOSPITAL NUMBER (IF KNOWN) ☐☐☐☐☐☐☐

NAME _____

DATE OF BIRTH ☐☐/☐☐/☐☐   AGE ☐☐

ADDRESS _____

_____

Patient Questionnaire

_____

TELEPHONE _____

These questions ask about the effects that your erection problems have had on your sex life <u>over the last four weeks</u>. Please try to answer the questions as honestly and as clearly as you are able. Your answers will help your doctor to choose the most effective treatment suited to your condition. In answering the questions, the following definitions apply:

- **sexual activity** includes intercourse, caressing, foreplay, & masturbation
- **sexual intercourse** is defined as sexual penetration of your partner
- **sexual stimulation** includes situation such as foreplay, erotic pictures, etc.
- **ejaculation** is the ejection of semen from the penis (or the feeling of this)
- **orgasm** is the fulfilment or climax following sexual stimulation or intercourse

---

Over the past 4 weeks: *Please check **one** box only*

☐ **Q1** **How often were you able to get an erection during sexual activity?**
- 0 No sexual activity
- 1 Almost never or never
- 2 A few times (less than half the time)
- 3 Sometimes (about half the time)
- 4 Most times (more than half the time)
- 5 Almost always or always

☐ **Q2** **When you had erections with sexual stimulation, how often were your erections hard enough for penetration?**
- 0 No sexual activity
- 1 Almost never or never
- 2 A few times (less than half the time)
- 3 Sometimes (about half the time)
- 4 Most times (more than half the time)
- 5 Almost always or always

☐ **Q3** **When you attempted intercourse, how often were you able to penetrate (enter) your partner?**
- 0 Did not attempt intercourse
- 1 Almost never or never
- 2 A few times (less than half the time)
- 3 Sometimes (about half the time)
- 4 Most times (more than half the time)
- 5 Almost always or always

☐ **Q4** **During sexual intercourse, <u>how often</u> were you able to maintain your erection after you had penetrated (entered) your partner?**
- 0 Did not attempt intercourse
- 1 Almost never or never
- 2 A few times (less than half the time)
- 3 Sometimes (about half the time)
- 4 Most times (more than half the time)
- 5 Almost always or always

☐ **Q5** **During sexual intercourse, <u>how difficult</u> was it to maintain your erection to completion of intercourse?**
- 0 Did not attempt intercourse
- 1 Extremely difficult
- 2 Very difficult
- 3 Difficult
- 4 Slightly difficult
- 5 Not difficult

☐ **Q6** **How many times have you attempted sexual intercourse?**

    0   No attempts
    1   One to two attempts
    2   Three to four attempts
    3   Five to six attempts
    4   Seven to ten attempts
    5   Eleven or more attempts

☐ **Q7** **When you attempted sexual intercourse, how often was it satisfactory for you?**

    0   Did not attempt intercourse
    1   Almost never or never
    2   A few times (less than half the time)
    3   Sometimes (about half the time)
    4   Most times (more than half the time)
    5   Almost always or always

☐ **Q8** **How much have you enjoyed sexual intercourse?**

    0   No intercourse
    1   No enjoyment at all
    2   Not very enjoyable
    3   Fairly enjoyable
    4   Highly enjoyable
    5   Very highly enjoyable

☐ **Q9** **When you had sexual stimulation <u>or</u> intercourse, how often did you ejaculate?**

    0   No sexual stimulation or intercourse
    1   Almost never or never
    2   A few times (less than half the time)
    3   Sometimes (about half the time)
    4   Most times (more than half the time)
    5   Almost always or always

☐ **Q10** **When you had sexual stimulation <u>or</u> intercourse, how often did you have the feeling of orgasm or climax?**

    1   Almost never or never
    2   A few times (less than half the time)
    3   Sometimes (about half the time)
    4   Most times (more than half the time)
    5   Almost always or always

☐ **Q11** **How often have you felt sexual desire?**

    1   Almost never or never
    2   A few times (less than half the time)
    3   Sometimes (about half the time)
    4   Most times (more than half the time)
    5   Almost always or always

☐ **Q12** **How would you rate your level of sexual desire?**

    1   Very low or none at all
    2   Low
    3   Moderate
    4   High
    5   Very high

☐ **Q13** **How satisfied have you been with your <u>overall sex life</u>?**

    1   Very dissatisfied
    2   Moderately dissatisfied
    3   Equally satisfied & dissatisfied
    4   Moderately satisfied
    5   Very satisfied

☐ **Q14** **How satisfied have you been with your <u>sexual relationship</u> with your partner?**

    1   Very dissatisfied
    2   Moderately dissatisfied
    3   Equally satisfied & dissatisfied
    4   Moderately satisfied
    5   Very satisfied

☐ **Q15** **How do you rate your <u>confidence</u> that you could get and keep an erection?**

    1   Very low
    2   Low
    3   Moderate
    4   High
    5   Very high

ADDITIONAL RESOURCES

Cappelleri, J. C., Rosen, R. C., Smith, M. D., Quirk, F., Maytom, M. C., Mishra, A., & Osterloh, I. H. (1999). Some developments on the International Index of Erectile Function (IIEF). *Drug Information Journal, 33,* 179-190.

Rosen, R. C., Riley, A., Wagner, G., Osterloh, I. H., Kirkpatrick, J., & Mishra, A. (1997). The International Index of Erectile Function (IIEF): A multidimensional scale for assessment of erectile dysfunction. *Urology, 49*(6), 822-830.

Female Sexual Function Index (FSFI)

R. Rosen et al.

The Female Sexual Function Index (FSFI) is a reliable, self-administered assessment tool for clinicians and clients to assess sexual functioning in women. The 19-item questionnaire assesses functioning in six domains: (a) desire, (b) arousal, (c) lubrication, (d) orgasm, (e) satisfaction, and (f) pain. Each domain captures a unique dimension of responses related to female sexual functioning. The questions ask about the woman's sex life over the last 4 weeks, and the instrument is appropriate to use with women of all adult ages.

INSTRUCTIONS

Participants are asked to check one answer for each question that describes their sexual feelings and responses during the past 4 weeks. It will be helpful to define for participants that "sexual activity" includes caressing, foreplay, masturbation, and vaginal intercourse. "Intercourse" is defined as penile penetration (entry) of the vagina. "Sexual stimulation" includes foreplay with a partner, masturbation, and sexual fantasy. "Sexual desire or interest" refers to feelings of wanting to have a sexual experience, thinking or fantasizing about having sex, and feeling receptive to a partner initiating sex.

SCORING

Each item is scored on just one scale as listed below. In addition, because the number of items on scales varies, a domain factor multiplier is applied as noted.

Domain	Questions	Domain Multiplier	Minimum Score	Maximum Score
Desire	1,2	0.6	1.2	6.0
Arousal	3,4,5,6	0.3	0	6.0
Lubrication	7,8,9,10	0.3	0	6.0
Orgasm	11,12,13	0.4	0	6.0
Satisfaction	14,15,16	0.4	0.8	6.0
Pain	17,18,19	0.4	0	6.0
Full Scale Score Range			2.0	36.0

Individual domain scores are obtained by adding the scores of the individual items that comprise the domain and multiplying the sum by the domain multiplier (see preceding page). The full scale score is obtained by adding the six domain scores. Note that within individual domains, a score of zero indicates that no sexual activity was reported during the past 4 weeks. When zero activity is reported in a domain, the full scale score is also lowered. Lower scores indicate increased problems of sexual function. A score of 26 or lower is used as a cut-off for distinguishing members of the normal and clinical samples.

Female Sexual Function Index (FSFI)*

Question	Response Options

1. Over the past 4 weeks, how **often** did you feel sexual desire or interest?

5 = Almost always or always
4 = Most times (more than half the time)
3 = Sometimes (about half the time)
2 = A few times (less than half the time)
1 = Almost never or never

2. Over the past 4 weeks, how would you rate your **level** (degree) of sexual desire or interest?

5 = Very high
4 = High
3 = Moderate
2 = Low
1 = Very low or none at all

3. Over the past 4 weeks, how **often** did you feel sexually aroused ("turned on") during sexual activity or intercourse?

0 = No sexual activity
5 = Almost always or always
4 = Most times (more than half the time)
3 = Sometimes (about half the time)
2 = A few times (less than half the time)
1 = Almost never or never

4. Over the past 4 weeks, how would you rate your **level** of sexual arousal ("turn on") during sexual activity or intercourse?

0 = No sexual activity
5 = Very high
4 = High
3 = Moderate
2 = Low
1 = Very low or none at all

5. Over the past 4 weeks, how **confident** were you about becoming sexually aroused during sexual activity or intercourse?

0 = No sexual activity
5 = Very high confidence
4 = High confidence
3 = Moderate confidence
2 = Low confidence
1 = Very low or no confidence

6. Over the past 4 weeks, how **often** have you been satisfied with your arousal (excitement) during sexual activity or intercourse?

0 = No sexual activity
5 = Almost always or always
4 = Most times (more than half the time)
3 = Sometimes (about half the time)
2 = A few times (less than half the time)
1 = Almost never or never

For a complete FSFI questionnaire, instructions and scoring algorithm, please see www.FSFIquestionnaire.com, or contact Raymond Rosen, PhD (Department of Psychiatry: UMDNJ-Robert Wood Johnson Medical School, 675 Hoes Lane, Piscataway, NJ 08854).

Question	Response Options
7. Over the past 4 weeks, how **often** did you become lubricated ("wet") during sexual activity or intercourse?	0 = No sexual activity 5 = Almost always or always 4 = Most times (more than half the time) 3 = Sometimes (about half the time) 2 = A few times (less than half the time) 1 = Almost never or never
8. Over the past 4 weeks, how **difficult** was it to become lubricated ("wet") during sexual activity or intercourse?	0 = No sexual activity 1 = Extremely difficult or impossible 2 = Very difficult 3 = Difficult 4 = Slightly difficult 5 = Not difficult
9. Over the past 4 weeks, how often did you **maintain** your lubrication ("wetness") until completion of sexual activity or intercourse?	0 = No sexual activity 5 = Almost always or always 4 = Most times (more than half the time) 3 = Sometimes (about half the time) 2 = A few times (less than half the time) 1 = Almost never or never
10. Over the past 4 weeks, how **difficult** was it to maintain your lubrication ("wetness") until completion of sexual activity or intercourse?	0 = No sexual activity 1 = Extremely difficult or impossible 2 = Very difficult 3 = Difficult 4 = Slightly difficult 5 = Not difficult
11. Over the past 4 weeks, when you had sexual stimulation or intercourse, how **often** did you reach orgasm (climax)?	0 = No sexual activity 5 = Almost always or always 4 = Most times (more than half the time) 3 = Sometimes (about half the time) 2 = A few times (less than half the time) 1 = Almost never or never
12. Over the past 4 weeks, when you had sexual stimulation or intercourse, how **difficult** was it for you to reach orgasm (climax)?	0 = No sexual activity 1 = Extremely difficult or impossible 2 = Very difficult 3 = Difficult 4 = Slightly difficult 5 = Not difficult
13. Over the past 4 weeks, how **satisfied** were you with your ability to reach orgasm (climax) during sexual activity or intercourse?	0 = No sexual activity 5 = Very satisfied 4 = Moderately satisfied 3 = About equally satisfied and dissatisfied 2 = Moderately dissatisfied 1 = Very dissatisfied

Question	Response Options

14. Over the past 4 weeks, how **satisfied** have you been with the amount of emotional closeness during sexual activity between you and your partner?

0 = No sexual activity
5 = Very satisfied
4 = Moderately satisfied
3 = About equally satisfied and dissatisfied
2 = Moderately dissatisfied
1 = Very dissatisfied

15. Over the past 4 weeks, how **satisfied** have you been with your sexual relationship with your partner?

5 = Very satisfied
4 = Moderately satisfied
3 = About equally satisfied and dissatisfied
2 = Moderately dissatisfied
1 = Very dissatisfied

16. Over the past 4 weeks, how **satisfied** have you been with your overall sexual life?

5 = Very satisfied
4 = Moderately satisfied
3 = About equally satisfied and dissatisfied
2 = Moderately dissatisfied
1 = Very dissatisfied

17. Over the past 4 weeks, how **often** did you experience discomfort or pain during vaginal penetration?

0 = Did not attempt intercourse
1 = Almost always or always
2 = Most times (more than half the time)
3 = Sometimes (about half the time)
4 = A few times (less than half the time)
5 = Almost never or never

18. Over the past 4 weeks, how **often** did you experience discomfort or pain following vaginal penetration?

0 = Did not attempt intercourse
1 = Almost always or always
2 = Most times (more than half the time)
3 = Sometimes (about half the time)
4 = A few times (less than half the time)
5 = Almost never or never

19. Over the past 4 weeks, how would you rate your **level** (degree) of discomfort or pain during or following vaginal penetration?

0 = Did not attempt intercourse
1 = Very high
2 = High
3 = Moderate
4 = Low
5 = Very low or none at all

ADDITIONAL RESOURCES

Female Sexual Function Index (FSFI). (2000). The Index and related materials are available online at www.FSFIquestionnaire.com

Rosen, R., Brown, C., Heiman, J., Leiblum, S., Meston, C., Shabsigh, R., Ferguson, D., & D'Agostino, R., Jr. (2000). The Female Sexual Function Index (FSFI): A multidimensional self-report instrument for the assessment of female sexual function. *Journal of Sex and Marital Therapy, 26*, 191-208.

Wiegel, M., Meston, C., & Rosen, R. (2005). The Female Sexual Function Index (FSFI): Cross-validation and development of clinical cutoff scores. *Journal of Sex and Marital Therapy, 31*, 1-20.

The Complexity Of Sexual Diversity: Sexual Identity Cube and Self-Awareness Exercise*

Frederick L. Peterson, Jr.

The "Sexual Identity Cube" (see p. 298) is a a conceptual tool designed to help you expand your understanding of the many forms of human sexual identity. It is a synthesis of the work of Alfred Kinsey, John Money, and Sandra Bem. A cube has three equal dimensions (height, width, and depth) and is created by enclosing the space along each of these three axes. If you divide each axis into three equal parts, you will have a cube containing 27 smaller cubes, or ID cubes if you will (a three by three by three cube with 27 ID cubes). Each ID cube represents one of 27 basic sexual identities, ranging from "heterosexual masculine males" to "bisexual androgynous transgendered" individuals.

1. Axis A is *gender orientation*, divided into female, transgender, and male. Gender is defined as the state of being male or female, and goes beyond biological sex (the identification of a person as male or female based on genetic and anatomical characteristics) to include gender identity (the psychological sense of being male or female). There are at least eight criteria used to determine gender: genetic, prenatal hormonal, external genitalia, internal reproductive organs, pubescent hormonal, gender assigned at birth, gender child is raised as, and gender identity. A transgendered individual (TGI) is a person that has one or more of these criteria divergent from the rest.

2. Axis B is *sexual orientation*, divided into homosexual, bisexual, and heterosexual. This division uses the one-dimensional continuum concept of sexual attraction (same-sex attraction on one end and opposite-sex attraction on the other). This perspective ignores the concept of asexuality until further research can empirically support it.

3. Axis C is *gender role orientation*, divided into masculine, androgynous, and feminine. Gender role is a set of socially defined expectations that men and women are expected to fulfill in a particular culture. Androgynous individuals, either men or women, have high degrees of characteristics traditionally attributed to both males and females (e.g., being both nurturing and aggressive). This concept is more applicable to cultures with high degrees of gender role polarization (as in America) than cultures with low gender polarization.

---

*F. Joshua Peterson is the illustrator of the Sexual Identity Cube.

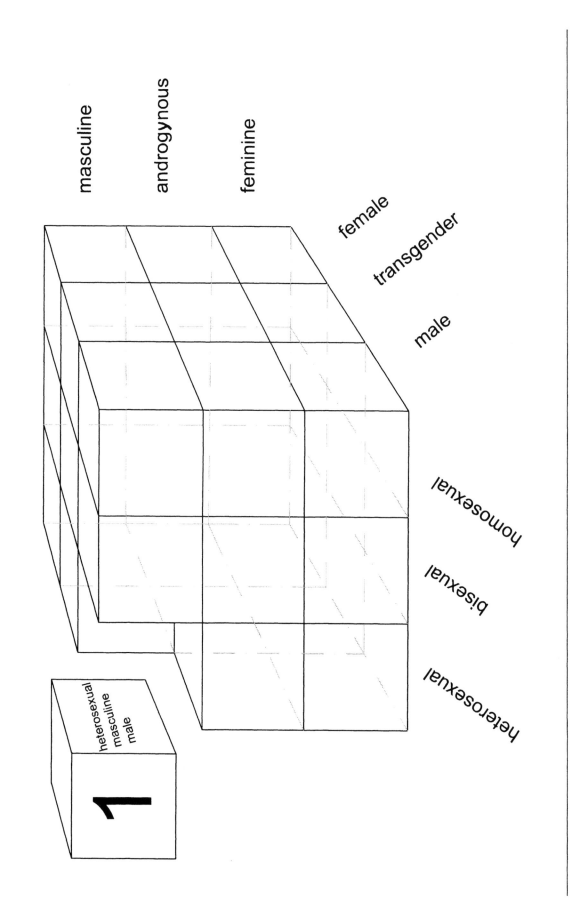

Figure 1. Sexual Identity Cube.

The Complexity of Sexual Diversity – Sexual Identity Cube: A Self-Awareness Exercise Using the Sexual Identity Cube

INSTRUCTIONS: As an awareness exercise, try writing out each of the 27 combinations and conceive what each sexual identity represents to you. As a check that you identified all 27 ID cubes, now reference the list provided. Remember, the final decision of where a person is represented in the identity cube is based upon their self-identification in terms of gender, sexual, and gender role orientations. For the purposes of this awareness exercise and as a measure of your life experience with sexual minorities, check your perceptions of where others would be represented in the identity cube. Count how many of the basic sexual identities are represented in your family, social network, and clientele (if you are a therapist). Place the person's initials or first names in the column to the right. With which ID cube do you identity yourself? Your partner?

Heterosexual Masculine Male	
Heterosexual Masculine Female	
Heterosexual Masculine TGI	
Heterosexual Androgynous Male	
Heterosexual Androgynous Female	
Heterosexual Androgynous TGI	
Heterosexual Feminine Male	
Heterosexual Feminine Female	
Heterosexual Feminine TGI	
Bisexual Masculine Male	
Bisexual Masculine Female	
Bisexual Masculine TGI	
Bisexual Androgynous Male	
Bisexual Androgynous Female	
Bisexual Androgynous TGI	
Bisexual Feminine Male	
Bisexual Feminine Female	
Bisexual Feminine TGI	
Homosexual Masculine Male	
Homosexual Masculine Female	
Homosexual Masculine TGI	
Homosexual Androgynous Male	
Homosexual Androgynous Female	
Homosexual Androgynous TGI	
Homosexual Feminine Male	
Homosexual Feminine Female	
Homosexual Feminine TGI	

CONTRIBUTOR

Frederick L. Peterson, Jr., PsyD, is a health psychologist at the Veterans Healthcare System of Ohio, Dayton Campus, where he coordinates a Sexual Health Clinic and the Smoking Cessation Programs. Dr. Peterson is the Co-Director of the Psychology Internship Program. He completed postdoctorate training as a Clinical Fellow at the Masters and Johnson Institute. Research interests include sex therapy, tobacco use treatment, and the effects of masculinity-related personality factors on health. He holds three academic appointments at Wright State University, including the School of Medicine (Department of Psychiatry), the School of Professional Psychology, and the College of Education and Human Services. Dr. Peterson can be reached at the Sexual Health Clinic, VA Medical Center, Dayton, OH 45428. E-mail: Docpete100@aol.com

Sharing the Treatment Plan for Sex Therapy

Frederick L. Peterson, Jr.

This Draft Treatment Agreement is an example of what is shared at a results-sharing conference (RSC). The RSC is usually the third or fourth meeting in a multiple-session assessment protocol. During the RSC, three basic sets of information are shared with the client (and the partner): (a) a brief summary of the key information learned about the client from all sources (data from interviews, psychological testing, other providers, etc.), (b) what the therapist concludes about the information, including diagnosis, and (c) what the client is most interested in – the therapist's recommendations concerning what to do about the presenting problems. The RSC document includes the summary of data, diagnosis, desired outcomes, treatment goals, recommendations, evaluation criteria by which to determine if the recommendations are making positive change, and standard language regarding consent and client responsibilities. To avoid overwhelming the clients, they should first be told that the RSC document is a draft to allow client input and modification; that they are in charge of what recommendations to accept, what the time frame will be to implement any recommendations they do accept; and that they are not expected to make an immediate decision regarding the entire plan at the RSC, but that they are asked to take the document with them for their review and decision.

Draft Treatment Agreement

Developed Between Marcia* and Robert and
Dr. Frederick L. Peterson, Jr.

I. DIAGNOSIS, TREATMENT OUTCOMES, AND GOALS

Robert is a 72-year-old Anglo-American male and Marcia is a 61-year-old Anglo-American female who have been married about 2 years. Whereas Marcia and Robert demonstrate strength in their love for each other in their marriage, each has expressed concerns related to communicating with the other and improving the satisfaction with their sexual relationship. They have experienced a history of health concerns, including Robert's vascular disease, bypass surgeries, congestive heart failure, and a history of erectile dysfunction secondary to heart disease and medication effects. Marcia has a history of ovarian cancer and hysterectomy after which she used hormonal treatment for several years but stopped because she was not sexually active. She has to use vaginal dilators to permit containment during penile-vaginal intercourse because both Marcia and Robert report her vagina is "small sized." She is not orgasmic during sexual intercourse with Robert but able to have multiple orgasms during masturbation.

Both Marcia and Robert were previously married and both of their spouses are deceased. The couple have known each other for decades and culminated their friendship in a romance after each was widowed. Each has advanced graduate education; Robert is a retired leader of a religious community and Marcia is retired from a job in human services. They are currently seeking treatment to enhance their relationship and sexual satisfaction.

On the Beck Depression Inventory, Robert reported he has less energy and gets fatigued more than he used to but was within the normal range of symptoms for depression. Marcia was within the moderate range of depressive symptoms, reporting less energy than she used to have, thinking of herself as a failure, and not seeing herself as attractive. On the Sexual Health Inventory for men, Robert reported a severe level of symptoms for erectile function but also reported a high level of satisfaction with sexual relations with Marcia. On the Female Sexual Function Index, Marcia reported sexual health symptoms with sexual desire, sexual arousal, the swelling/lubrication response, orgasm, and sexual satisfaction.

Diagnosis: Erectile Dysfunction (R)
Depressive Disorder, moderate, recurrent (M)
Hypoactive Sexual Desire Disorder (M)
Female Sexual Arousal Disorder (M)

Robert and Marcia are consulting with Dr. Peterson for a comprehensive mental health and sexual health assessment. As such, they are conjointly developing the components of this Draft Treatment Agreement. Hence, the following are *desired treatment outcomes* for ensuring the mental and sexual health as defined by:

1. enhancing the couple's satisfaction with their overall relationship.
2. specifically enhancing their satisfaction with their sexual relationship.

This outcome will be accomplished through *specific treatment goals*, which include:

1. increasing satisfaction with, and frequency of, nondemand, nongenital touch, employing sensate focus therapy techniques.
2. increasing satisfaction with, and frequency of, sensual and erotic touching, with and without intercourse.
3. increasing satisfaction with, and communication about, their sexual and overall marital relationship, specifically addressing feelings of security, emotional intimacy, and physical intimacy.

---

* Names and characteristics have been changed to protect confidentiality.

These treatment outcomes and goals, as well as the following recommendations, may be accomplished at whatever pace and amount of time Robert and Marcia wish to proceed, acknowledging that these difficulties took considerable time to develop and will not be resolved "overnight." Please take this draft with you, review and discuss it, then decide to start treatment.

II. TREATMENT STRATEGIES

Treatment strategies employed to achieve these outcomes and treatment goals will be:

1. Couples sex therapy, as provided by a therapist of Robert and Marcia's choosing. Should this be Dr. Peterson, multiple techniques will be employed, including but not limited to sex education and therapy (including video-based education), cognitive-behavioral prescriptions/contracting, and existentially focused psychotherapy. Treatment sessions will be on a biweekly basis until such a time as both parties agree to move to a monthly schedule or end treatment.
2. Behavioral prescriptions will be employed, including but not limited to:

   a. Robert effectively overcoming the challenges of erectile dysfunction (ED) through use of a vacuum-constriction device (VCD) or one of the first-line treatment options for the clinical practice guidelines on primary care management of ED.
   b. Sexual self-image affirmations being assigned and completed toward a goal of enhanced self-esteem.
   c. Relaxation exercises enhancing willful control over the level of tension in the body, including optional Kegel exercise or biofeedback training of vaginal tension.
   d. Sensate focus exercises concentrating on the exploration and sharing of each other's sensuality.

3. Marcia employing an at-home female orgasmic training program with support from the couple's sex therapy and involving Robert as indicated by program guidelines.
4. Bibliographic strategies (journaling, reading assignments) focused upon expanding sexual literacy and improving marital communication.
5. A women's therapy group or individual counseling for Marcia to decrease anxious mood and facilitate support. Group treatment can either be on a concurrent or consecutive basis with individual therapy.
6. A men's support group for Robert to increase level of support and buffer the effects of stress related to age-related losses as well as to diminish his cardiovascular risk.
7. Diagramming, monitoring, and engineering the couple's social support system to serve as a mediating buffer to stress and to provide structuring of time for leisure together.
8. Participation in a regular exercise program together, such as walking for a minimal period of 20 to 30 minutes of increased heart rate, several times a week.
9. Testosterone evaluation of Robert to ensure he is within normal limits and, if he is not, consideration of a supplemental hormone treatment.
10. Specific recommendations for sexual adjustment secondary to health changes related to client's medical conditions:

    a. Increased sensual play to change the pattern of sexual relations as "work."
    b. Bathing each other/mutual showers for sensual play and relaxation as well as reduction of spacisity and muscular pain.
    c. Emphasis on morning sensual/sexual activity rather than evening to reduce the impact of the fatigue factor.
    d. Maintenance of an air conditioned environment and avoidance of lengthy exposure to heat which can "sap" energy and strength.
    e. Employment of different positions when having sexual intercourse, which can add variety and reduce continued pressure of body parts that cause discomfort.

f.   Consideration of the use of mild stimulants if fatigue continues to be an obstacle to sexual activity as well as activities of daily living (e.g., caffeine).

g.   Use of lubricants to supplement Marcia's vaginal lubricating response.

h.   Use of vibration stimulation for increased intensity and reduction of fatigue.

11. Establishment of a personal and family mission for the integration of physical, emotional, and spiritual goals for this stage of the couple's life development, including end-of-life decision planning.

12. Consideration of a second trial of hormonal supplement treatment employing estrogen transdermal patch if behavioral treatment of hypoactive sexual desire disorder does not increase sexual desire to the level of patient satisfaction.

13. If improvements are not witnessed within 3 months of treatment, consideration of psychiatric consultation for evaluation of medication management related to history of depressive episodes.

III. EVALUATION

Evaluation of treatment progress will be conducted on a regular basis using a combination of subjective satisfaction ratings and completion of behavioral contracts. Subjective ratings will be on a 1 to 10 scale (1-10) with 10 representing the highest level of satisfaction. Frequencies are recorded in episodes per time unit (3X/week) or percent of time (10%). Criteria are specific to the client's presenting complaints. This treatment agreement will be for a 3-month period, with review and modification or termination every 3 months thereafter.

Criteria	1 Yr. Ago	TX Start	Mid-TX	TX End	6 Mo. F/U
Her Sexual Self-Esteem					
His Sexual Self-Esteem					
Satisfaction With Nondemand Touch					
Frequency of Sexual Desire					
Intensity of Sexual Desire					
Frequency of Female Orgasm With Manual Pleasuring					
Frequency of Female Orgasm With Oral Pleasuring					
Frequency of Female Orgasm With Vibration					
Frequency of Female Orgasm During Intercourse (With Clitoral Stimulation)					
Frequency of Exercise					
Utilization of Support System					

Criteria	1 Yr. Ago	TX Start	Mid-TX	TX End	6 Mo. F/U
Frequency of Sexual Relations					
Her Satisfaction With Sexual Relationship					
His Satisfaction With Sexual Relationship					
Her Satisfaction With Overall Relationship					
His Satisfaction With Overall Relationship					

IV. CLIENT RESPONSIBILITIES

1. Maintain personal responsibility for one's own health and satisfaction, using professionals only as consultants and resources for treatment/healing process.
2. Maintain personal safety by removing any weapons from the home and never bringing weapons to the treatment center. Abstain from any acts of physical aggression unless one's own safety is threatened.
3. Keep the therapist informed of any contemplation of suicide, harm to others, or separation and divorce.
4. Participate in treatment plan as conjointly developed and agreed upon at the start of treatment, including, but not limited to, consistently attending sessions, being on time to sessions, completing assignments, and paying fees for services.

V. CONSENT FOR TREATMENT

The contents of this agreement have been developed as a draft for my review and input. The draft agreement has been explained to my satisfaction and I understand I may withdraw from this treatment at any time. I understand the rules of confidentiality and that any disclosure of imminent harm to self or others (intent of suicide or homicide) or abuse to minors or elders will be reported to appropriate authorities, by obligation of law and professional ethics. The signatures below represent an agreement to this statement of treatment outcomes, goals, strategies, and evaluation methods.

_____   _____
Marcia   Date

_____   _____
Robert   Date

_____   _____
Dr. Frederick L. Peterson, Jr.   Date
Clinical Psychology and Sex Health

CONTRIBUTOR

Frederick L. Peterson, Jr., PsyD, is a health psychologist at the Veterans Healthcare System of Ohio, Dayton Campus, where he coordinates a Sexual Health Clinic and the Smoking Cessation Programs. Dr. Peterson is the Co-Director of the Psychology Internship Program. He completed postdoctorate training as a Clinical Fellow at the Masters and Johnson Institute. Research interests include sex therapy, tobacco use treatment, and the effects of masculinity-related personality factors on health. He holds three academic appointments at Wright State University, including the School of Medicine (Department of Psychiatry), the School of Professional Psychology, and the College of Education and Human Services. Dr. Peterson may be contacted at the Sexual Health Clinic, VA Medical Center, Dayton, OH 45428. E-mail: Docpete100@aol.com

Sex History Questionnaire

Jill W. Bley and Associates

Since William Masters and Virginia Johnson introduced their revolutionary ideas about how to help people with sexual problems, sex therapists and counselors have been trained about the importance of taking a thorough history of the presenting complaint. Later, sex therapists such as Helen Singer Kaplan introduced the importance of understanding the presenting sexual complaint within the context of the developmental history of the person and/or the couple.

The "Sex History Questionnaire" that follows is a comprehensive questionnaire that asks clients to respond to questions related to their psychosexual development starting with questions about their parent's relationship to each other and to the client, sibling relationships, dating history, abuse history (if any), important relationships prior to the current one, and then the history of the current relationship, as well as some questions concerning their medical history. There are important questions related to sexual development, such as when the client first masturbated and the emotional reaction to the experience, how the client learned about sex, and whether or not the information was accurate. Although the questionnaire is rather lengthy, most clients feel that it is well worth their time and effort to fill it out because it causes them to think about certain aspects of their development and sexuality that they may not have thought about or considered to be important or relevant to their presenting problem.

Sex History Questionnaire

Client Name: _____   Today's Date: _____ / _____ / _____

INSTRUCTIONS: *Please answer the following questions and return the questionnaire to your therapist. If you and your partner are both completing this survey, DO NOT discuss the contents of the following questionnaire while you are filling it out. There are no "right" or "wrong" answers to the following questions, only what is accurate for you. Give honest and complete answers, but do not spend a great deal of time on any one item. If you need more space for an answer than is provided, use an additional sheet of paper and number the continued answer. This questionnaire is very important to our assessment procedure and treatment plans, so take the necessary time to complete it as well as possible. If there is any information that you wish to keep confidential from your partner, please indicate by writing your response in __red__.*

Your gender (circle one)?   Male   Female   Your age? _____   Birth date? _____ / _____ / _____

Your current marital status (circle one)?   Single   Married   Separated   Divorced   Remarried   Widowed

If married, is this your first marriage? ❑ Yes ❑ No   If no, which (number) marriage is this? _____

How long were you married to your previous spouse(s)? _____

If married or living with your partner, how long have you been married? _____ Living together? _____

What is your average alcohol consumption? _____ How long does it usually take you to fall asleep? _____

Have you recently found yourself waking in the middle of the night and having difficulty falling asleep again? ❑ Yes ❑ No

    If yes, how often does this occur (e.g., every night)? _____

    How long has this been going on? _____

Have you noticed a change in your appetite for food? ❑ Yes ❑ No

    If yes, briefly explain: _____

Have you recently lost or gained a significant amount of weight? ❑ Yes ❑ No

    If yes, how much and over what period of time? _____

Do you suspect that you might have a physical problem that you have not seen a physician about? ❑ Yes ❑ No

    If yes, briefly explain: _____

Would you like a referral to a physician to investigate a possible medical problem? ❑ Yes ❑ No

Are you currently being treated or have you in the past 5 years been treated by a psychologist, psychiatrist, or other mental health professional? ❑ Yes ❑ No

    If yes, briefly explain: _____

Would you like for your physician, psychiatrist, and so on, to be notified of your progress in therapy? ❑ Yes ❑ No

    If yes, please list his/her name and address: _____

_____

Your signature here gives your therapist permission to discuss your treatment with the physician/therapist you designate:

_____

Do you have any physical problems that interfere with your sexual enjoyment/performance? ❑ Yes ❑ No

    If yes, briefly explain: _____

Is your mother alive? ❑ Yes ❑ No

    If yes, what is her health? _____ If no, when and how did she die? _____

Is your father alive? ❑ Yes ❑ No

    If yes, what is his health? _____ If no, when and how did he die? _____

Did you grow up living with your natural parents? ❐ Yes ❐ No

    If no, briefly explain: _____

Describe your memories of how your parents (stepparents, guardians, etc.) got along with each other while you were growing up:

_____

_____

Describe your memories of how your mother (or stepmother, etc.) treated you while you were growing up: _____

_____

_____

Describe your memories of how your father (or stepfather, etc.) treated you while you were growing up: _____

_____

_____

Were you ever physically abused as a child (beating, etc.)? ❐ Yes ❐ No

    If yes, please explain: _____

_____

Were you ever psychologically abused as a child (regular criticism, accusations, threats, etc.)? ❐ Yes ❐ No

    If yes, please explain: _____

_____

Were you ever sexually abused (incest, fondling, invasion of your privacy)? ❐ Yes ❐ No

    If yes, please explain: _____

_____

If your parents or stepparents are alive, how would you describe your relationship with them? _____

_____

What were your parents' most important personal values that they attempted to pass on to you? _____

_____

_____

Who or what had the largest influence on your emotional development during your childhood and adolescent years?

    Briefly explain: _____

How many brothers do you have? ____ Sisters? ____ What was your relationship with them like while growing up?

_____

What is your current relationship with your brother(s)/sister(s)? _____

Within most families, children are often "labeled" by other family members (e.g., "the smart one," "the troublemaker," "the athlete," etc.). What was your label? How did you get it? Was it accurate?

_____

_____

Where or from whom did you gain most of your sexual knowledge? Looking back, was the information helpful? Accurate?

_____

_____

Did your parents discuss sexual facts with you? ❐ Yes ❐ No Sexual feelings? ❐ Yes ❐ No

What was the general message that they (verbally and nonverbally) transmitted to you about sexuality? _____

_____

Do you recall ever playing "sex games" (e.g., playing doctor) <u>prior to age 6</u>? ☐ Yes ☐ No

    Were you caught or punished? ☐ Yes ☐ No

    Explain: _____

_____

Do you recall ever playing "sex games" (e.g., playing doctor) <u>between ages 6 and 12</u>? ☐ Yes ☐ No

    Were you caught or punished? ☐ Yes ☐ No

    Explain: _____

_____

As a child or adolescent, do you recall watching someone behave sexually? ☐ Yes ☐ No

    Explain, including your memories of your reaction to it: _____

_____

At what age do you remember having your first sexual/genital feelings? _____

What are your memories of your reaction to these feelings? _____

_____

_____

At about what age did you first experiment with masturbation (or any other solitary activity which produced pleasurable sensation)? _____ On the average, how often did you masturbate during adolescence? _____

What was your emotional reaction after you masturbated during that period of your life? _____

_____

Were you ever caught or punished for masturbating or stimulating yourself sexually? ☐ Yes ☐ No

    Explain: _____

_____

On the average, how often do you masturbate now? _____

What are your feelings now about masturbation? _____

_____

Do you usually have a particular image or fantasy during sexual intercourse? ☐ Yes ☐ No

    If yes, briefly explain: _____

_____

FEMALE ONLY: At what age did you begin menstruation? _____ Did you understand menstruation when your first period arrived? ☐ Yes ☐ No

    How did you learn about menstruation? _____

FEMALE ONLY: Please describe any menstrual difficulties that you have experienced in the past or currently experience:

_____

_____

MALE AND FEMALE: What are your feelings about intercourse during menstrual periods? _____

_____

When did you first learn about nocturnal orgasms (wet dreams)? _____

Did anything negative happen to you in adolescence having to do with nocturnal orgasms (e.g., getting caught or punished)? ☐ Yes ☐ No

    If yes, briefly describe: _____

Did you have any sexual experience involving a person/persons of the same sex, either in adolescence or as an adult? ❏ Yes ❏ No

Briefly explain, including your current feelings about the incident(s): _____

_____

Has any member of your family ever involved you in sexual activity? ❏ Yes ❏ No

If yes, explain: _____

_____

Have you or anyone close to you ever been raped? ❏ Yes ❏ No

If yes, briefly explain, including your current feelings about the incident(s): _____

_____

About how old were you when you began to date? ____ Did you "steady-date"? ❏ Yes ❏ No

What was the most common activity you participated in on dates in high school? _____

_____

_____

How old were you when you began to "make out" and pet on dates? ____ Did you pet on most dates, or only with certain individuals? Did you enjoy touching your partner's genitals on these occasions? Did you enjoy having your genitals touched?

Comments: _____

_____

_____

At what age did you first have intercourse? _____ Did you or your partner use a birth control device/method on this occasion? ❏ Yes ❏ No

Describe the first occasion, including your memories of your reaction and your partner's reaction to it: _____

_____

_____

How much pleasure and freedom from concern did you experience during your first few sexual interactions? _____

_____

Were you ever suspected or caught behaving sexually? ❏ Yes ❏ No

If yes, were you punished? Explain: _____

_____

Describe your most serious nonmarital relationship prior to your current one. Include, briefly, why it ended and whether you continue to have any form of relationship with the person presently.

_____

_____

_____

Have you ever been previously married? ❏ Yes ❏ No

If yes, describe on an additional piece of paper, courtship, length of marriage, and why the marriage ended.

Does your current spouse/partner know (in general) about past love and sexual relationship(s)? ❏ Yes ❏ No

If no, briefly explain why not: _____

_____

Describe briefly how you and your current partner first met and the courtship that followed: _____

_____

_____

What were your partner's physical and personality characteristics that first attracted you to him/her? _____
_____
_____

MARRIED ONLY: Did you and your partner live together before marriage? ☐ Yes ☐ No

    If yes, for how long? _____ Speaking for yourself only, why did you decide to marry your partner? _____
_____
_____

Briefly describe your first sexual encounter with your partner (when, where, how, why, and what was the outcome as you remember it)?
_____
_____

If you have children, were they planned? ☐ Yes ☐ No

    How do your children affect your current relationship? _____
_____

What forms of contraception (if any) are you using now? Are you satisfied with this method? _____
_____

Do you plan to have children in the future? ☐ Yes ☐ No

In your own words, describe the current sexual difficulties:
_____
_____

How has your sexual relationship with your partner changed since you first had sexual intercourse with him/her? ____
_____
_____

If you had to choose, which of the following two statements are most true for you (circle one)?

    (A) Our nonsexual problems in our relationship are the main cause of our current sexual problems.

    (B) Our sexual problems are the main cause of problems in the nonsexual part of our relationship.

How often did you and your partner have intercourse (on the average) during the first 6 months of your sexual relationship? Were you satisfied with the frequency level? If no, what would you have preferred?
_____
_____

How often (on average) have you and your partner had intercourse over the past 6 months? _____

Are you satisfied with this frequency level? ☐ Yes ☐ No

    If no, what would you have preferred? _____

Do you feel free to express yourself SEXUALLY at any time with your partner and be warmly received? ☐ Yes ☐ No

Do you feel free to express AFFECTION toward your partner at any time and be warmly received? ☐ Yes ☐ No
    (If the answer is no to either of these questions, describe or explain on an additional sheet of paper).

Describe a typical sexual encounter between you and your partner (be very specific on what each of you says, does, and feels from beginning to end of the encounter).
_____
_____

Now describe what an "ideal" or "perfect" sexual encounter would be like with you and your partner (again, be specific).
_____
_____

Which of you usually chooses to begin lovemaking? _____ Does lovemaking lead to intercourse? ❏ Yes ❏ No

    How would you change the lovemaking that occurs prior to intercourse? _____

_____

What would you like to change about intercourse itself? _____

_____

What would you like to change about the time immediately following intercourse? _____

_____

Are you happy with the variety of methods that you and your partner use to express yourselves sexually? ❏ Yes ❏ No

    If no, what changes would you like to occur? _____

_____

Do you feel loved by your partner during lovemaking? ❏ Yes ❏ No

Do you usually feel loved by your partner when not behaving sexually? ❏ Yes ❏ No

What would you like to see your partner do more (or less) of to make you feel more valuable and loved by him/her?

_____

_____

Do you have a preference for a time of day or specific situation for lovemaking? ❏ Yes ❏ No

    If yes, briefly explain: _____

_____

When you and your partner are making love, what are some of the typical things that you think about? _____

_____

_____

How do you let your partner know what pleases you and displeases you sexually (be specific)? _____

_____

_____

Are you, or have you ever had one or more extrarelationship sexual affairs? ❏ Yes ❏ No

Does your partner know about this? ❏ Yes ❏ No

    If yes, how do you think your partner feels about this? _____

_____

    If no, how do you think he/she would feel about it if he/she knew? _____

_____

What topics do you and your partner AGREE about most? _____

_____

Has your partner had an extrarelationship sexual affair? ❏ Yes ❏ No

    If yes, what are your feelings about this? _____

_____

What trait, habit, and so on does your partner have that tends to reduce your sexual feelings for him/her? _____

_____

_____

What does your partner do too much that you would like to see him/her change? _____

_____

What does your partner do too little that you would like to see him/her change? _____

_____

What do you want most from your partner that he/she does not provide now (be as specific as you can)? _____

_____

_____

Do you feel that you are an attractive person? ☐ Yes ☐ No

    Do you feel that your partner thinks you are attractive? ☐ Yes ☐ No

    If no to either, please explain: _____

_____

Which do you feel are your best attributes or characteristics that you have to offer your partner? _____

_____

_____

What do you notice most when you touch your partner (be specific)? _____

What do you notice when your partner touches you (be specific)? _____

Under what conditions do you find touching your partner to be irritating, annoying, embarrassing, and so forth?

_____

Do you and your partner use body contact FREQUENTLY to express your feelings? ☐ Yes ☐ No

    If yes, what form does it take?

_____

What is the most comforting or pleasing form of touching that you remember from childhood? _____

_____

Do you enjoy oral sex (giving and receiving)? ☐ Yes ☐ No

Is the frequency of this activity satisfactory? ☐ Yes ☐ No

Do either of you like to wear special clothes or devices during lovemaking? ☐ Yes ☐ No

    If yes, describe: _____

_____

Do you need to physically hurt or emotionally humiliate your partner in order to become sexually aroused? ☐ Yes ☐ No

    If yes, briefly explain: _____

_____

Do you enjoy looking at your partner's nude body? ☐ Yes ☐ No

    If no, briefly explain: _____

_____

Do you enjoy having your partner look at your nude body? ☐ Yes ☐ No

    If no, briefly explain: _____

_____

Are you particularly aware of odors during lovemaking? ☐ Yes ☐ No

    If yes, describe and briefly explain: _____

_____

Does sound or noise tend to get in the way of your enjoyment during sexual activity? ☐ Yes ☐ No

    If yes, describe and explain: _____

_____

How does the sexual problem affect YOUR sexual functioning? _____

_____

How does the problem affect your partner's sexual functioning? _____

_____

How have you and your partner handled the problem up until now? _____

_____

How often (on the average) do you orgasm (climax) during intercourse (e.g., every time, about half the time, never, etc.)?

_____

FEMALE: Do you have difficulty getting lubricated during lovemaking? ❏ Yes ❏ No

    If yes, please explain: _____

_____

MALE: Do you have difficulty getting or keeping an erection during lovemaking? ❏ Yes ❏ No

    If yes, please explain: _____

_____

Do you have problems climaxing too soon during lovemaking? ❏ Yes ❏ No

    If yes, please explain: _____

_____

Do you ever experience unusual pain during intercourse or penetration? ❏ Yes ❏ No

    If yes, please explain: _____

_____

If you have any final comments you wish to make, please use another sheet of paper to do so.

Jill W. Bley, PhD, is a clinical psychologist. She is certified by the American Association of Sexuality Educators, Counselors, and Therapists as both a sex therapist and a supervisor. She taught sex therapy to graduate students in clinical psychology at the University of Cincinnati. During that time she trained and supervised many students. Dr. Bley wrote a syndicated column, "Speaking of Sex," which appeared in some downtown newspapers. Her columns addressed the diverse issues related to human sexuality. She is a founder of Women Helping Women/Rape Crisis Center and a Sex Therapy Clinic, both in Cincinnati. She has lectured extensively on topics of sexuality. Dr. Bley is a Volunteer Associate Professor in the Department of Psychiatry University of Cincinnati Medical Center. Dr. Bley may be contacted at 750 Red Bud Avenue, Cincinnati, OH 45229. E-mail: drjillbley@cinci.rr.com

Sexual Pleasuring (Sensate Focus Exercises)*

The pleasuring exercises that are described in this handout are intended to help people who are having certain sexual problems to regain their previous level of functioning, and to give couples who cannot have sexual intercourse (permanently or temporarily) ideas about how they can continue to have a loving sexual relationship through loving touch, sometimes referred to as "outercourse."

If you or your partner has a sexual problem such as inability to have orgasm, premature ejaculation (ejaculating too fast), no lubrication, or erection problems, following these exercises step by step from Sensate Focus I to Sensate Focus III will probably help to resolve the problem.

—— REMEMBER ——

If you want to correct the problem, you need to follow the instructions carefully and not be tempted to jump ahead to the next level too soon.

If you and your partner cannot have sexual intercourse but neither of you has a sexual problem (or the male partner is permanently unable to have an erection), Sensate Focus I and II along with creative use of creams, lotions, oils, fabrics with soft, sensual textures, and so on, will help you to feel close, loving, and sensually connected.

The first and most important rule for using these exercises to correct a sexual problem such as those listed above is that both of you must agree that you will not try to have intercourse until you progress through the steps to Sensate Focus III, nor have an orgasm or pressure your partner for orgasm. In other words, there must be an agreement to put a ban on intercourse and orgasm during the time that you are working through the steps.

Sensate Focus I: Nongenital Pleasuring

You should decide ahead of time who will initiate the request to do the exercise. The best way to arrange this is to agree that whoever asks first will not initiate again until the other initiates. That way, each of you will have the responsibility to ask for sexual pleasuring about 50% of the time. Most couples are used to leaving that responsibility to one or the other partner most of the time. If you share the initiating, you will both have an opportunity to learn how to ask for sex and how to say "yes" or "no." If your response is "no," then a rule should be that the one who says "no" must offer an alternative time and then be there ready to do the exercise at the alternative time with no reminders from the other.

Before you get started, it is helpful for you to talk about the kind of sexual language you have. If you have none — that is, you don't say anything when you want sex, just start to kiss or touch or give some other nonverbal indication — you may find it very helpful to figure out together whether that is okay with each of you or if you would like to be able to ask for a sexual encounter. You could also discuss how to say "no" without the other's feelings being hurt.

The person whose turn it is to initiate the pleasuring exercise is responsible to make sure the room temperature is comfortable enough to be nude without clothes or blankets. That person should also set the "mood," paying attention to the lighting, perhaps soft music, having lotions, oils, or creams available that are at room temperature, and so forth. Then the initiator begins to touch the partner all over the body excluding genitals and breasts. The touch should be like a loving massage, making sure that the pressure is comfortable (not too soft or too hard).

---

*This handout was prepared by Jill W. Bley, PhD.

The initiator should be focused on touching the partner for his or her pleasure, allowing himself or herself to be "lost" in the experience of giving pleasure and touching. The receiver just relaxes and focuses on the pleasure of receiving loving, sensual touch and allows himself or herself to be "lost" in the sensations of the body. No one talks during the pleasuring except to indicate pleasure or ask the receiver to turn over or to check out whether or not the touch is comfortable. The receiver may talk to indicate if something is uncomfortable and may show the initiator how to touch in a particular area in order to make the touch more comfortable.

When the initiator feels that he or she is ready to stop touching, change places; the receiver then becomes the one who touches and the initiator receives the pleasuring touch. Remember that both should focus on "getting lost" in the sensations of touching and being touched.

Sensate Focus II: Nongenital and Genital Pleasuring

You are ready to move on to this step only when both partners are enjoying the sensations of "getting lost" in the feelings of pleasure produced by the loving touch. The rules and suggestions for Sensate Focus II are the same, except that this time the genitals and breasts are included in the pleasuring touch. However, there should be no more emphasis on the breasts and genitals than on the other parts of the body. In other words, the difference between these two exercises is to merely include the breasts and genitals in an overall body sensual massage with the person whose turn it was to initiate the exercise going first and being responsible to set the mood.

If you are doing these exercises to correct a sexual problem, there continues to be a ban on intercourse and orgasms!!! Do not sabotage your progress by putting pressure on your partner to violate this ban. If either partner simply must have an orgasm, do it privately by masturbating yourself so that the partner does not feel pressured or guilty for not "giving" you the orgasm.

If you are hoping to correct an orgasm problem, this exercise is great for learning to control the orgasmic response (if the problem is coming too fast) and for enjoying the teasing and building of sexual tension (if the problem is inhibition of orgasm).

If you are hoping to correct an erection or lubrication problem, pressure to "use" it right away if an erection or lubrication occurs will usually only be successful for the moment. Ridding oneself of "performance anxiety" and/or inhibitions to receiving pleasure will not be overcome if you try to have intercourse as soon as you have an erection or begin to lubricate.

If you are using these exercises as a way to maintain sexual closeness during a period of time when you cannot have intercourse, there is no ban on orgasm. However, you may want to occasionally have an agreement that you will have a ban so that you can keep the emphasis and focus on the touch and loving sensations instead of orgasm.

Sensate Focus III: Intercourse Pleasuring

This exercise is only for those who are using these instructions to correct a sexual problem. There continues to be a ban on trying to achieve orgasm. You are ready to move on to these exercises only when both of you are enjoying the feelings of "getting lost" in the sensations of being lovingly touched and caressed all over the body, including the breasts and genitals, and the partner with the identified sexual problem is feeling comfortable and secure about lubrication or erection; that is, he or she can depend on it and does not feel inhibited or worried about performance.

The rules about how to initiate are the same. Begin this exercise by doing Sensate Focus II. Do not take turns touching each other now. Sort of "choreograph" a mutual "dance" of loving touch. Then when both partners feel ready, begin to pleasure one another with intercourse, starting out in one position and then gracefully and rhythmically changing to another position. After a while, change positions again. You may want to get a book, such as *The Joy of Sex: Fully Revised and Completely Updated for the 21st Century* (Alex Comfort, 2002, New York: Crown) to give you some ideas; *The Joy of Sex* includes graphic illustrations of many positions for sexual intercourse.

If premature orgasm is the problem, be sure that you do not start this exercise until you are confident in your ability to prolong your pleasure and withhold the ejaculation for an agreed-upon time. Achieving this skill is done by using the "Stop-Start" technique for stimulating the penis during Sensate Focus II pleasuring. The instructions for doing "Stop-Start" are published in many books about male sexuality. One good book is *The New Male Sexuality* by Bernie Zilbergeld (1992, rev. ed., New York: Bantam).

If inhibited orgasm is the problem, Sensate Focus III, with no pressure at all to produce an orgasm, may help an orgasm to happen. If it does not and you cannot have an orgasm even with masturbation, then you need to continue to work on learning how to give yourself an orgasm. Once that is accomplished you should then teach your partner how to touch your genitals to replicate your own touch and then "bridge" these sensations to intercourse. There are many books on female sexuality that give very clear instructions to women for learning to be orgasmic. One old but good book is *For Yourself: The Fulfillment of Female Sexuality* by Lonnie Barbach (1975, New York: Doubleday). The Zilbergeld book mentioned previously has information about inhibited orgasm for men.

Kegel Exercises
(Pelvic Floor Exercises)*

The exercises that your therapist has asked you to do are very important because they are a key element to the success of your treatment. These exercises, if done as directed, will strengthen the muscles of your "pelvic floor." The pelvic floor is a large group of muscles that stretch from side to side across the floor (bottom) of your pelvic area. The muscles are attached to the pubic bone which is in front of your body, and to the lowest part of your spine (the coccyx), which is in the back of your body. All of the openings in the lower part of your body pass through these muscles, that is, the urethra, anus, and vagina. These muscles support your pelvic organs and control the flow of urine and feces. The primary muscle group in the pelvic floor is the pubococcygeal muscle (PC muscle).

How to Do Pelvic Floor Exercises

The first thing to do is to clearly identify the muscles that you need to control. Other muscles near the pelvic floor muscles can easily get involved. Therefore, you should spend some time making sure that you are working only with those muscles in the pelvic floor by making sure that you are not pulling in your stomach, not tightening your buttocks, not tightening your thighs, and not holding your breath. To make sure that you are not using muscles that should not be included, place your hand on your abdomen while you do the exercises. Your abdomen should not move.

Now try to isolate your PC muscle. To accomplish this, sit on the toilet. Spread your legs. Begin to urinate. Squeeze the muscles that will stop the flow of urine. Pay attention to the muscles that you are contracting in order to stop the flow. Finish urinating and then insert your finger into your vagina or just rest your finger on the opening of the vagina and see if you can feel the muscle contract. If you can insert your finger, you will feel the muscle contract around your finger. These are the muscles that you will be exercising. Here are the exercises:

- Tighten the PC muscles quickly by contracting them powerfully. Then relax the muscle completely after each contraction. Do 10 repetitions.
- Tighten the PC muscles and hold them for 3 to 5 seconds and then relax them for 3 to 5 seconds.

The quick contractions build muscle strength. The slow contractions build stamina. Do these exercises 3 times per day. Every week increase the number of repetitions by 5 until you reach 30. The contractions that you hold for 3 to 5 seconds should be increased from 3 to 10 seconds.

You need to remember to do these exercises every day. One way to remember to do the exercises is to link them with a predictable daily activity. For example, if you drive to and from work you can decide to do your exercises every time you have to stop your car for a red traffic light. If you are a stay-at-home person, you could decide to do your exercises every time you need to urinate during the day, or every time you have to walk up or down the stairs.

---

*This handout was prepared by Jill W. Bley, PhD.

A Health Care Professional's Guide to Contemporary Sexual Myths*

Sexual health is defined as the integration of the physical, emotional, intellectual, and social aspects of being sexual in ways that are positively enriching and that enhance personality, communication, and love (World Health Organization [2001]. *Promotion of Sexual Health: Recommendations for Action.* Proceedings from a regional consultation convened by Pan American Health Organization and the World Health Organization in collaboration with the World Association for Sexology, Antigua Guatemala, Guatemala). Hence, sexual misinformation and myths interfere with the intellectual understanding of sexuality, which in turn can affect perceptions of self and others (emotional and social aspects) as well as risk for transmission of disease (physical aspects). In short, the perpetuation of sexual myths serves as a significant obstacle to achieving sexual health.

The sexual myths are listed below as "red flags" for misconceptions that complicate sexual lives. This is not by any means a comprehensive list but rather a representative list of some of the most common myths. Review the list and evaluate if you have been (or currently are) influenced by any of them during your own sexual development. Ask yourself, "What impact have these sexual myths had upon my view of sexuality, physical attractiveness, sexual function, self-esteem, relationships, and how I communicate (or do not communicate) about sexual matters?"

Sexual Myths Regarding Age
(Children and Seniors)

- The most potent myth of childhood sexuality is the idea of childhood nonsexuality: The myth that children do not have any interest in sex, or if they do, it is to be discouraged.
- The idea that kids are not sexual also leads to the common myth about sex education of children – talking to children about sex will "pollute" them by putting ideas in their heads.
- Children always tell the truth about sex.
- People have to be young and beautiful to be attractive to others and sexually happy.
- Aging itself will bring an end to sexual function (e.g., old age causes impotence).

Sexual Myths Regarding
Anatomy and Physiology

- The size of sexual organs is related to a person's sexual satisfaction.
- The absence of the hymen (maidenhead) proves that a girl is not a virgin.
- Menopause or hysterectomy ends a women's sex drive and sex life.
- Each person has a designated number of sexual experiences (orgasms, ejaculations) and when they are used up, the person is no longer sexual.
- Only men have "wet dreams" and they are a sign of a sexual disorder.
- Masturbation results in physical and mental disorders.

---

*This handout was prepared by Frederick L. Peterson, Jr., PsyD, and Christina C. Peterson, BS.

Sexual Myths Regarding Sexual Performance

- Optimal health (as well as athletic performance) is achieved through sexual abstinence.
- Real men are to be the active lovemakers, "doing it" to passive women who tolerate it being "done to them." It is the man's role to initiate.
- If a good girl has to do it, then she should have the decency not to enjoy it.
- Men are "sexual experts" who impart their sex knowledge to pure and virginal brides.
- Honeymoons are times of great sexual satisfaction and release after long "waiting."
- Real men are supposed to have erections at the drop of a bra.
- Good women, God bless them, better fake it well – just smile and moan but never yell.
- To be true to your marriage in love and bliss, you are never to find another attractive enough to kiss.
- Marital sex is a delightful routine of the missionary position only after 9:00 p.m. in the master bedroom with the lights out resulting in mutual and simultaneous orgasms.
- Erections for men and climax for women are necessary for sexual satisfaction.

Sexual Myths Regarding Pregnancy and the Postpartum Period

- Women cannot conceive during their menstruation period.
- Women cannot get pregnant if the man withdraws before climax, or if the woman is on top.
- During pregnancy, the baby can get hurt from the probing penis or it may "break the bag" of amniotic fluid protecting the baby.
- Sex during pregnancy is unnatural and repulsive.
- Pregnancy changes the woman's body in ways that will make her unattractive.
- Natural childbirth doesn't hurt and anyone can do it.
- Breastfeeding is a "woman's thing" and there is no role the father plays.
- Breastfeeding is not as healthy as bottle feeding a baby.
- Breastfeeding mothers don't mind if their husbands "belly up to the bar."
- Resuming your sex life postpartum will be simple and anxiety free.
- Good parents never have thoughts about abusing their children.

Sexual Myths Regarding Sexually Transmitted Infections (STI) and Diseases (STD)

- You can tell a person has an STI by their appearance.
- Just by chance, there is a low probability of getting an STI.
- An STI is a punishment for bad behavior more than a result of an infection.
- If a person does not have any symptoms of anything wrong, they don't have to worry.
- With all the medicines today, I can get treated and cured if I get an STI.
- Rubbers (condoms) don't really make a difference in protecting a person from STIs.
- People cannot get an STI if they don't have sex.
- There are no sexual activities that protect you from AIDS that are still satisfying.
- In general, men have more severe consequences of STIs than women do.
- By law, physicians have to report all cases of an STI to the public health authorities.

Sexual Myths Regarding Sex Offending (Rape, Child Molestation)

- Women want to be raped and "ask for it."
- Women are primarily raped by strangers.
- Woman can always avoid being raped if they want to.

- Women "cry rape" for revenge.
- Rapists are always crazy (psychotic) or low-life sociopaths.
- Child sexual abuse is rare and only happens in poor families with uneducated parents.
- When child sexual abuse occurs, it usually gets reported and the child gets help.
- Child sexual abusers are usually strangers to the child.
- Child sexual abuse usually involves force and physical coercion.
- Child sexual abuse really doesn't hurt the child as there are no long-term effects.

Sexual Myths Regarding Same-Sex Attraction

- Gay people are pedophiles that want to have sex with children.
- Homosexuality (or heterosexuality for that matter) is a lifestyle choice.
- You either are or are not gay.
- Feminine men HAVE to be gay and highly masculine men HAVE to be straight.
- Gay people are out to recruit or turn heterosexuals gay.
- Same-sex activity is doing something unnatural.
- A child conceived through rear-entry coitus (doggy style) will be homosexual.

Sexual Myths Regarding People With Disabilities

- People with disabilities are asexual, innocent, and childlike, or predatory.
- People with disabilities should only be sexual with other disabled individuals or they will have disabled offspring.
- Sexual problems experienced by people with disabilities are caused by their disability.
- If an able-bodied person has a sexual relationship with a person with a disability, it is because the nondisabled person cannot attract anyone else or is predatory.

Sexual Myths About Sex Therapy and Sexual Medicines

- Sex medicines give all men instant, sustained erections that do not subside after climax.
- Using a pill to resolve concerns about erections will make your sex life satisfying.
- It is safe to "try out" sex pills by borrowing some from a friend.
- Sex therapy involves being observed while having sex or having sex with a therapist.
- My physician, psychologist, or therapist received training in sex therapy while completing academic requirements and is comfortable discussing sex.

Sexual Myths About Masturbation

- Masturbation is abnormal and unhealthy.
- Masturbation is unnatural and it is not observed with animal behavior.
- Masturbation leads to illness or disability, such as blindness or insanity.
- Men have limited sperm, so don't waste them through masturbation.
- Men with available sex partners shouldn't want or need to masturbate.
- Masturbating is immature and should never be discussed with a partner.
- Young children do not masturbate and if they do, it is a sign of sex abuse.
- Elderly people do not masturbate because they lose interest in sex.
- The Bible condemns masturbation as the "sin of Onan."
- There is no room for masturbation in a "Christian marriage."
- Parents should be punitive towards children caught masturbating.
- Masturbating more than a couple times per week, and especially more than once per day, is always a sure sign of "sex addiction."

Subject Index

Continuing Education Available for Home Study

The most recent volumes of *Innovations in Clinical Practice* are available as formal home-study continuing education programs. This best-selling, comprehensive source of practical clinical information is complemented by examination modules which may be used to earn continuing education credits.

Credits may be obtained by successfully completing examinations based on those contributions in each volume which have been selected by the editorial advisory board. Each of these contributions explores a timely topic designed to enhance your clinical skills and provides the knowledge necessary for effective practice. After studying these selections, a multiple-choice examination is completed and returned to the Professional Resource Exchange for scoring. Upon passing the examination (80% of test items answered correctly), your credits will be recorded and you will receive a copy of your official transcript.

At the time of publication of this volume, continuing education modules are available for Volumes 17 through 20 of *Innovations in Clinical Practice: A Source Book*. Each module contains examination materials for 20 credits (equivalent to 20 hours of continuing education activity). Twelve-credit programs are available for *Innovations in Clinical Practice: Focus on Children and Adolescents* and *Innovations in Clinical Practice: Focus on Violence Treatment and Prevention*. Fourteen-credit programs are available for *Innovations in Clinical Practice: Focus on Adults* and *Innovations in Clinical Practice: Focus on Health and Wellness*. A 20-credit program is available for *Innovations in Clinical Practice: Focus on Sexual Health*.

The *Innovations in Clinical Practice* Continuing Education (CE) programs are one of the most efficient ways to stay current on new clinical techniques and obtain formal credit for your study. If your professional associations and state boards do not currently require formal CE activities, you may still wish to consider these programs as an excellent means of receiving feedback on your professional development. These self-study programs are . . .

- *Relevant* - selections are packed with information pertinent to your practice.
- *Inexpensive* - typically less than half the cost of obtaining credits through workshops and these expenses may still be tax deductible as a professional expense.
- *Convenient* - study at your own pace in the comfort of your home or office.
- *Useful* - the volumes will always be available as a practical reference and resource for day-to-day use in your professional practice.
- *Effective* - as a means of staying up to date and obtaining feedback on your knowledge acquisition and professional development. In most states with continuing education requirements, credits earned from American Psychological Association (APA) approved sponsors are automatically approved for licensure renewal. Consult your profession's state board for their policies regarding the status of programs offered by APA approved sponsors.

Specific learning objectives are available upon request.

To receive additional information on these CE programs, please see next page. ⟶

Do You Want More Information?

Yes! Please Send Me . . .

❒ Information on the other volumes in the *Innovations in Clinical Practice* series (Tables of Contents for all volumes and ordering information).

❒ Information on your Home-Study Continuing Education Programs.

❒ Your latest catalog.

Name: _____
(Please Print)

Address: _____

Address: _____

City/State/Zip: _____

Telephone: (_____) _____

E-Mail: _____

My Primary Profession Is: _____

For Fastest Response . . .

Fax to Our 24 Hour FAX Line at **1-941-343-9201**

OR

E-mail to **orders@prpress.com**

OR

Visit Our Website at **http://www.prpress.com**

Or Mail This Form To . . .

Professional Resource Press
PO Box 15560 • Sarasota FL 34277-1560